WHEN A BABY S

WHEN A BABY SUDDENLY DIES

Cot Death — The Impact and Effects

Janet Deveson Lord

HILL OF CONTENT
Melbourne

First published 1987

by Hill of Content Publishing Company Pty Ltd
86 Bourke Street Melbourne Australia

Copyright © Janet Deveson Lord 1987
Grief Diagram copyright to R. Trivan and J. Lord
Cover design by Helen Semmler

Typeset in Australia by
Midland Typesetters Pty Ltd, Maryborough 3465

Printed and bound in Australia by
Australian Print Group, Maryborough 3465

National Library of Australia
Cataloguing-in-Publication data
Lord, Janet Deveson, 1942–
   When a baby suddenly dies.

   Bibliography.
   ISBN 0 85572 162 6.

   1. Sudden death in infants. I. Title.

618.92

In over thirty years of attending many conferences, seminars and workshops, a few speakers stand out in my memory. The grand oratory of Professor C.W.D. Lewis of Auckland, the knowledgeable exposition of Dr A. Aldis of Cardiff, the emotional guidance of Dr Peter Barr of Sydney, and the pithy summaries of Dr John Maloney of Melbourne. However, I have never heard so much wise advice in a short lecture as in that given by Janet Lord at the National Association for Loss and Grief Conference in Adelaide in 1981 when she spoke of the organisation and responsibilities of self-help groups.

From that time I have been a great admirer of Janet and listened avidly whenever I have been able to attend her lectures. I was therefore delighted when I heard she was writing a book and honoured when she invited me to write the foreword.

Like such people as Elizabeth Kubler-Ross and Katherine Kingsbury, Janet succeeds in bringing her subject out of the 'taboo closet'. In her book she too helps accept death and dying as a normal event in human existence while acknowledging that certain aspects of cot death need special attention.

Sudden unexplained infant death *is* special, and grieving for this infant has several specific features:

Sudden — When death is sudden and unexpected there has been no preparatory grieving and the impact can be incredibly shocking.

Unexplained — The cause of death is not known and the reason the infant died is not understood. Startling and dramatic (and usually incorrect and misleading) 'breakthrough' reports of the cause of death are disturbing and confusing for the parents — and anyway healthy people shouldn't be dead!

Infant — Acceptance of death of the elderly, especially if they have lived a long and full life, is usually easier than accepting the death of an infant. Infant death seems a particularly cruel and unfair blow, and it is no wonder the parents feel angry. For the parents there is also a feeling of having been completely responsible for the health and well-being of this small baby. With its death comes incredible guilt.

When an adult dies, there is usually one person who stands out as the most important grieving person; for example, when a spouse dies the surviving partner is seen as the chief mourner and when a parent dies, a bereaved adult is given a certain prominence within the family. When a child dies there are two principal mourners who usually attempt to share their grief. Sharing grief is not easy because it is individually felt.

To want to run away or be left alone is a normal grief reaction, and to 'share' in this circumstance would be extremely difficult. Nevertheless, parents who are able to support each other while grieving individually, can forge the strongest bond that can ever exist between two people.

Janet's book, I am sure, will prove to be a great help to grieving parents, giving them reassurance and hope. It will be a wise guide to family, friends and members of the community who come into contact with these grieving parents and it will be invaluable to people such as Sudden Infant Death Syndrome Parents' Association volunteer counsellors, clergy, doctors, nurses, ambulance and police officers, funeral directors and social workers who are committed to helping the bereaved.

Susan M. Beal, M.B.S., A.T.C.L., Coordinator of Child Development, Research Counsellor for S.I.D.S. in the Department of Histropathology and Neurology Research Assistant at the Adelaide Children's Hospital

THIS book is about Sudden Infant Death Syndrome commonly called cot death. Sudden Infant Death Syndrome (S.I.D.S.) was defined by the 2nd International Conference On Causes of SIDS, held in Seattle in 1969, as the: 'Sudden death of any infant or child which is unexpected by history and in which a thorough post-mortem examination fails to demonstrate an adequate cause of death'.

Although it opens with these few remarks in preface, there is no introductory chapter to this book. Irregular though this may seem, it is correct, nonetheless, in relation to Sudden Infant Death, its impact, and its effects on families.

Families who experience the sudden, unexpected and unexplained death of their baby step into a void. Entry is swift, shattering and potentially soul destroying. Most families emerge from this event with changed views and values about the world in which they live. This book is about their journey, from impact, through the maze of grief to acceptance and some form of resolution. Some parents search for a long time and with a great deal of energy for the person/family they once were. It takes time for parents to understand that life can never be the same again; and though they have been changed by this most unwelcome event, this does not necessarily mean that life can never be 'good' again.

Parents are in a state of confusion and bewilderment after the sudden and unexpected death of their baby. They do not understand what is happening to them. They are vulnerable in this situation and because of their shocked state they are amenable to ideas and suggestions which often hinder rather than help the devastated parents. Both the emergency responder and the community often try to hasten the process by which the parents and siblings resolve their grief.

The Sudden Infant Death Research Foundation (under whose auspice this book is written) has found that the process by which parents return to their full potential is individual, painful and takes many, many months; most commonly a period of about three years passes before families regain a level of former happiness. If the community becomes aware of the differences and difficulties encountered by parents who have experienced cot death, it follows that they are in a better position to allow parents to exercise options and alternatives as they struggle towards an individual resolution of their infant's death. The effects of Sudden Infant Death Syndrome are compounded by the myths that abound in the community about how we react to death and how we should cope. Misinformation about the causes of S.I.D.S. contributes to the unnecessary burden of guilt parents take to themselves.

The Sudden Infant Death Research Foundation: is a self-help based organisation whose aims and directions initially were in response to the cot death parents' acknowledgement of their needs. These included:

- How did my baby die? (Need for information about the syndrome)

- Why did my baby die? (What causes S.I.D.S.)

- Will it happen again? (What research is being undertaken)

- What is happening to me, and why are people avoiding me? (Recognition of the overwhelming devastation and despair)

- It's been three months now and I feel worse than in the beginning. (Support needed during their long bereavement)

The aims and directions of the S.I.D.R.F. broadened as the parents' needs were allowed to become visible in the community. The community then responded with requests both for information and more knowledge about how they could effectively support grieving parents.

This led to a demand for the S.I.D.R.F. to become involved with the in-service training of Ambulance Officers, the Police, Infant Welfare Sisters, Casualty Staff at hospitals, etc. Feedback from parents and emergency responders alike has shown that the Foundation's input was beginning to decrease their sense of isolation as the community began to gain an insight into the difficulties encountered by families during resolution of their grief.

The S.I.D.R.F. adheres to a policy of balance between professionals and lay personnel. The basic tenet here is the belief that both have much to contribute to the resolution of the grief that is the aftermath of cot death, and that both can support parents.

As parents who have been on this long journey fully understand the pain and despair of newly bereaved families, they are in a position to offer empathic support which they undertake as volunteer parent visitors and supporters on behalf of S.I.D.R.F. The self-help nature of this kind of support has proved to be extremely successful in breaking down dependency, and has allowed families to manage their lives in ways which suit them best.

When my daughter Clare died from S.I.D.S. in 1972, resolution of the grief associated with cot death was made even more difficult by the dearth of information available and the absence of any support systems slanted towards sudden infant death.

In 1979 I was employed by the Sudden Infant Death Research Foundation and in this way became involved with other cot death parents. Then began a long learning and training process under the supervision of the Counselling Unit of S.I.D.R.F. Gradually I developed the skills to support other parents, act as a facilitator in the training of parent supporters, and became involved in the planning, preparing and presenting of seminars, workshops and lectures to health professionals.

While the aetilogy of the Sudden Infant Death Syndrome continues to challenge research workers on a worldwide basis, 'what to do until the answer comes' is of vital importance to parents, emergency responders, and those who wish to support them. If the content of this book encourages the reader to acknowledge the individual's reaction to the sudden and unexpected death of a loved baby, it will have done much to alter the myths that abound in our community about how we react to sudden death and how we cope—and will have met its aim.

Janet Deveson Lord
Melbourne, 1986

To Ruža
who laid the foundations

ACKNOWLEDGEMENTS

M ANY people have assisted, supported and encouraged the writing of this book. Parents, friends, relatives, doctors, nurses, ambulance officers, police, infant welfare sisters, clergy and civil celebrants, also those associated with the funeral industry, S.I.D.S. support groups and my colleagues at the Sudden Infant Death Research Foundation who gave so generously of their time and personal experiences. To these I wish to express my sincere thanks for permission to include their stories, comments and accounts in the manuscript.

I also gratefully acknowledge support and assistance from the Frankston SIDS Support Group and the ANZ Executors and Trustee Company Limited (Charitable Trusts), whose belief in the project in its early stages allowed it to come to fruition.

While encouragement was received from many quarters of the Community, Clinical Associate Professor, T. M. Adamson, Department of Paediatrics, Monash University, Queen Victoria Medical Centre, and Professor J. E. Maloney, Professor of Obstetrics and Gynecology and Medical Physiology, Faculty of Medicine, University of Calgary, Canada, suggested the need for such a book. I am particularly grateful to Elspeth Longney for her enthusiasm and encouragement over a long period of time. I am also indebted to Dr Jan Fraillon, Medical Coordinator, Education, Training and Research, and Dr Lindsey Knight, Senior Medical Officer of the Victorian Academy for General Practice for their suggestions and improvements to Part 1.

Acknowledgement is made to all authors and publishers of works quoted within this book. If any names of writers, their assigns or publishers have been inadvertently overlooked in the bibliographical acknowledgements at the end of the book, they are requested to contact the publishers.

To my friends who allowed me to seemingly take over their lives at times, and who provided spaces and places and other comforts so that the writing could continue, I express my heartfelt thanks.

Janet Deveson Lord

CONTENTS

Foreword   v
Preface   vii
Acknowledgements   xi
Prologue   xiv

PART I   THE IMPACT
1   Cot Death and Its Impact   3
2   The First Emergency Responders   14
3   The Doctor, The Hospital and Cot Death   30
4   The Infant Welfare Sister   52

PART II   THE AFTERMATH
5   An Overview   69
6   The Journey Through Grief   76
7   Preparing for the Funeral: The Physical Goodbye   96
8   The Funeral, the Clergy and Civil Celebrant   114

PART III   THE PEOPLE TOUCHED BY COT DEATH
9   The Complexity of Women's Grief   135
10   Men I Have Known Who Have Grieved   146
11   Relationships   162
12   Children and Their Responses   181
13   The Community   198

PART IV   THE FUTURE
14   The Next Child: A Dilemma   215
15   Facing the Reality   228
16   In Conclusion   246

Appendix   251
References and Bibliography   269
Index   275

PROLOGUE

TO say: 'It must be unreal' is to be in touch with the real situation.

To state that it must be difficult to believe, is an expression of what the parent is struggling to accept, but acceptance is a long, long way off. This point (impact) is just the beginning of a journey that will take many months, perhaps years, to complete.

To allow the parents full expression – and this often means chaotic expression at the time of impact – facilitates *recognition of the real-life event* that has taken place.

This is no fantasy – no nightmare from which one can wake with pounding heart to be reassured 'it is just a bad dream'!

PART I

THE IMPACT

Death is one idea that has no history . . .

Milton Mayer

CHAPTER ONE
Cot Death and Its Impact

A T 8.10 p.m. I checked Bruce. He was sound asleep. I walked into Clare's room and stood irresolute. Should she have an extra blanket, I wondered? It was a cold, silent night. The morning would sparkle with frosted cob-webs and swirling mists. I walked closer to the cot and looked down. I smiled to myself and thought how lucky I was. Two sons and a daughter, just perfect. Still smiling I leant further into the cot.

'I can't let her sleep with her head turned down like that, she might become uncomfortable as the night wears on.' I slid my hand under her head . . .

The night and I split in two. Silent night and silent me stand and watch a frantic creature screaming something. It sounds like 'My baby's dead!' She screams it over and over into the night.

This parent's account typifies the way in which Sudden Infant Death Syndrome brings disbelief, disorder, devastation and despair. These words probably describe the reaction to any sudden death, but certainly the emotions they represent crowd in with particular severity upon the unsuspecting parent who finds their baby dead in its cot, bassinette, bouncinette or car-seat.

While these deaths often occur during the night, they also take place at the supermarket, during feeding times, while the parents are visiting friends or relatives, and some occur while the baby is in the care of another person, perhaps a grandmother or the care person at a creche. Whoever finds the baby dead, whatever the circumstances, will experience overwhelming shock in discovering that the baby in their care has died. 'If only we had known, we would *never* have: put the baby down—gone visiting—asked Mum to have looked after him—left her to cry—gone out to dinner—played that game of tennis—gone back to work.'

In short, families who experience Sudden Infant Death Syndrome certainly would not have lived or gone about their daily lives in the ways that we all do had they been able to *foresee* their experience, because nobody wants their baby to die. The fact that S.I.D.S. cannot be prevented, and to date has no known cure, is of scant use to the parents at the point of impact. Because they truly believe that apparently perfectly healthy babies, or even ones with a slight cold, simply do not die, they initially will feel guilty.

Any human being who has looked into the eyes of a parent whose baby is lying dead between them, can hear the scream, silent or otherwise, that says *tell me it's not true—tell me this isn't happening—this isn't my baby!*

Disbelief Accompanies This First Tremendous Shock

Following the discovery, the mother's most commonly reported response is to scream—then run for help. But to whom? To the telephone, to a neighbour, to a husband or sibling, to someone in the street, or to rush helplessly into the garden? Those people around at first scatter—and then close in. *Disorder* is immediate, and does not necessarily abate with the arrival of the emergency responder.

The family structure is ruptured, is irrevocably changed. The family unit as it existed five minutes, one hour, twelve hours ago is gone forever. 'If only we had known.—' The family is shattered, and as the confusion mounts the destructive elements of cot death become all too obvious. It is impossible to convey the overwhelming devastation of this impact. Life is laid waste and parents are in continual conflict as they dare to sense the truth of what they see— then push it away with all their might.

Day one ends with the glimmer of the despair to come. Parents know their baby is dead because everyone tells them so. Confirmation is what is needed, but it is impossible to absorb the reality at that point. The kaleidoscope of emotions are jagged, intense, and turn relentlessly.

Another parent's account
(Written by Janet Taylor six weeks after the death of her daughter Beth)

It was Thursday about 7.15 a.m. I was waking up and I realised Beth had not as yet stirred. Peter and I got up at the same time, I asked him to check Beth, while I pulled on a tracksuit and made the bed. Peter checked her and then went upstairs to the bathroom.

I went into her room and saw that the doona was pulled up, like the bed had been made. I looked, and realized that I couldn't see her. I thought perhaps Peter had got her up, but then remembered that he always left the cot with the doona pulled back. I went cold. I pulled the doona back and there she was. She had gone halfway down the cot. Her head was on the side and her face looked very blotchy. I screamed to Peter as I picked her up, and then screamed out again. I ran to the dining room where I placed her on the couch. By this time Peter had come down and I realised that she wasn't breathing.

I started mouth-to-mouth resuscitation, trying to remember what you did for babies. Peter started to ring for an ambulance. It seemed only minutes until they came. I could hear the siren for miles before they arrived. I was continuing mouth-to-mouth until they arrived. I remember talking to her, telling her to breathe and that I loved her, but deep down, I was sure we had lost her.

The ambulance men came and took over, taking off her clothes and moving her onto the dining room table. There was equipment everywhere. I stood by the kitchen door just watching, feeling utterly helpless. Peter was trying to distract the boys—Marcus, 5 and Justin, 3. They couldn't understand what all the commotion was all about.

One of the ambulance men, then rang the Mobile Intensive Care Ambulance Unit. The man next door came in, found out what was happening and went and got his wife. She bundled the boys up, still in their pyjamas and took them next door. The M.I.C.A. men arrived.

I kept watching (there was no way I was going to leave her) and asking if she was breathing, but no-one would answer. They worked and worked on her for what seemed a long time. One of the ambulance men then made me sit in the kitchen and explained to me that she wasn't breathing, but that they exhaust the procedure three times. I just sat there blank and numb. It seemed quite a while before another ambulance officer came and sat down with me. He held my hand and told me that they had tried everything including adrenaline but with no response. He said he could imagine how we felt as he had lost a baby of his own eight years before.

I started to cry. I don't remember where Peter was at this stage. I think he was out the front with my mother, as she was taking the boys to her place. I went to him and just stood. I just shook my head. He knew, and we both hugged each other and cried. We went back into the house. I was asked would I like to nurse Beth, and I said 'Of course I do'. I nursed and cried for quite a while and then Peter nursed her. The ambulance officer asked would I like to go with them to the Royal Children's Hospital, or follow in the car. I had to go with her. Peter would follow in the car.

We both got dressed, in what seemed like slow motion. I then took Beth again, and was helped into the ambulance. I nursed her all the way into the Hospital. Paul, the ambulance officer sat with me. I don't remember much about the trip in. It seemed very slow. We talked, but I don't really remember what about. One thing I do remember, is that he asked me was I religious. I said 'Do you mean do I believe in God?' And I added 'Yes'. He informed me that the police would be calling as a matter of routine.

When we got to the Hospital one of the sisters took Beth and we were ushered into a private rom. We just sat. A doctor came in and asked us a few questions. The sister came back and asked could she contact anyone for us. All I could think of was my cousin, Joseph, a Priest, who had baptised Beth only three weeks earlier. She tried to ring him for us but with no luck. When she finally got through to his parish, she was told that there had been a death in his family and that he had gone to them. It was us.

He was waiting for us, with my father and sister when we got home. It was about 9 a.m. My sister had packed some clothes for the boys to take to Mum's, but all I could think of was having them home. It was important for us to have them near us, as much as I am sure they wanted us near them. I was dreading facing them, but we realised we had to be as honest as possible. We explained that Beth had died, and Marcus then said that she had gone to Heaven to be with God. His main concern was who was going to feed her. He then decided that Mary would feed her.

Beth was totally breast-fed, and by this time I was getting very uncomfortable. My sister and her husband arrived. She was marvellous. She contacted my doctor and organised tablets for drying up my milk.

By about 10.30 a.m. the police had arrived. All I could think of was 'What will the neighbours think?' This sounds silly, but I have always associated police with solving crimes.

. . . It's all like a dream. I keep seeing it over and over. I know I will never forget, but I hope the hurt will soon start to ease, even if just for a little bit.

The Impact on Paul, a Melbourne Ambulance Officer

After a wonderful month's holiday, it was with much reluctance that I returned to work. I was rostered to work a 7.00 a.m. to 5.00 p.m. shift and thought that it would be an easy day. How wrong I was! At about 7.10 a.m. we were called to a 'Child Collapse'.

During the trip to our case, I wondered out loud what we may expect to see. My partner, Alex seemed quite relaxed and he stated it was probably a child with asthma, croup or maybe even an infantile convulsion. I remember saying, 'Yeah, you're probably right, anyway as long as it's nothing too serious'.

As we entered our patient's street, I saw a man, in his late twenties, waving to us about a hundred metres away. I wasn't alarmed by his sense of urgency because I have found that many people panic over minor things.

Down the long narrow hallway of the house I trotted, oblivious to the tragedy that awaited me. The man, who had been waving was now bending over a baby that was lying on a couch. As I approached I still wasn't unduly worried, whereas now, in hindsight, I'm disappointed that I failed to notice in either the man's urgency or the haggard appearance of his wife, that they were already experiencing personal tragedy.

I bent down over the baby and I observed that she had good colour, but she was motionless, that she was not breathing and she didn't have a pulse. My mind was now oblivious to the surroundings. I was now facing the reality of the situation. A non-breathing baby without a detectable pulse, a dead baby. All the theory in the world was of no value to me now, action, and positive action at that, was all that mattered now. I gave five quick puffs of air into her nose and mouth, rechecked her breathing and pulse. Still nothing, so I commenced cardio-pulmonary resuscitation (C.P.R.). My partner arrived with the oxygen, noticed the baby's good colour and suggested, perhaps we could make a dash to hospital, which was only about five minutes away. I didn't feel happy about moving the child, or about my own ability to perform C.P.R. adequately in a fast moving ambulance, darting in and out of peak hour traffic. Instead I asked my partner to ring the controller and request the Mobile Intensive Care Ambulance (M.I.C.A.) which I estimated would be only as many minutes away from us as the hospital.

While we were doing C.P.R., I was aware that there were some other children in the house. I remember during my initial assessment of the baby, that another child had inquired about his sister and his mother had hurried him back into the kitchen, and thus out of sight. I also remember that someone else had come into the dining room and rushed out to the kitchen, but it happened so fast, and I was concentrating so hard, that I didn't see who it was. I later learnt that it was the baby's grandmother and she had come to pick up the other children to take to her place. I believe this was a mistake. The trauma the parents were going through wasn't solely their problem. It was a family one and the two other children should have gone through the same experience as the parents. Even though they were young, children have a great ability to cope with reality and to accept it in their own way, and therefore should not have been sheltered.

Also, while we were doing C.P.R., the mother asked us whether her baby was breathing. I searched my mind trying to give her the correct answer — a truthful, but gentle answer; unfortunately I couldn't find one and I said nothing. It's so easy when one's in a classroom and we're discussing the correct answers to give, but when you're outside in a real-life situation, it's so damned hard to know what to say. Every situation is so different and I don't believe there is one simple answer that one could use in all cases.

I had been working on the baby for what seemed like an eternity, when in actual fact it was only about five to six minutes. I was now starting to worry about M.I.C.A. We weren't getting anywhere positive with C.P.R. and I was wishing for M.I.C.A. to hurry up and arrive. I didn't think we were going to be successful in reviving the baby and the longer M.I.C.A. took, the less chance they had.

The M.I.C.A. officers arrived a minute or two later, observed what was happening and took immediate control. I was still ventilating the baby, but now the M.I.C.A. officers were in charge, I was able, for the first time, to observe the parents and to really explore my own feelings.

The mother was sitting in a chair in the kitchen doorway and her eyes were very red from crying. Her husband was standing next to her and with his hand on her shoulder, his eyes were also red. I could see, in both of them, that they knew their baby girl had died, and although I'm sure they still hoped she could be revived, I felt they knew it was all over.

Up to this stage I really hadn't felt much emotion because I had been concentrating and working so hard, but now I was starting to feel very sad and annoyed that such a thing had to happen to these people. I found myself staring at the baby and I couldn't believe that she was dead. How can such a healthy young baby die so suddenly? I tried to imagine her yesterday giggling and crawling around full of life, but as she lay so motionless, in front of me, I couldn't put the two pictures together. She couldn't be the same child. I've always associated death with either trauma, such as road accidents, shootings, etc., or with simply just growing old, but to see a young baby dead for no reason is just too hard to comprehend.

We continued to work for a further ten minutes until it was obvious to everyone that the baby couldn't be revived. One of the M.I.C.A. officers sat down with the parents and told them their baby girl was dead. The mother burst into tears and her husband, although comforting her strongly, was also crying. I felt a complete emptiness inside and my stomach started to knot. My eyes were also watering and I just bowed my head and closed my eyes for a few moments.

My partner and one of the M.I.C.A. officers were organising with the parents about transport to the Royal Children's Hospital [R.C.H.]. It was suggested that the parents should both come to the 'Kids' because it was believed that it could be good therapy for them.

While they were arranging this, I wrapped the baby up in a bunny rug and then handed her to her mother.

The mother cuddled her child and kissed her on the forehead. It was really nice to see her respond to her baby and it just looked so natural. A typical normal mother giving her baby daughter a cuddle. She then passed the child to her husband who also took the baby into his arms with care and warmth. I started to feel a lot of empathy towards the parents. My greatest wish in life is to be a caring, understanding and loving parent and it was just so wonderful to watch these two people, who so obviously have all those qualities, cuddling their baby girl.

We arranged for the mother and baby to come with us and the father would follow in his car, so they would have transport home later. The mother sat on one of the stretchers with her baby in her arms, and I sat opposite.

From the moment we had first arrived and until then, I had had very little contact with the mother, solely because I had been with the baby all that time. However, now I found myself sitting about one metre away from the mother and thinking as far as I could about what I should do. Should I talk consistently, or perhaps say nothing? Do I wait for the mother to speak first or do I lead? Do I talk about trivial matters or more important social issues? What does one say or do?

I found we were both looking at the baby simultaneously on a few occasions, so when she looked up at me, I started to discuss her baby with her. Now, in hindsight, I realise that it was silly of me to worry about what to say because, although we hadn't spoken to each other previously, we already had something in common, her baby.

I developed a great liking for the mother. I couldn't help but admire the way in which she was handling the situation and I was very glad that she had decided to come with us. It gave her the opportunity to have a bit of time with her daughter and I am sure her long-term recovery will be simplified because she spent those last few moments with her baby.

On route to hospital, she told me she had two other children, both boys aged three and five. She stated that the boys absolutely adored their new baby sister and were constantly telling other kids at school all about her.

I hadn't before thought about what effects a S.I.D.S. baby would have on other children. I have always only considered the parents' feelings, but now I was being made aware of how this tragedy affects everyone in the family. Indeed, what a tragedy these children will have to contend with. Having a baby sister one minute and the next nothing. Perhaps, what is even worse, is the fact that they weren't given the opportunity to say goodbye to their sister. As I've stated earlier, I believe the parents will benefit immensely from being with their daughter and spending those last few precious moments with her, but unfortunately the children have been deprived that privilege and, I feel, that will lengthen their long term grieving.

When we arrived at the Children's, I went into Casualty and informed them that we had a probable S.I.D.S. baby. The sister-in-charge came out to the ambulance, met the mother and father and escorted them to a room which is solely used for grieving parents. I took the baby from her mother and gave her to one of the doctors. My partner and I said goodbye to the parents and we left them in the competent hands of the sister-in-charge.

For the rest of the morning I was very low and depressed. I only started to feel better in the afternoon, thanks mainly to my partner. He saw that I was affected and he encouraged me to talk about it. It certainly helps when one can talk to others about problems.

I often think about the family of our S.I.D.S. baby and I have learnt a great deal from them. Regardless of what personal tragedy one faces, it's always better to face it head on and to accept reality — the reality of the situation as it is happening — not necessarily understand it, but to always accept it. The other point is that it's also easier to cope with it if one has a partner with which to share the burden.

The impact of a cot death on this ambulance officer relates specifically to a baby dying at home, but the impact the sudden death of a baby has on the parents and health professionals involved, can be extended to include stillbirths, neo-natal deaths, and some miscarriages.

Brothers and Sisters:

Children have an acceptance of death that sometimes astonishes their parents. Children grieve, have their own feelings of grief and want to share those feelings, and they need acknowledgement of their understanding that their brother or sister has died.

The most forgotten participants at the scene of a cot death are the other children. Whether we like the idea or not they are usually present, and sometimes are the ones who find their brother or sister dead. Even older children of perhaps nine, ten, thirteen and fourteen years probably haven't left for school when their parent's scream, closely followed by the wail of a siren, draws them inexorably into the confusion.

Children's reactions appear in a later chapter, but it is important that their presence and their place in the family is not overlooked at impact. Others have noted that children are the 'forgotten mourners', and in the case of the S.I.D.S. death it needs to be emphasised that gently delivered, honest explanations of what has occurred are of paramount importance to the future behaviour and well-being of the child. Their active involvement can be encouraged. Even the youngest of children can absorb minute details with accuracy, and provided they too are allowed to trust their own eyes and are not given conflicting information and confused messages, it appears they are able to integrate the experience with little, if any, long-term harmful effects.

Significant Factors

There are some significant factors and major concerns that emerge with Sudden Infant Death Syndrome (S.I.D.S.).

Lack of an adequate explanation for the cause of death is the crux of the issue:
(It is without apology that the author repeats the definition already given in her Preface.)
Sudden Infant Death Syndrome (S.I.D.S.), commonly called 'cot death', was defined by the 2nd International Conference on Causes of S.I.D.S. in Seattle 1969, as 'the sudden death of any infant or child which is unexpected by history and in which a thorough post-mortem examination fails to demonstrate an adequate cause of death'. This death is not only totally unexpected but also has no satisfactory explanation, at least it hasn't if we accept the premise that apparently healthy babies just don't die.

While minute changes in the baby's organs and immune systems are sometimes present at autopsy — there are no outward and visible signs that anything at all is wrong. The most significant changes a parent recognises (with hindsight) include evidence of a 'sniffle', or that the baby was recovering from a cold or mild illness, or perhaps that the baby was listless, or more restless — that 'he cried more than usual'. These variations are accepted by parents and health professionals as being well within a baby's 'normal' range of health.

The very nature of S.I.D.S. means there can be no emotional preparation for the death: S.I.D.S. differs here from some other causes of infant/child death such as leukemia, or significant congenital abnormality, in that there is no warning of the death. This means that there is no fantasy — no fantastically prepared rehearsal of what it might be like to suffer the death of the baby.

Another significant factor with S.I.D.S. is the age of the average S.I.D.S. baby: Between two to five months is the critical age for S.I.D.S., although younger and older infants can succumb. Usually both parents and baby are beginning to settle into a routine and the baby is beginning to recognise and respond to its parents. The baby is still totally dependent on the care-giver, but in this dependence there is recompense for the nights of interrupted sleep and general tiredness that accompanies the arrival of a new baby. In other words bonding is intense.

The disruption to natural order that has taken place with the sudden death of the baby: Most of us have a natural, social expectation that at some point in our lives are parents will die. This is within the natural order of the universe, and although preparation for this event is taken to lesser and larger degrees, shock is registered nevertheless. How much greater the shock when this 'natural order' is reversed?

The guilt factor: As stated previously, the lack of an adequate explanation leaves parents with almost no other option but to attempt to find one of their own. It is of no consequence to them that these explanations may have no basis in fact or reality. Their reasoning goes something like this:

Babies are helpless and have parents to provide the life-sustaining care necessary for their survival, therefore if my baby dies and there is no cause that science/medicine can provide, somehow I am at fault — guilty!

It needs to be said that parents will take this self-imposed label (guilty) to themselves in lesser and larger degrees. Some parents will hurdle this barrier with relative ease. Some will need careful and skilful support while they deal with this issue. Certainly all parents will look at themselves, or those who had care of the baby at the time of death, in an attempt to answer the question 'Why did my baby die?'

If the parents raise the issue of who is to blame, often contained in the question, 'How did my baby die?' or the statement, 'I should have checked in on him again', the emergency responder (doctor, police, ambulance officer, friend, neighbour) could reply, 'Nothing can be done to prevent S.I.D.S.'. This won't ease their pain, but it is the truth, and parents will check and re-check their every move (their own involvement) in the months to follow, and the echo of those words will be there.

Some parents will decide, or assume, there and then that 'it's my fault' or assume that the non-attendant spouse will heap blame on them. To respond, 'Don't be silly, there's no need to feel guilty' is useless. That guilt and blame are components of grief has been well documented. In relation to 'cot-death', these feelings are intensified and can in a few cases have disastrous results. Maternal suicides have been recorded after 'cot-death'. A response that will allow the guilty feelings to stay near the surface where they can be talked about and be seen as a normal reaction to this kind of death could be: 'Parents do feel guilty when their baby dies in this way, but unfortunately S.I.D.S. cannot be prevented' (echo?). Nothing more needs to be said than this. The significance lies in what has been conveyed to the parent:

(a) that guilt feelings *are* common

and

(b) (to date) that the death could *not* have been prevented.

CHAPTER TWO

The First Emergency Responders

THE crisis and how it is managed can have far-reaching repercussions for the future psycho-social adjustments that parents are required to make, post cot death.

How the ambulance officers, police, casualty staff, doctors, friends, neighbours, relatives, infant welfare sisters and clergy respond to the crisis is covered in the following pages. The information contained here and elsewhere in Part I has been culled from the reports of responders themselves and from case studies made available to the S.I.D.R.F. This chapter deals in particular with those emergency responders usually first in attendance at a cot death.

Emergency Responders

Although emergency responders can arrive in any order, the arrival of the ambulance first is a most common occurrence. This results from dialling the emergency telephone number for the area. For this reason the role of the ambulance officer is dealt with first here. To follow in this chapter and then later in Part I, are:

- the arrival of the police,
- the trip to casualty,
- the doctor's presence at the scene of a cot death,
- friends, neighbours, relatives, clergy,
- the response of the infant welfare sister,

There are some general points to remember if you become involved as an emergency responder. They include:

(a) Handle a baby, not a body. (Even though the baby is dead, the parents may be responding as though the baby is still alive.)

(b) Take as much time as you can spare:

(i) to provide parents with information about Sudden Infant Death Syndrome;

(ii) to provide parents with options, thus encouraging them to make decisions for themselves.

(c) Avoid the use of cliches, e.g. 'time heals', 'you have the other children', 'you can always have another baby'.

(d) Be aware that your physical presence may be the strongest comfort.

(e) Be aware that although parents are in shock, they move in and out of it. When they 'touchdown' on reality they are extremely vulnerable to your words and actions.

(f) Parents need to know what is going to happen next. Where their baby is being taken, where and when can they see their baby again.

Who is involved at the point of impact?

With the first cry for help, parents set in motion a series of events over which they have no control. While some familiar faces will surround the parents, many will be strangers. Strange faces add a dimension of unreality — 'This can't be happening.' 'Who is that man with my baby? What is he doing?'

Procedures differ slightly in different parts of the world when the first emergency call is made, and in Australia either the ambulance officers, doctor, police, or a counsellor from S.I.D.R.F., a friend, or neighbour, or clergy, could be among the first emergency responders. Another alternative is the frantic dash by distraught parents to the Casualty Department of the nearest hospital.

The Ambulance Officers as Emergency Responders

How do they know what to do for S.I.D.S. parents? The Ambulance Service in Melbourne, Australia, has been in close contact with S.I.D.R.F. since 1978, and all officers through their training, at initial stages, and later during in-service updating training programs, receive lectures by S.I.D.R.F. staff and trained Volunteers. It is interesting to note that the ambulance officers themselves requested a S.I.D.S. parent deliver the lectures. The reason given is that they feel comfortable taking up the suggestions and options which are provided by the lecturer, but are sometimes contrary to commonly held beliefs that a dead baby should not be touched, or held by the parents, and that speedy removal of the body is the best alternative.

We know from feedback from many many parents, that the

ambulance officer as first emergency responder, is held in high esteem by parents. Their sensitive handling of the baby's body, the concern they show for the parents mind-numbed reactions, and the amount of time they spend with the family, are all facets of the well deserved praise they receive. Through their knowledge of cot-death and its effects on families they are able to offer immediate support, and assist greatly in laying the foundations for parents to move through the grief that follows.

What is happening at the scene of a S.I.D.S.?

The scene when the ambulance officers arrive varies considerably, but contains some constant elements. Constant is the chaos, the confusion and the bewilderment of the parents. Variations include a single stricken parent staring vacantly and showing little emotion, alone with his/her baby, or a lone parent distraught to the point of distraction, crying hysterically to the ambulance officer to 'do something, quickly'. Sometimes the scene will be very crowded. Family members may have already converged on the scene; neighbours or friends may be present; the police might be in attendance at this stage, and general confusion could be paramount. The ambulance could be directed to a creche or day-care centre, or to the home of the baby's grandparents.

Somewhere in this *melee* is a parent or parents who want you to 'do something'. What they want is for the emergency responder to say 'It's okay — really, you're just having a bad dream'. What they need is confirmation of what they already know: 'Yes — your baby is dead'. Ambulance officers are aware of this conflict the parents are facing.

Ambulance officers can bring some order to the chaos, and frequently do:

After attempting resuscitation, if this is feasible, or at least checking for a pulse the ambulance officer can say that he thinks the baby has possibly died from Sudden Infant Death Syndrome (cot death). Parents need to see with their own eyes that everything possible was done to save their baby. If the baby is obviously beyond resuscitation the use of a stethoscope provides parents with a reality focus, as well as enabling the emergency responder to be seen to be searching for any sign of life.

While no one will know the cause of death with certainty until a thorough post-mortem (autopsy) has been completed, the reality of the situation demands a temporary possible diagnosis. Provided the ambulance officer or emergency responder prefaces his remarks with 'If it is a S.I.D.S.', much preparation for the grief work that is so necessary for resolution can begin *now*. This cannot be emphasised too strongly. Whether or not the post mortem examination reveals a cause other than S.I.D.S., he is dealing with the sudden and unexpected death of a baby.

When the ambulance officer decides to proceed on the basis of 'possible S.I.D.S.' he can begin to reassure the parents that nothing they could have done would have prevented their baby's death. Ambulance officers who are aware of the effects of cot death on families, can calmly explain what does not cause S.I.D.S. If autopsy confirms S.I.D.S. he will be correct (at this time 1986) in saying the baby did not smother, did not choke on vomit, did not die because he was crying, did not die because he was fed on formula etc.

Parents need to express their guilt feelings. At the same time they need to be reassured their feelings are normal and are shared by other parents whose infants die. While the guilt may have no basis in fact, it is real enough for some parents to agonise over for many months. It needs to be remembered too that some parents will feel very guilty, others hardly at all.

Ambulance officers can provide parents with options:

There are several important options that parents may not be aware they have. Many parents report their feelings of helplessness, that they have no control over what is happening, and later regret that they did nothing—took no active part in this first goodbye. The emergency responder, in this case the ambulance officer, can do much to assist the parents to become active participants if they so choose. Not all parents want to be active at this point, but many do.

Some parents will vigorously reject their baby because the baby who is rigid with rigor-mortis, hideously disfigured or discoloured bears no resemblance to the baby the parents put down to sleep. Unfortunately this is common enough to be a major haunting concern for many parents. If this is the case parents can be told they can see their baby later at the funeral parlour. They need to know that then the baby will look much more like the one they knew and want to remember. It is important to note that some parents will attempt to sever the physical tie with their baby swiftly, regardless of its condition, and parents who have been observed to do this appear to be reacting to the absence of the life force. Parents who are sensitive to this rarely have any interest in being very involved with the baby's body at this stage, although may be very active with the funeral and burial. Parents who respond in this way have exercised an option — the option not to touch, hold, kiss and cuddle the baby before she or he leaves home.

In other cases however, especially where the baby shows little or no disfigurement or discolouration, ambulance officers can have difficulty with separating the baby from his parents. To understand some issues involved here we need to look for some of the reasons the parent can't let go.

This is the first 'goodbye' and the first 'letting go'. Parents have their first opportunity to say goodbye and let go at the time of impact — the crisis. Parents need time to adjust to the idea as well as the reality that their baby has died. They will make many attempts to bring together what is for them the fantasy of their baby's death and the reality of its non-existence.

Some parents will hold on to their baby in the way they always have; some parents rock their baby, or croon; some will pace the floor with the baby in their arms. Others will sit, crying quietly, almost oblivious of their surroundings. This brings into focus the difficulty the ambulance officer can have here. The parents are reacting or responding as though their baby is still alive and the ambulance officer is only too aware that the baby is dead. Ambulance officers who are remembered with affection by parents later are those who are sensitive to this dichotomy, and acknowledge the parents' reality. This then enables the ambulance officer to produce perhaps a familiar blanket or toy to travel in the ambulance with the baby. If the ambulance officer is comfortable using the baby's name, he can facilitate departure (his objective-removal) by saying 'Soon we will have to take (name) to the Hospital', or 'Would you like to get a blanket and in a little while we will walk him to the ambulance'. Parents will be reassured by familiar actions such as the tucking of the baby into bed (in the ambulance) this is something they have done many many times. *Note*: In Melbourne, Australia, there is no difficulty in parents travelling with their baby in the ambulance.

Two parental responses have been reported here. The parent who chooses to have nothing to do with their baby and the parent who can only hand over their baby with great difficulty. More common is the response that lies between these two, and it is here that the emergency responder, the ambulance officer in this case, can involve/allow these parents to become active in this first goodbye, this first letting-go.

Parents can be immobilized by the shock that accompanies the discovery of their dead baby, and can stay in this stage of suspended animation for some time. This other state of being, other state of awareness, wherein parents variously report 'I knew what was happening, but couldn't feel anything' is so common that there is a temptation here to say all parents experience these feelings of alienation. Some parents go into shock, which is defined as: 'prostration of voluntary and involuntary functions caused by trauma', and stay there. But most parents step in and out of this state of feeling and non-feeling during the first twelve hours or so. Numbness does come and usually lasts for several weeks, but at impact this shocked and numbed feeling comes and goes. If time is on the side of the ambulance officer or emergency responder and he/she is able to observe these 'shifts', the laying of healthy foundations for grieving can begin.

Parents are extremely vulnerable during these first hours and will take-in messages delivered unknowingly. Such messages have been repeated verbatim two or three months later when numbness is beginning to wear-off. The words used, and the subtle messages given by emergency responders cannot be undervalued. If this contact with parents is the *only* contact made, then these messages are vitally important. Equally, any suggestions of 'guilt', any subtle physical avoidance of the parent can produce an indelible imprint that is not only negative but may require a counsellor's patience, skill and understanding to erase. A careless word by neighbour or by-stander can cause self-recrimination, and a rift that may never be healed between the parent and the unfortunate by-stander.

The case below demonstrates clearly enough the problems that can arise if the parents are passive by-standers because they are unable to participate, or because they have not been offered options or invited, by word or gesture, to become actively involved. These parents mentioned had no clear idea of where their baby was taken when the ambulance left the house. Again, this does not necessarily mean that they were not told, but rather that they did not 'hear'. Amidst the chaos and confusion, the shock, disorder and despair, it is important to understand that parents may need repeated simple explanations of the procedures that emergency responders take for granted in the carrying out of their duties. If parents are unable to make contact easily with their baby again, an extra element of distress can be added.

S.I.D.R.F. home visitor's account

'A parent who reported: "My baby was torn from my arms" had severe panic attacks when, after the birth of the next baby twelve months later, anyone offered to take her baby son from her or asked for a cuddle. On my first visit to this mother, she had just finished bathing the baby and I offered to hold him while she removed the bath, etc. She handed her son to me and then began to shake. Her story revealed: At her scream that "S— isn't breathing", her young husband (he was twenty years and she was nineteen years) 'wrenched' him from her and tried to resuscitate him. He continued until the ambulance arrived and the ambulance officers then took over. She said "I just stood there watching it all—I couldn't move and it was like I wasn't there". She didn't touch her son again.

'This parent had no clear recollection of whether she was asked if she wanted to see, hold, touch her baby again. She reported "by the time I came to, it was all over" and S— was gone. There are several possible explanations: she wasn't asked; she was asked, and didn't reply due to the shock; someone else made the decision for her.

If the emergency responder says, 'S.I.D.S. has no known cause and cannot be prevented', they can then acknowledge the parent's reality with the remark, 'It must seem very strange and unreal'. Such an approach does not rush the parents into making decisions. It also helps the emergency responder to resist the trap of making decisions for them. He or she can then feel that they have supported and assisted the parents in a positive way.

If the emergency responder is also able to wait for the arrival on the scene of the family doctor and/or the husband, he or she will be able to leave knowing there was little else that could be done for the parents (siblings are another issue), except, perhaps, to ring the S.I.D.R.F. (always with the parent's permission and after having explained their role) should they say they would like the support of a counsellor or home visitor.

The Police Arrive

As previously mentioned the emergency responders can arrive at the scene in any order, but usually the police arrive shortly after the ambulance, or while it is still at the home. It needs to be stated at the outset that most policemen and police women are aware that their presence brings added distress to the family.

In the case of any sudden death, an investigation is required by law and the police must follow the procedures laid down by the law. The policemen and women who are sensitive to the effects of cot death on families complete their information-gathering in as gentle a manner as is practicable. They have questions to ask the parents which can seem both cruel and ambiguous if put without care for the parent's position, that is, that they have just discovered their apparently healthy baby dead, and they don't know why.

This extremely delicate position between devastated parents and enquiring police is most often handled with commonsense, and on the premise that the cause of death probably/possibly is S.I.D.S. Gentle questioning will usually release a flood of information which the police officer can sift, and in so doing complete their *Form 83*, or equivalent report.

Parents want to check and re-check their own moves and involvements in the hours leading up to the death, and usually need little or no prompting to supply the most minute details of the care administered to their baby prior to death. Parents readily volunteer 'I gave him/her his usual medication'; 'He had his last feed at . . .', 'I looked in at eleven, or twelve o'clock on my way to bed', 'I fed and bathed her, put her down to sleep early because we were going shopping', and so on and in this way supply this emergency responder, whose task it is to gather the information, with a comprehensive picture of the hours leading up to the death.

In Melbourne, Australia, the Coroner has acquainted himself with the special problems facing cot death parents and has streamlined some procedures. For example, the requirement for a visual identification of the baby's body has been waived in an effort to avoid adding distress to the parent's situation. In an article written by the Melbourne Coroner and printed in the S.I.D.R.F.'s newsletter, the Coroner states:

However, account must be taken of the priorities that a legal investigation conducted by the Coroner necessitates. If there are to be changes made in the procedures, and certainly whatever information comes from the Foundation would be taken into account, they would not be made without very careful consideration of all the consequences that may flow from them.

Accounts of this visit which is required of police by the Law vary. The following examples demonstrate both the positive and negative aspects:

A parent's response:

The poor young police officer . . . the awful duties they have to perform. When I saw him I thought for one dreadful moment that I was going to be charged with something. Don't ask me what, but it occurred to me at the time.

A father's response:

I think that guilt is reinforced with the appearance of the police. They come to do their job; they asked the questions, and I seemed to be trying to justify it. 'What happened to the baby? What medication was she on? Where did you get it from? Was it prescribed by the doctor?' I was thinking gee-whiz. They are there to do their job, but it is still pretty hard to take.

A mother's response:

By about 10.30 am the police had arrived. All I could think of was 'what will the neighbours think?' This sounds silly, but I have always associated police with solving crimes. The police that came to the house were marvellous. A young fellow and a girl. The boys thought this was terrific. The young fellow went out into the backyard and played football, and Marcus and Justin had a lovely time with the handcuffs. They really tried to make it as painless as possible.

The following case study was reported to S.I.D.S.F. in 1983

Basic outline:

- Housing Commission flats
- ambulance called – possible S.I.D.S.
- baby found dead in bed beside mother when she woke about 8 a.m.
- police arrive (uniformed)
- 2 more police arrive (plain clothes)
- parents interviewed separately
- required to produce baby's birth certificate

- parents asked to leave flat – prevented from returning for approx 7 hours
- parents not informed by police they could return to flat.

Mother:

They kept questioning me, pumping me. Altogether I must have made about four statements. The same questions were asked over and over again. 'When did you put him down? When did you feed him last?' They gave me the impression that they were suspecting I had murdered him.

I kept thinking and saying 'I murdered him, I murdered him'. His nose was all pushed in and I thought he had smothered in the b – bed. The pillows were thin though and separated – he wasn't lying between pillows – he could breathe. The way the police questioned me made it worse.

If they had explained what they were doing I might have understood better. We were locked out of the flat and didn't know what was happening. I don't know if it's true, but I believe they were taking photos of the bedroom. I wished I hadn't washed out his bottle from his night feed – they could have tested it. Maybe if he had been in his bassinette and not in bed with me it might have been different – they may have treated us differently. Living in the Housing Commission flats didn't help.

The detectives said they would come back the next day: they didn't. I think they realised they were wrong the way they treated us, and that they found out it was cot death. They should have come back and apologised.

I felt better when the call came from the Royal Children's Hospital (confirming S.I.D.S.). I knew the police could ring the Royal Children's Hospital if they didn't believe me.

Father:

When I arrived back from work the ambulance officers were present with two policemen. The ambulance officers left fairly quickly. The police didn't speak much. They virtually kicked us out of the flat – 'find somewhere to go'. They took over – they said they had to 'make investigations'.

When the detectives arrived they took me aside and asked me about my wife. Was she coping with the child, etc? I felt that they reckoned there was funny business going on. They didn't care – that was the impression I got. I know I was upset, but that's how I felt.

This was about 10 a.m. and we were in another person's flat till about 5 p.m. Seven hours! My wife was still in her night clothes. I went back a couple of times and they said they were still checking things off. At about 1 p.m. I had asked them to let us know when they had finished. At 4.30 p.m. I went back again and they had all shot through. I felt really wild with them — they just didn't care. All they were looking at was — she must have suffocated him — they hardly spoke to us, except the detective. He was questioning me about my wife. Right from the start they were looking for something. I guess I can understand some of it. I don't know how I would react in their place. Maybe the same. I don't know.

The detective who questioned me wasn't bad. He was a bit sympathetic I suppose, but all his questions were along the lines of 'Your wife — is she coping? How is she with the kids? Does she look after them — feed them?' It was making my mind tick over — he thinks she has done something.

At one point they asked for his birth certificate. I went up there and it was a struggle just to get into our flat — to the front door. 'What do you want? No-one's allowed in here!' — that sort of caper. I got the birth certificate from the top of the fridge and gave it to the detective. We tried to get it back a week later and were told they didn't have it — God knows where it's gone. It drives you mad. It's all routine. They don't care — and their first thought was that she'd done something.

At the time, and looking back, that's the impression I got. They left, said nothing, never returned, didn't tell us a thing. When you get the report (from the R.C.H.) you feel better. You know for sure. With the baby being in bed, you wonder — you might have rolled over — you just don't know. When I have been in bed asleep with the other ones, you are asleep but you are that conscious of them there, that it just doesn't happen, but the question is there 'but I might have, I might have.' Once you get the report back that it wasn't suffocation, it's a real load off your mind.

I think living in these flats made it difficult. My mate at work had a cot death two weeks later, and he got it very different. Not the questions we got. It was the line of questioning and their lack of caring that made me so angry. We got pushed around — I thought we got it pretty rough. I thought if they handle all these cases like that — it's crazy. I think being in that situation in the flats played a big part of it. I don't think it would have happened if we had been living in this house. A whole situation — a picture — is created that makes it hard for them too.

The case quoted above is an example of mishandling, and how that mishandling affected the family concerned. At the Sudden Infant Death Research Foundation we are also aware of the more common response of the police at the scene of a cot death.

The following interview with a policewoman from the Community Policing Squad (C.P.S.) is consistent with reports from parents which show the police do their difficult job with sympathetic understanding. It shows also that when police take the time to explain to parents the purpose of their visit, what their role is, and why they have to investigate, the outcome for the parents can be quite different.

On responses and expectations

I think that any death of a child would be really heart-breaking, but the death of a little, tiny baby that you have literally carried for longer than it lived, I would find absolutely devastating.

It's a lot different from suicides I've been to, or even old people that die, because a new baby is such an exciting time and everyone is really happy.

On the emotional impact and its effects

The last S.I.D.S. I attended brought problems for me when I visited my nieces. While I was in their home I kept running in and looking at them all the time, although they were probably fourteen or fifteen months old. I couldn't talk to my sister about it. I thought I'm not going to worry her, that's the last thing she needs to hear about.

People don't want to talk about cot death. Especially girls my age who are either pregnant or who have got young children. They just don't want to know about it . . . if we don't talk about it, then it doesn't happen. My husband, also a policeman, didn't want me to talk about it — he hasn't been to a cot death.

Because I couldn't talk about it, I showed my affection more; gave my nieces more hugs than I normally would, and probably self-consciously thought, if anything happens to you I know I hugged you a lot today.

Another S.I.D.S. I went to brought a different reaction. When we got back (to the station) I started doing the necessary things — treated it like any other job where there is necessary paper-work, until the girls asked me where I had been. Then I blurted out: 'A dreadful cot death. The mother wouldn't give the baby up. She kept hold of it, and it was awful sitting in there with her holding the baby.'

We had a cup of tea and I was still thinking about it — still seeing. Even now I can still see her holding it and those little blue feet. I avoided kids, I suppose for about a week, after that. I just didn't want to go and see any children, and when I did see them it was overwhelming.

I really didn't think it would affect me like that. I had been to a S.I.D.S. before, but I didn't see the baby. I think if you see the child you really feel it. I know it did upset me, but it took me a while to accept it had upset me.

When we were notified (by the Coroner) it was a S.I.D.S., and therefore an inquest was unnecessary, again I saw the shape of the baby and the markings on the face. If you don't see the baby you have no connection [with it]. When I go I hope the baby is not there.

The feelings and memories cling to me for a while. I have to accept that. I am a great believer in talking things out, whether they are pleasant or otherwise. If you bottle them away they are going to start doing harm. By talking about the experience it eventually subsides, except for occasional reminders, for example when another S.I.D.S. call comes.

On the difficulties of the job

Sometimes it is difficult not to cry. I can get tears in my eyes and have to wipe them away. If I start to really cry then no-one in that room has control of the situation. Perhaps if I am strong, I think to myself, it will help the mother to pull herself together a little bit; . . . I have a job to do . . . so I take a little bit of a step back . . . I have to do it without having tears all over my face. My tears would show a bit more of me than I really want to show. I try to be caring, but there is still a part of me that I want to reserve just for me and my family . . . The part I take home with me I deal with at home . . . I cry.

I think both police and the public are reading more about cot death, and are becoming more aware of the problems associated with it, and that cot death isn't infanticide. Maybe what terrifies parents when we appear in uniform is that they imagine we think they have killed their child. I find this the hardest; they see the uniforms and think — crime, offences.

It is hard . . . some people will kill their children. It is hard to have to sit down and say this is our job. We have to take these statements, and we realise it is probably cot death.

Being in uniform can be looked at from two sides. In uniform you can take a statement and *dispel* the fear that a crime has been committed, as well as have your uniformed presence suggest you think they have murdered their child.

I try and explain that we are more welfare based, being Community Policing Squad, and that we are there mainly to help them through that initial crisis . . . . Also, if we can take a statement that day I think it is a lot better than leaving them for a week, going back, and asking them to remember the morning, afternoon or night they found their child.

. . . when we get a call as possible cot death, we proceed on that basis unless we are made aware of other circumstances. It didn't enter my head with the couples I saw that they would have killed their baby. Besides it would come up in the autopsy. That's how I look at it.

On gathering the information

Basically I suppose when I take a statement, I actually write down my own version of what has gone on. As we talk I jot things down. Like the time the baby was put to bed, and the time the parents wake up, rather than get the parents to say word by word what happened. When I have written up the statement I ask them to read it through and check the accuracy of the report without it having to be perfect. In one case the mother said, 'No, I didn't tuck him in, I just threw the blankets over him', so we had to alter that. It's not so much questions and answers; I try to get a bit of a story about the child.

I think I sometimes ask irrelevant questions . . . to take a statement in a crisis situation I try to bring things back to the normal everyday things we take for granted . . . like what time they normally got to bed and get up . . . sometimes I am trying to get them to realise they were just doing everything naturally; that it was a normal process and it was just unfortunate their child died that night.

To ask the parents questions about the baby before it died is very difficult for me; as soon as they start to think they just break down and cry. I really wonder then if I am doing the right thing in asking all these questions . . . but I know the sooner we get this over and done with the better . . ., so I keep prodding them along and talking to them . . . and not getting myself upset . . . reassuring them I am sympathetic . . . . Sometimes there is a good bond and I know I can help them, not just write things down and leave them.

I remember in one case the mother was almost hysterical . . . so many people around . . . she was sitting in a chair and I was kneeling beside her either holding her hand or knee and writing. The other policewoman was sitting on the other side comforting her as much as she could . . . . We jotted things down as we went.

In another case we followed the parents to the Royal Children's Hospital . . . and again I had to take a statement from a very distressed mother and father. She was a young woman — ten years younger than me, and she was in agony. There was a social worker sitting with her. In some ways I was more concerned with the father of the child; while the mother was sobbing, he was saying, 'What have I done?' 'What haven't we done?' and I could see the fight going on inside him by his actions and movements. I tried getting the message through [that] it wasn't their fault, for them not to blame each other or anyone else, and I also knew about the S.I.D.S. programme [S.I.D.R.F.'s Counselling and Support Service]. The social worker said they would get in touch.

At that time I was unaware that they did not have to identify the child at the morgue, but was already thinking of ways around adding to their distress. I knew in the back of my mind that I could probably take a statement of identification . . . . I knew at least I would try, and so I incorporated the two statements.

On educational aspects

There seems to be more publicity now about cot death. More people are reading about it and becoming more aware of the problems associated with it, and that cot death isn't infanticide.

The apparent bruising . . . which some police still think is the result of 'baby bashing' . . . is just the pooling of the blood. [Known in medical terms as post-mortem lividity, it occurs because the blood pools in the lower parts of the body after death.] I know the police who did the training course [S.I.D.R.F. Lecture Series to the Police Training Academy at Glen Waverley, Victoria] were made aware that discolouration of the baby was present in many cot death babies and should not be confused with bruising.

I feel a little more confident now when I go to a cot death because:

(a) There is back-up by:
   • The S.I.D.R.F.'s twenty-four hour service
   • The social worker at the hospital

(b) I know the procedures:
   • Where the baby goes
   • That the autopsy is performed at the [in Victoria] Royal Children's Hospital
   • That identification is not needed

Cot death is a little easier to handle now; I think because I have been through it before. I have done it before — and I survived.

The police men and women who attend these deaths rarely find their task simple. Like any human being who is confronted with a dead baby and devastated parents they may find they have the skills to deal with the situation, or they may find themselves wishing they were better equipped to handle both the grief of the parents and those parts of the job that must be performed.

Community education is a positive advantage for both the

Community Policing Squad and the parents. The role of the policemen/women (see Appendix) at the scene of a cot death requires that they carry out an investigation and make a brief report of the circumstances of the death. In the cases quoted the same information was passed on to the Coroner, but the gathering of that information left different impressions on the parents.

It is hoped that with greater public awareness parents will understand more easily that the unannounced arrival on the scene of a police car plus uniformed police, does not mean that they are somehow being accused of their baby's death, rather that:

the procedures are designed to protect the rights, and the interests of all concerned in the investigation, and that includes the rights of parents as well.

(Quoted with permission from B. Stocks, Coroners Court.)

CHAPTER THREE

The Doctor, the Hospital and Cot Death

DOCTORS are people who share the ups and downs of life. They share an awareness of death that is shared by the rest of society. They are a special group of people who, like ambulance officers, police, and hospital casualty staff may have the skills to deal with the sudden and unexpected death of a baby – or they may not.

Death is a particular problem for doctors. Their medical training, advances in science and technology, and society's expectations of the doctor's capabilities have combined to place the doctor in a most unenviable situation when a death occurs. Although doctors are closer to death than most of us, this does not protect them from vulnerability in the cot death experience.

Doctors who contributed their experiences to this chapter include, Dr Peter Barr, Dr David Conron, Dr Jan Fraillon, Dr Howard Goldenberg and Dr Peter Longney. The author wishes to express her gratitude and thanks for their interest and cooperation in this project.

Doctors' Comments

Comment 1: First Cot Death experience

When you get there you wonder what you are going to find. You obviously hope your gut feeling is wrong; you wonder what you are going to face when you come across a dead baby, which is probably the first dead baby you have seen professionally. Even though you have worked in the Children's Hospital, babies don't often die, and if they do die, they die in hospital where there are the usual support services. But you are there [in the home] and someone is saying their baby is dead: you have to confirm that. Questions run through your mind. Could this have been prevented? Have I missed something myself? This is an instinctive emotional response, and the answer is usually no. It is important that the parents know the death was unpredictable, unpreventable, and it probably does help the doctor emotionally too.

In a sense it is the suddenness and unexpectedness of it that grabs everybody.

Comment 2: *Doctor's first experience with cot death as a locum in an outer-suburban practice*

The mother brought in this baby which was nearly a year old. It was still and white in the nightdress and she said 'it's sick, it's sick'. She came in screaming and I had a look at the baby, and it looked dead. I put the stethoscope on its chest and no heart beat, no respiration, and I felt dreadful. The baby was warm; that really threw me. I have seen dead babies, but it was warm. Actually, it had probably been dead two hours and it had been in a warm cot, or a warmed cot I think. Because it was warm I thought there was hope, and there was an obligation to treat the child, not like a dead child but as a living or liveable child, so I tried mouth-to-mouth resuscitation. Fifteen minutes later it was obvious the baby was not going to respond. (People who knew the baby were telling me the baby was born with deformities and was not expected to live beyond twelve months.) It turned out it was not the mother who brought it in, but some helping person, a friend. I am not sure whether the friend had been babysitting, or what. I felt really quite shattered and I said to the other people in the waiting room, 'That is the end of surgery today. I am going.'

On subsequent occasions when I came in contact with cot death I was able to be a little more philosophical, was more experienced, and did not send home a room full of people who had come with their own problems.

Comment 3: *Doctor's third cot death experience*

The baby had died during the night and they [the parents] came in the next morning. They had taken the baby to the hospital I think. So we were not actually confronted with a dead baby on this occasion. They were infrequent attenders until then and they were both just sobbing in our morning tearoom for some time together. She was asking 'Why? Why? What have I done wrong?' I felt more composed [than with previous S.I.D.S.]. There wasn't a dead baby occupying the centre of the stage, and I felt less threatened and more able to be of use to them.

Comment 4: *Disbelief is a factor for everyone*

I had seen the mother and baby two weeks before, a healthy, happy, strong, little baby. We commented on it. Two weeks later a teary mother was saying 'My baby is dead'. It was unbelievable. Complete disbelief. She had put down a really healthy baby — then it is dead. I am really fond of the family so it really does hit you. Doctors are not immune from feeling. You are trained to suppress your feelings and look at the positive things you can do. Training is what you can *do*.

As a support for the grieving parents, the doctor is in a commanding position. In most cases, we can assume a pre-existing bond which, again in most cases, both parents and doctor will want to maintain,

Families feel a special bond with the General Practitioner or Obstetrician who cared for the mother during pregnancy and confinement, who delivered the baby and congratulated the father. When a baby dies from S.I.D.S. and neither the doctor, coroner nor medical science to date can tell the parents why, feelings of guilt and resentment between parents and doctors can be a fairly natural consequence.

Doctoring is most often a busy 'doing/fixing' job, which is also seen by the community as a 'helping/caring' one. Sometimes it seems that because the doctor could not *fix* or *do* anything about the dead baby, he has failed to meet the unrealistically high expectations that the family had of him, and he had of himself. The family may even feel he has failed in his caring. The link between family and doctor can break down.

Sometimes something goes wrong—as this doctor's comment shows:

The baby had a bib around its neck and she (mother) had found it dead in the cot. She said
'I think it's dead'. She was screaming while we worked on trying to start the baby and couldn't. My colleague's questions were along the lines of, 'The bib — how long has it been on?', 'Was it on too tightly?', and that sort of thing. In fact I thought he was terrific in the way he tried to care for that baby. He cared for that baby more than he cared for the mother, but I say his energies were directed at that time towards the baby and not towards the mother.

The mother came to me some months later, when I was feeling awfully guilty about not having been able to save the baby. I saw her and I thought 'Oh crikey, what am I going to do?' I felt dreadful. Her recollection of the occasion was that the other doctor [my colleague] who had been trying to save the baby, had been accusive towards her and had made her feel guilty and responsible. She had come to me because I had been the opposite.

In fact I had been feeling feeble and helpless, and all I had done was commiserate with her because there was nothing I could do for the baby.

As far as the baby's chances of life were concerned he [my colleague] was really extraordinary skilful, prompt and effective. Anyway, I was really quite struck that her [the mother's] retrospect of it was that I had been of use to her . . . .

How Does the Doctor Respond?

The following responses are examples given by doctors.

(1) He could respond as an individual. Simply as any member of society would respond when they are confronted with a dead baby – with disbelief.

'I had only checked her out yesterday – just a routine check-up – and she was perfectly okay.'

(2) He could respond as a doctor who feels his medical training has failed him – leaving him feeling helpless.

'There is always going to be a first time. It is the first time for them [parents] and for the doctor too. It is always the first time emotionally for these two groups of people, whether the good Lord has said you are parents, or whether the good Lord has said you are a doctor. There is no training that helps parents and there is no training that helps doctors.'

(3) He could respond as an individual who has acquired some special awareness.

'Support their feelings, their beliefs and what they are thinking. We do very little else . . . get in there with them; give them permission to do whatever they want to do.'

(4) He could respond as an efficient doctor.

The undertaker has to be contacted. One has to discuss the organising of a post mortem at the Children's Hospital. One has to either sign a death certificate or organise a coroner type situation. Basically one comes into a house in which a baby has just died, and one leaves the house with the baby being taken away by the undertaker to the Children's Hospital. Basically that is a simple mechanical role one has played. One has made the phone calls, written the pieces of paper, and that is the simple mechanical role. It has to be done. It . . . is not easy.'

There is little the doctor can do. The baby is dead and he simply can't 'fix it'. However there are some tasks the doctor can perform at the scene of a S.I.D.S. If he has not been called immediately the baby died he can take the opportunity to make himself available to the parents as soon as possible—preferably in their home.

If you can't 'fix it'—what can you do?

1 *The doctor can give accurate information about Sudden Infant Death Syndrome.*

In doing so he is credible in both his own eyes and the parents. Parents response: 'He sat with us and told us all he knew about it. He was wonderful'.

Information given can include:

(a) *Sudden Infant Death Syndrome (cot death) is not predictable and therefore not preventable.* When the parent asks 'But what if I had gone into him earlier?' or 'If only we had not taken him out last night' or 'He had a sniffle. I should have taken him to the doctor', the doctor could respond: 'It would not have prevented the death. *No one* is to blame for your baby's death'.

(b) *Sudden Infant Death Syndrome is not increasing.* It is visible in the community because babies rarely die any more from diptheria, smallpox, pneumonia or poliomyelitis.

(c) *Other children in the home are not at risk.* The point to make here is that S.I.D.S. is not an infectious disease.

(d) *If a baby has died from S.I.D.S., it has not suffocated or choked.*

(e) *Sudden Infant Death Syndrome occurs in all socio-economic and racial groups.*

(f) *The baby did not suffer.* There is no indication that these babies go through any period of pain and distress. As in the case of any sudden death, whatever the cause, general body movement and vomiting may sometimes occur during or even after death. This can account for displaced blankets and unusual positions in which the babies are sometimes found. Facial or body discolouration may also occur because of the baby's position. Apparently the babies simply turn pale and die, usually while asleep, but it appears whichever way they die, they first become unconscious.

(g) Sudden Infant Death Syndrome occurs in both bottle and breast-fed babies.

Two points can also be made where relevant

(i) If the elder of two babies has died, e.g. an eighteen month old whose sibling is five or six months old, parents may need extra reassurance about the younger baby.

(ii) Because some babies are found lying face-down or under the blankets suffocation is still a major concern for many parents; they too may need extra assurances.

2   The doctor can call an ambulance

Commonly when a person dies at home, after confirming the death, the doctor would call the Government undertaker. For parents this type of removal can be abhorrent. (Although it is not common practise for an ambulance to be called to remove a dead person; an exception has been made in Melbourne for cot deaths. Doctors could normally be assured of cooperation from the Melbourne Ambulance Service in these instances.)

As previously explained in the section on ambulance officers as first emergency responder, parents at this point can respond/act as though their baby is alive, even though they know it is dead. Ambulance officers are trained to adopt a caring, supportive role. Parents sense this even though they are deeply shocked, and often recall the gentleness with which their baby is removed from their care.

3   Advise the parents that the police will visit

Following the unexpected death of the baby in their home, for most parents the unannounced arrival of two uniformed police at their door somehow confirms for them that they were in some way responsible for their baby's death. It is important to explain to parents that it is a legal requirement that investigations be carried out to be sure the death was from natural causes. This is so for any person who dies at home, regardless of their age.

4   Explain to parents that an autopsy will be performed

(a) Although the thought of an autopsy being performed on their baby is a difficult one for parents to contemplate, confirmation that their baby's death was unpredictable and unpreventable—that they therefore were not to blame—

can bring great relief. It could also be pointed out that autopsy may reveal a cause other than S.I.D.S., e.g. a previously undiagnosed condition, or a congenital abnormality.

(b) Parents can be prepared at this time too for the sight of suture marks when they view their baby before burial. While not all parents wish to see their baby again, many do. Viewing is especially important when the baby is disfigured and discoloured when found. Rarely do parents realise that after autopsy these distressing signs of death, which may be present in some S.I.D.S. babies, are absent.

(c) Pathologists may need to be made aware that many parents wish to see their baby before burial.

(d) Doctors can endeavour to obtain the autopsy results as soon as they are available and pass this information to the parents without delay, by telephone or during a visit to the parents' home if this is possible.

Parents do have questions about the above points, but often hold them back for fear of appearing morbid. It is not morbid to care about what is happening to the baby. Caring about the baby's welfare continues for a long time after its death. Doctors could prepare themselves for questions about the autopsy and/or initiate them when they feel it is the appropriate time. S.I.D.R.F. Counsellors have found substitution of the word 'autopsy' for 'examination' can facilitate this process.

The tasks outlined above are the 'doing' or active ones a doctor can undertake following cot death.

Parents need two things from the doctor: accurate information about the Syndrome and a human response

Dispensing accurate information is perhaps the most active the doctor can be. This role fulfills some expectations parents and doctors have of each other.

A human response will give the parents acknowledgement that their distress, pain and bewilderment is natural — that the 'storm going on inside them . . . is very real'.

As well as the skills a doctor has already accumulated, there are new ones he can acquire which will assist him in his dealings with sudden infant death. Any person wishing to support the bereaved family with compassion (and some understanding of their needs) may commit himself to learning as much about himself as he can. By discovering his own strengths and vulnerabilities, recognising his own humanness, i.e. 'I can't believe it', and acknowledging his own mortality, he is in a better position to understand what is happening to the parents and why he is feeling as he is.

The doctor who says 'it must seem unreal' is in touch with the real situation. 'It must be difficult to believe' is an expression of what the parent is struggling to accept. To allow parents full expression, and this often means chaotic expression, facilitates recognition of the real-life event that has taken place.

How to Develop the Skills to Do Nothing:

An indication that contact has been successful is contained in this parent's response: 'He didn't do much — explained about S.I.D.S. I just felt better because he came'. Or this response: 'Living in a small community the doctor is well known to us, and it is lovely when he arrives and I am Jocelyn and he is Chris. No rush to see Laura, just a warm welcoming pair of arms which engulf me, a kind voice encourages me to let it all out, have a good howl'.

Doctors who seek information about the effects of cot death on families will have some understanding of the families' needs. While there is still a great deal of research to be done on the effects of S.I.D.S. on families, some observations have been documented.

Acquiring the skills to support parents can be summarised as:

    (a) Obtaining self-awareness — taking stock of our own strengths and vulnerabilities;

    (b) Obtaining knowledge of the effects of S.I.D.S. on families;

    (c) Acquiring the skills of supportive therapy.

The skills of supportive therapy may be ones the doctor needs to acquire or they may not. For any supporter there can be difficulties or barriers to be overcome.

What gets in the way of supportive therapy?

There are four areas in which doctors and the S.I.D.S. parents can find difficulty. They are: expectations, helplessness, anger, and guilt.

1   Expectations

Family medicine as it was once practised has changed. In some city practices the doctor is seen primarily as a source of referral (to a specialist for this and that) by many patients. In outer-urban and country practices this emphasis may not be as strong, but still may be an influence. This can result in a 'disappointment experienced by general practitioners as their expectations to practise family medicine are not met. The difficulties they then encounter in a S.I.D.S. case can result in the breakdown of the patient/doctor relationship'. Put very simply (perhaps over-simplified) the expectations each has of the other are not met.

Parents often have an expectation that their doctor can make it better'. After all, he has been able to in the past. As one doctor said 'if your patient gets diabetes you give insulin; for pneumonia (you) give antibiotics, if he gets cancer, you can do something'.

In the case of cot death, parents expect their doctor to 'fix it'; tell them 'It's not true'; 'take away the pain'. The doctor can do none of these in this situation. Some however will try to take away the pain.

Doctors too have expectations of themselves. Their training has taught them to be active. The same doctor quoted above said, 'We think something, then *do* something'. The doctor's active or doing part of the management of cot death is recorded under the heading 'If you can't fix it what can you do?' If we used a scale or diagram to illustrate the management of S.I.D.S. the 'doing' part would occupy a very small portion.

2   Helplessness

Doctors have described situations where it becomes clear there are variations in his normal role. The doctor may not be in a hospital situation, he may not be in his surgery, and it may be the first time he has confronted a dead infant away from his familiar surroundings. In this situation he may feel as helpless as the parents. There may be no medical team at his right hand, and no equipment either. As with the parents, the doctor's normal supports may be non-existent in this moment.

If the bond is to remain intact—or be strengthened—the helplessness needs to be acknowledged, and perhaps a new type of treatment be applied—that of support.

3 *Anger*

Anger is a well documented grief reaction, and yet the surprise and force of it when it is directed at us personally is very discomforting.

When discussing grief reactions in Unexpected Infant Death, Dr G. L. Higgins says:

. . . there is anger, perhaps unexpressed but certainly felt. The anger may be directed toward a physician who may have seen the child recently, and reassured her [mother] it was only a cold, or it may be directed toward a babysitter who was caring for the child. Sometimes she may be angry with her other children, wondering if they perhaps had done something to the baby.

Where the anger is directed at the doctor, if he is able to recognize the anger is part of the much deeper 'why?' and is not being directed at him personally, he is in a good position to offer and provide the long-term support most families require. (Especially important during the subsequent pregnancies, birth and first months of the new baby's life.)

4 *Guilt*

Guilt can be a major or minor issue as an effect of S.I.D.S. Doctors may ask 'Did I miss something?' 'Could I have prevented this death?' Parents say 'I should have taken him to the doctor,' or ask of themselves 'What did I do wrong?' While the causes of S.I.D.S. are not known there is no way to prevent it happening, and no one is to blame for these untimely deaths.

Doctors can assist parents to understand guilt feelings are natural. He may be able to acknowledge that he too has questions; that medical science has not provided him with the answers yet as to why their baby died.

These are some of the issues that can get in the way of supportive therapy.

What is supportive therapy?

One doctor described it this way:

Doctors who give supportive therapy let the 'doing' take care of itself. They simply support the person while they have this storm going on inside them. Let them feel they are not abandoned, [let them feel] they are not helpless. What they are feeling is very real. You (the supporters) will support them if they ask for it, for as long as they want it. The supporter needs to be conscious of what he is doing and why. Otherwise the risk is there of putting your needs onto the person you are supporting. [This is] equally true for doctors, other helping professionals and lay supporters. We need to have a way of checking out whose needs we are meeting.

Another responded to the question, 'Can you describe a kind of support that you see as being most effective?'

It needs to be a one-to-one relationship with somebody whom they (the parents) perceive as having some of the answers, and (someone who) will obtain additional information where necessary. (Someone) who is not too worried about saying I do not know.

Like the ambulance officers described earlier as emergency responders whose main task was to transport the baby to the hospital, and at the same time support and care for the distraught family, doctors too can be both facilitators and supporters. Parents indicate time and time again that they want and need their doctor's support. Laying healthy foundations for the grieving which will follow the baby's death can also be the concern of the family doctor.

To facilitate and to support are similar, but not the same. 'Facilitate' is to make easy or easier: 'support' is to bear the weight of, to hold up, to endure, to sustain. *Supportive Therapy* in S.I.D.S. is about making it easy for parents to exercise options—to encourage them to do what *they* want, and to support them in those choices for as long or as little a time as they indicate a need. When the parents find their baby dead, their world is out of control. They cannot take in what is happening to them and around them. 'I can't feel anything'; 'This is a nightmare'; 'Why are the police here?'; 'Where is my baby?'

To assist them to regain some measure of control doesn't mean forcing their emotions and feelings back inside so they appear more in control; it means allowing expressions of disbelief and anger, and patiently encouraging them to make decisions for themselves. For any emergency responder it is sometimes difficult not to take in the situation at a glance and immediately begin to take over.

Parents who are deeply shocked may seem unable to think or act, but the S.I.D.R.F.'s experience shows that offering choices, even the simplest of choices, e.g. 'Would you like me to wrap (baby's name) in this blanket, or that one for his trip to the hospital?' allows parents to begin to bring their world (their reality) back under control.

There are many options you can provide. For example:

'Would you like me to ring your husband/mother/friend'

or

'Would you like to ring?'

or

'Would you like to travel in the ambulance with your baby?'

or

'Would you like to/will you hold your baby while I . . . (call the ambulance)?'

If the parents do not wish to hold/cuddle their baby:

'You will be able to see him again at the hospital or the funeral parlour'.

You can ask if they would like tablets for suppression of lactation or not.

Parents may want their other children present, or they may not. Resist deciding for them. Ask them.

You can advise parents of support organisations and ask if they would like you to make contact with them or not. (This is one call parents find difficult to make, and yet they have assured the S.I.D.R.F. that the contact was important. Only a very small number of parents say they do not want contact.)

It is important that parents do not feel rushed while making these decisions. They will be confused, but most often will make decisions for themselves if given the opportunity. When parents have made choices support their choice. No two people, let alone two couples, will respond in the same way when their baby has died. 'I was so relieved he explained to the children what had happened'. 'I wanted to tell them myself. Although they were only two and four years old they had been part of the commotion and I wanted to make sure they understood what had happened'.

The following are two examples of how parents responded to the suggestion they may wish to see their baby again:

'I didn't want to see him again. I wanted to remember him as he was when I put him down to sleep'.

'I was encouraged to see him again in his coffin. At first I thought it would be horrible. It wasn't. I felt so much better being able to say goodbye'.

Resources

Supportive therapy takes time. There is short term and long-term support to be considered. In either case the support required by parents may entail the doctor giving time he does not have at his disposal. If this is the case, it is useful to be aware of the resources within the community.

As the knowledge of S.I.D.S. and its effects on families becomes more widely known, the chances of locating other health professionals who have the time to undertake supportive therapy increases. Community health centres, local hospitals, infant welfare centres, citizens advice bureaus, and telephone 'life-line' organizations will usually be able to direct the doctor to such support service if neither the doctor nor agency approached are able to help directly. Some S.I.D.S. organisations employ psychologists or trained counsellors, and local S.I.D.S. groups can offer both emphatic support and information about the syndrome. Many parents painstakingly seek out information that will help them understand why their baby died, and in so doing gather information that may be helpful to those who are supporting families.

To engage in supportive therapy requires being 'a good listener'. Attentive listening is a basic counselling skill which can be acquired if desired. For instance, a component of attentive listening is the paraphrasing of the parent's words. This will let the parent know they have been heard and understood. For example

'I can't believe this is really happening' becomes
'It must be very difficult to believe'.

'Where did I go wrong?' 'What could I have done?' means
'The lack of an adequate explanation for cot death causes an awful frustration and heartache for S.I.D.S. families'.

'I want my baby back. Why did it have to be him?' is
'It is so very difficult to understand. You must miss him dreadfully, long to hold him again'.

'It's been three weeks now and I still hear him crying, I think I am going crazy', can be heard as
'That is a very common response to a sudden infant death. You must be wishing and longing for your baby. Intense feelings can produce hallucinations of this kind'.

To be misunderstood or misheard is shattering to the parents. For example:

'I want my baby back. I don't want him to be dead', misheard can receive the reply:

'You can have another baby'
'You are young, there will be other babies'
'You have the other children'
'You still have the surviving twin'
'Be strong. There are others to consider; they need you'
'Time will heal the pain'
'He was so good God took him'.

Experience has proved these responses bring no comfort to parents at the height of their distress, no matter how much they may wish to find solace in such words.

Finally, supportive therapy for S.I.D.S. involves follow-up. Doctor's comment:

I went to see this mother because she was distraught. I felt I had a role and could help her in her distress. We had a drink. It was evening; we talked about it. She was still concerned she had done things wrong. She was worried about what to say to her two year old and how to cope in future. The baby died on the mother's birthday. I knew this would be a huge reminder.

Sometimes follow-up is made easier if the doctor is aware of those times when there is a resurgence of intense grief for the parents. Individuals will adhere to their own pathway, and there are some common markers when grief is likely to surface with intensity. Some of these markers include:

(a) Two to four months — most commonly around three months, in the experience of the S.I.D.R.F. At this time community and family supports begin to wane; at the same time the reality of the situation hits parents with full force.

(b) family celebrations, birthdays and other significant family anniversaries.

(c) mother's and father's day, Easter, and Christmas.

(d) the baby's first birthday, and

(e) the anniversary of the baby's death, particularly the first one.

(f) subsequent pregnancies and births.

When a person is under severe stress, illnesses can occur. Even if the illness is influenza or some other mild ailment which brings the patient to the doctor's surgery, the doctor who is aware that his patient may have a hidden agenda, is in a position to treat the cause of the illness rather than its symptom. This is not to suggest that every bereaved parent who visits his doctor is in the 'doldrums' or in crisis and should be looked on in such a light, but rather that a kindly enquiry about how the parents are feeling is another way of saying: 'I remember her too. Sometimes life is hard, and will go on in spite of us'.

Parents do need recognition that they are managing a difficult process as well as they can, and they value this recognition from their doctor.

The Question of Sedation

Parents will sometimes apply pressure on their doctor and ask to be sedated in the hope that their emotional pain will be eased. Many parents who have taken this course of action have later reported regrets. One explained: 'It didn't take away the pain anyway, and now I can't remember what people said to me, or even who was there, or who took my baby away. I wish I knew these things. Other people can tell me, but I don't remember them.'

Dr G. L. Higgins in his excellent article 'The lost infant: Impact on the family' (*Canadian Family Physician*, Vol. 26. November 1980) says:

Drug therapy has little place in management, compared to the importance of encouraging ventilation of feelings. Short-acting benzodiazepam hypnotics may be used for a short period where sleeplessness is a major problem. Occasionally a depressive illness may develop during the grieving process. Although tricyclic anti-depressants may be used throughout the depression, there is no place for them in the management of the normal grief reaction.

It is in these first hours after the death that the foundations are laid for the many months of grieving that follow. This process has been likened to a very lengthy journey. At best sedation can only delay the process, and at worst cloud the reality of the death so strongly that parents are unable to grasp what has happened. How can a journey be completed if it has not yet begun?

At the Hospital

Whether a suspected S.I.D.S. baby arrives at the emergency station of a hospital in the care of distraught parents, or enters the hospital via the ambulance, the staff on duty are thrust into a role which demands much of their emotional energy.

Emergency or Casualty wards are places well used to trauma of all kinds. The staff are trained to respond to emergencies, they are used to crises and treating children in distress, and yet the Counselling Unit of the Foundation was told by the staff of the Royal Children's Hospital that it was difficult to put that training into action when a cot death occurred. Their situation is similar to that of a doctor or ambulance officer who attends the scene of a cot death. Who do you treat? Action is required, but it seems certain that babies who die a cot death cannot be revived.

The information contained in this section results from two pilot sessions, each conducted by the Foundation to assist the emergency staff in defining their role when a dead baby is brought to hospital. The participants numbered twenty and included:

(a) Staff on the enquiry counter (casualty staff clerks are frequently the first point of contact for families) and ambulance officers.

(b) Nursing sisters

(c) Two doctors — one a psychiatrist

(d) Nurses in training

The first session focused on the feelings of the emergency staff, and in the second session the Foundation provided case studies which demonstrated the bewildering effects of cot death on the parents.

The staff wanted a great deal of information. (Preliminary questionnaires were sent to participants to determine their needs.) They wanted a clearer picture of what happens to parents before they arrived at casualty, and were deeply concerned about what happened to them when they left the hospital. Clearly, they saw their work of crisis intervention as only part of the wider experience.

The first task in the first session was to identify how the emergency staff felt when a dead baby arrived at the hospital. They said they felt:

'Upset, I felt like crying'; 'compassion'; 'pity'; 'angry'; 'sad'; 'I felt empathy'; 'I felt inadequate'; 'helpless and hopeless'; 'flat — the day was changed'; 'anxious'; 'fearful'; 'I wanted to follow-up because I felt responsible'; 'shut out'; 'relief' (knowing the baby and parents were on their way to the hospital produced an anxiety that was lessened when the family actually arrived).

As shown by the range of feelings listed, it became evident there could be a medley of emotions felt by each person. For example, the helpless and hopeless feelings could lead to a multiplicity of emotional expressions.

In the discussion that followed, two feelings emerged more strongly than the others. They were the feelings of helplessness and the feeling of 'flatness' that prevailed for the rest of the day.

The staff did all they could do for the families. They were asked how they responded to the crisis. They said that they:

'Provided physical comfort (by touch)'; 'comforted – gave them tea and coffee'; 'gave reassurance – it's not your fault'; 'gave information – about the syndrome and the Foundation'; 'made phone calls'; 'allowed the parents and children time to say goodbye'; 'did nothing'; 'I listened'; 'I stayed with the parents and was available to them'; 'provided privacy'; 'didn't always follow hospital procedure'; 'where the family concerned showed cultural differences (in the manner in which they showed their grief) I made all the allowances I could – I recognised the differences'.

From the above list it can be seen that the staff responded to the families' needs in a variety of ways. They made every endeavour to meet the needs of parents and yet a feeling of helplessness and hopelessness was an overwhelming memory.

While the 'flatness' commented upon earlier could be due to the sadness any untimely death of a baby would bring, some opportunity to share the feelings generated by the event could:

(a) Allow staff to see for themselves they had done all they could do. (This emerged in Session 1.)

(b) Allow staff to release their own feelings of helplessness and anger and so meet some needs of their own.

Note well the second point listed here: *For all the staff's efforts to meet the needs of families, they had entirely neglected their own.* Providing 'time out' in a busy casualty or emergency ward is obviously a difficult administrative problem, but clearly the participants of these sessions had, at the time of their respective cot death experiences, needed to deal with their own responses and feelings.

Some examples from the evaluation sheets from the sessions revealed:

'I felt so much better after sharing with others in the group how they felt; everyone was able to express their feelings. At least you know you weren't the only one who felt that way .

'Unfortunately the second session was rushed and I felt a lot of people would have liked discussion'.

Evaluation of the second session also revealed, it was:
   (a) 'Useful to gain insight into parental views and feelings'.
   (b) 'Useful to remember that a lot of things have happened to parents prior to arrival at the hospital'.

The following two comments show the benefits of providing opportunities for emergency staff to express their feelings.

   1. 'I gained . . . an insight into the feelings of *all* the people involved with dealing with the parents of a S.I.D.S. We often tend to forget that the clerks and doctors also feel quite devastated after a S.I.D.S. has been through the department.'

   2. 'Just being able to talk openly about S.I.D.S. and the fears that we all have will help me be of more help to the parents instead of feeling scared of the situation'.

For parents who bring their baby to hospital without the prior intervention of trained emergency responders, the journey can take on a nightmare quality as the following case demonstrates. (This trip to casualty began 65 kilometres from Melbourne. The family lived in a small country town.):

I knew immediately that Nicholas was dead . . . . I tried to resuscitate him, shaking and crying all the while . . . I was completely in a state of panic . . . I rang the doctor and my closest friend . . . both numbers were engaged.

I felt I was going insane as I continued mouth-to-mouth . . . I rang the same two numbers again . . . still engaged. I tried another doctor a few miles away . . . . I hung up eventually because I could not make him understand. . . . I put Nicholas on my lap while I drove . . . all I could think of was to get him to a doctor or hospital.

I came to the driveway of my neighbour's house . . . I needed help . . . . As I braked, my two year old son's car-seat flew violently forward.

My neighbour was deeply shocked [but took over the driving]. I told her to drive faster . . . to the doctors . . . as if we still had time to save Nicholas.

At the doctor's surgery I was told 'yes he is dead'. I was given an injection, put back in the car with my neighbour, my two year old son, my dead baby, and told to take him to the Royal Children's Hospital because it was probably cot death.

Compare this case study with the much less traumatic arrival at casualty which appeared in Chapter 1.

Often in the hospital setting there is more confusion for the parents, and less opportunity for them to take up options as illustrated earlier—that is to become active in the first goodbye and the first letting go.

Parents who present at casualty with an apparently dead baby in their arms need:

1   confirmation that their baby is dead, and
2   a human response to their questions and their distress.

The moment of the first goodbye—the first letting go—needs to be as sensitively handled here as when it occurs at the parents home. Taking the baby to another room to confirm death, and leaving the mother and father behind can be too abrupt a removal. If the baby and parents are separated while the examination takes place, the parents need to be told where the baby is, what is happening, and that their baby will be returned to them.

Only after confirmation of the death can the parents begin to say goodbye. The sooner the parents receive this confirmation the earlier they can begin to deal with the turbulent emotions that are pushing for release. It needs to be remembered that for some parents the emotions are so overwhelming that they may not be able to release any of them at this time. The parents who appear detached could be immobilised by their pain.

As already stated the emergency staff are often placed in a difficult situation because they cannot bring back life to a S.I.D.S. baby. But if the needs of the parents are recognised they can be met. Hospital staff are becoming increasingly aware of the needs of parents and some provide a special room where the parents can vent their pent-up emotions in privacy, and such is the case at the Royal Children's Hospital, Melbourne.

An added advantage at this hospital is the presence, during normal working hours, of administrative staff who are able to come to the parents and give information about S.I.D.S., and offer understanding of the parents' plight. It is rare indeed to hear of parents who arrive at this hospital being sent home with a cursory 'your baby is dead, you will be notified of the cause in a day or two'. But this does happen to some parents where there is insufficient recognition of the impact the death brings to parents. Some parents have reported wandering in a daze into the street without even a cab fare home.

It is not suggested that anyone would consciously allow this to happen, but rather that each staff member involved in the case thought the other one was attending to the needs of parents. It is obvious that there is a need for clearly defined roles for staff when a dead baby is brought to casualty. It is a simple remedy to overcome the additional distress mishandling brings to the parents.

The following points will aid Emergency Staff in ensuring appropriate information is given to parents while they are still in the Department.

1   Reinforce that if the baby has died from S.I.D.S., nothing the parents or anyone else could have done would have prevented the death, but that to feel guilty is a normal and common reaction.

2   The cause or reason for these deaths is unknown. There are many theories about S.I.D.S. Some have been disproved, and further research is being carried out to discover why these babies die.

3   Explain to the family that the police will be visiting them if they haven't already called. Explain too the police must visit all sudden deaths regardless of the age of the person who has died. Emphasise no blame is being attributed to the parents when the police visit.

4   Advise the parents they will be told the cause of death as soon as the autopsy has been completed. [In Melbourne the pathology for all babies who die suddenly and unexpectedly is carried out at the Royal Children's Hospital. The pathologist personally rings the parents, and writes as well, explaining the cause of death. It is worth noting that many parents carry this letter with them for months and find it useful when explaining to others that their baby died from S.I.D.S.]

5   Ensure the records department has the address and telephone number of where the parents will be staying; they don't always go straight home, and may stay with friends or relatives for a day or so.

6   Tell the parents about the existence of the Sudden Infant Death Research Foundation, and that there are organisations in all states

of Australia. Ask them if they would like you to contact the Foundation for them.

7   Explain there is no need to rush into funeral arrangements. This can be done a little later. They may not know that many different options are available to them, and that they can take time to decide how and when they want to arrange the funeral of their baby.

8   If other children accompany their parents to the hospital *ask parents if they would like a member of staff to look after them for a while, or play with them*, especially toddlers who are getting fractious. Parents may wish their older children to be left with them. Remember many cultures expect children to be fully involved in the expression of grief, and that any family may wish their children to be included in all that is taking place. Children too sometimes blame themselves for the death of their brother or sister; being aware of this may allow you to explain to children that *they* have done nothing wrong.

9   If the baby arrives without the parents, and you know they are coming, try and keep the baby in the department until they arrive.

Finally, there are some extra points for all emergency personnel who find themselves in the hospital emergency department when a cot death baby has been brought in. Police and ambulance officers are among those frequently present in the emergency department and are often closely involved with the hospital staff on the occasion of a cot death.

1   Cot death seems to affect everyone, but reactions and feelings differ, likewise each individual's way of dealing with them.

2   Ambulance officers and police may need to *make* time to deal with, and share, their feelings and reactions.

3   If the department is 'too busy' for you to deal with your feelings – do it later.

4   The sense of flatness seems to be a common reaction; it may stay with you for a while.

5   You may or may not want to allow a spontaneous release of your feelings. This is OK. Everyone is different.

6 Try and set time aside for talking about your experience, perhaps with your colleagues at some later time.

7 You may suffer feelings of recrimination if you have allowed your distress to become visible before the parents. Experience has shown that parents do not resent and are not afraid of your being affected by the death of their baby.

8 Remember that the S.I.D.R.F. is available for *you* as well as the parents.

Squarely confronting the issues surrounding sudden infant death can diminish problems for doctors, hospital staff and others concerned, including the parents.

CHAPTER FOUR

The Infant Welfare Sister

THE Infant Welfare Sister has an important role to play in the lives of families. By being non-judgemental and caring she can represent for the family a knowledgeable person in whom they feel safe to confide.

They will be able to talk with her about their fears and sorrows, and can share with her their past and future joys. Nevertheless, that first visit to the mother or parents of a baby who has died of cot death can never be an easy one for the sister. For the parents themselves it may be an occasion they will try to postpone in fear of the emotions and memories it will arouse.

Some advice for the first visit — and indeed much of this chapter — has been contributed by Susan Lurie R.N., Community Education Coordinator with the S.I.D.R.F. Following this are some valuable case histories and comments from contributing Infant Welfare Sisters, Margaret Clemow, Christine Gray, Rita Hamilton, Dawn Hoy, Leonie Sartori, Glenda Stork and Dulcie Varney. The author feels that by sharing their personal experiences directly, they demonstrate the important part the Infant Welfare Sister can play in assisting the recovery of parents and families of cot death babies. To these contributors she records here her sincere thanks.

The Infant Welfare Sister and Cot Death

The Infant Welfare Sister may be one of the people outside the family who knows the baby best. She is often one of the last of the professionals to learn of the baby's death. She may also have been involved with other members of the family, and may feel closely connected to them. Usually she will be informed of the baby's death via a telephone call from the Health Commission. This call can be made from within a few hours to several days after the S.I.D.S. has occurred, and will be at the end of a chain of events:

Ambulance takes baby to nearest Casualty

↓

To Royal Children's Hospital for post-mortem

↓

To Pathologist, who informs Coroner cause of death S.I.D.S.

↓

Coroner notifies Health Commission ——— who informs the Infant Welfare Sister.

After the Infant Welfare Sister has been informed of the death she may rush to her record cards to check what was noted at the last visit. She may share with, for example the General Practitioner, the fact that the expectations society has of them, and which they have of themselves, may lay them open to feelings of:

- Guilt
- Frustration and powerlessness
- A sense of failure, and
- Anger — (it's not fair!)

These feelings can be accompanied by, and mixed with those of:

(a) intense sadness, and
(b) a sense of personal loss,

for had she not shared with the family the dreams and hopes for the future of that child? Had she not taken a personal pride in the development of the baby? Had she not had an emotional investment in the whole family, and formed a special bond with the mother and baby?

Occasionally the Infant Welfare Sister will learn of the tragedy earlier in an informal way: For example, through another mother. Whichever way she hears of the baby's death, the news will be shattering.

One of the contributing Infant Welfare Sisters said:

'My first experience with cot death was devastating for me. I was just settling into the centre here. The mother was well-known to the services here; she had been here for a long time and was very involved with the centre and the staff . . . .

'Everyone [in the community] here was shocked. I first heard about it when one of the neighbours came [to the centre]. I remember feeling stunned.'

It is often the case, especially when the infant was only a few weeks old, or had a mild cold, that he or she will have been at the Infant Welfare Centre within forty-eight hours prior to the death.

The first emotion the Infant Welfare Sister may feel could be likened to the shock and panic experienced by the parents. She will probably ask herself:

'What did I miss?'

'Will they think I am to blame in some way?'

'Perhaps this is true?' (what did I miss?)

'What can I say?'

'What if I cry? I feel as if I might, and when I trained I was told it was unprofessional to show emotion'.

'Should I mention the baby or not?'

'There was a really big question for me', recalled one Infant Welfare Sister, 'the baby had just had his first immunization, and I wondered did I encourage her [the mother] to have the immunization too early? That was a big professional question for me — was I to blame . . . and would the mother blame me . . . . I could see that some people might (blame someone) . . . that mother didn't.

'The other part was: would I change my professional advice in the future? The 'powers-that-be' say to start (immunization) at eight weeks, but I wondered then should it be later; say at three months. I eventually resolved that. Over a period of time and from reading information about cot death, I came to understand that the immunization was not to blame, that there is nothing and no one to blame for a cot death. The other issue involved the fact that I had not been working in the field for twelve months. I had been studying to become a community health nurse. Could I have missed something?'

Another Infant Welfare Sister questioned:

'In both cases I had seen the babies very recently, and they were thriving; there was no reason to suspect anything would happen. With one set of twins I had altered their formula, and I did wonder whether I should have done that — did I miss anything? Was I to blame in any way?'

One of our contributing Sisters had this important comment to make:

'The morning the baby died the Health Commission advisor was coming to see me on a routine visit, and she held the fort while I went straight up to visit the mother. I think that was a very positive thing for me to go and do it *right there and then* because I've since had another cot death experience. It happened over a weekend and I was busy at work on the Monday. I should have made more effort, but I didn't. I rang and spoke to the maternal grandmother. I didn't actually get to speak to the baby's mother. I was put off by the grandmother; I lost the chance, and I didn't ever make contact. Even now, I still don't feel too good about that.

'. . . That first day when the advisor was here, I was lucky. She was a good sport. Her physical presence made it easier for me. She said she had lots of information in her office and would send it to me. That was very positive for me. Since then I have compiled a file about cot death and have it here in the centre.'

'. . . I admire that first mother enormously. I took strength from her composure and her willingness to talk about it: I really learned something from her. She wasn't afraid to show her feelings – even the angry ones. She didn't try to push the experience away.

'. . . the only advice I would give to other Infant Welfare Sisters is to make that first contact early; not wait like I did in the second instance'.

Infant Welfare Sisters can be left with doubts about themselves:

'I don't think I have been very therapeutic . . . . I have felt inadequate in counselling parents . . . . I have referred them to others who are experienced . . . . I didn't feel supported by my peers, even though we were able to talk about it; . . . they hadn't known *that* child.

'I saw him forty-eight hours before he died – I felt I failed that baby . . . – that day I saw him (at the centre) I didn't get to enjoy him because he was sick, and of course I didn't see him again. I visited that mother often during the following months, and I know I was looking to her for reassurance tnat the visits were of some comfort . . . .'

Infant Welfare Sisters would like to be able to bring the subject of cot death into the open, but there is always a frustration in not having any real answers to give when the subject comes up:

'. . . Generally, mothers don't talk about cot death with me, unless there is a sensational report in the newspapers; they bring up the

subject of cot death then. I spend a lot of time then explaining . . .
I feel so angry because they are just theories'.

The Visit that is So Hard to Make

Professionals of all kinds, in their contact with S.I.D.S. families may
find their visit easier when they develop an acceptance that they
cannot do anything different, or more, than any other person. That
is, they can:

- *Be there* (physical presence) — giving permission for the
  bereaved person to express grief in any way they want,
  without trying to change it.

- *Listen.*

- *Acknowledge the reality* of what is happening for the bereaved
  person.

Having received the news of the death, the thoughts of the Infant
Welfare Sister will turn towards the visit she must make to the family.
She may find herself adding to her initial emotions of shock, dismay,
despair — and even guilt — those of fear and dread. It is best to make
the visit as soon as possible.

The Infant Welfare Sister may feel disadvantaged as a supporter
if she did not receive news of the death within the first forty-eight
hours. Effective support can be given, and is often easier to give
within the first twenty-four hours.

It is possible that the bereaved parent may be acting angrily. It
is important to understand that this anger is more likely to be part
of the parents' general feelings of anger and frustration, than a direct
attack on the Infant Welfare Sister. It is important to be very familiar
with the basic facts about Sudden Infant Death Syndrome, including
the fact that cot death cannot be predicted or prevented. It is
important also to avoid speculation about causes, airing personal
theories, and to stress that, to date, *no one* has the answers. The
S.I.D.R.F. Facts Booklet will help.

Platitudes such as 'time will heal all wounds', or 'at least you've
got the other children' may add to a parent's anger, whereas 'it must
be awful' and 'it must be very painful' acknowledges the parent's
reality. If the support giver can't think of anything to say, it is
appropriate to say 'I don't know what to say' or 'I can't think of
anything to say' for this also acknowledges something of what the
parent herself or himself is going through.

Some Infant Welfare Sisters who have experienced cot death bereavement tell of their experiences

'I have experienced two cot deaths. In both cases it was one of twins who died. In one case I received a call from the baby's Aunty, and visited the family the same day. In the other case, the local doctor phoned me early one morning and I visited the family at 8 a.m.

'During the first visit there were tears all round and we hugged each other. I had seen the baby just the day before, and told the mother I just couldn't believe it. I knew this family very well, and found myself wondering if I was imagining it . . . Was it a dream? With this family we talked, and I remember listening a lot.

'In both cases I was really devastated, as were the parents. I noticed in both families the surviving twin was not put down while I was there: [in each case] the surviving baby was cuddled and held.'

Parents have reported that they remember with particular affection the professional person with whom they have shared their emotional response to the death of their baby. Sharing the parents' experiences can mean a great deal to them, and is more meaningful than exchanging platitudes or cliches.

It has been stated in other sections of the book that parents need to talk about their baby, hear his or her name repeated often, and relate their baby's milestones to an interested listener.

Susan Lurie suggests:

Not only can you talk about the baby, but you may also facilitate the parents mourning by doing so, as well as allowing yourself to express sadness at the death of the baby who has been in your care.

Families usually have a sense of not wanting the baby to be forgotten; of always wanting him or her to be regarded and remembered as part of their family.

If parents are allowed to remember when . . . with you, if you have shown a willingness to talk about the baby's life and death, you will probably find that that is all you need to do.

Most families will welcome the visit, continuing support and the contact with their Infant Welfare Sister. Sometimes, however, they may wish to sever the connection. This may be part of the urge to flee that some parents experience, rather than indicating that they hold the Infant Welfare Sister responsible in some way. Some parents may find themselves wishing to avoid all contact with anyone they associate with the dead baby. It is possible that even these extreme feelings may be resolved with time.

A visit or telephone call from you to the parents will almost always be received with gratitude. Experienced counsellors have found that parents who may have appeared to be 'coping very well' often experience feelings of not coping' at about the three month period.

A telephone call or visit at this time may give parents the opportunity to express any fears or concerns they may have.

As the initial numbness wears off, parents are faced with the reality of their baby's death. Some fear they are going mad, or feel thrown into conflict by the often heard phrase, 'you should be getting better by now'. The Infant Welfare Sister can reassure parents that what they are feeling is 'normal' for now.

It has also been observed that there may be a resurgence of grief at special times such as anniversaries of the baby's birth and death, and other family occasions. A telephone call from someone such as the Infant Welfare Sister (or General Practitioner) at such times will never be forgotten.

If the links between the family and the Infant Welfare Sister are maintained, she is in a unique position to monitor the family as a whole, its individuals, and the effect the baby's death is having on the surviving siblings in particular. An excellent reading reference here regarding reactions of surviving siblings is: "S.I.D.S. and the family: the Pediatricians role" in Pediatric Annals by Zebal and Woolsey, March, 1984.

If the Infant Welfare Sister feels that specialised counselling is needed for emerging difficulties, she is in a position to help the family find it. While it is often helpful for bereaved parents to meet and talk with others who have had similar experiences, experience has shown it is unwise to arrange such meetings on a geographical basis only. Not all bereaved parents are ready to support others. It is preferable to put cot death parents in touch with the staff of the Foundation or Association in their State. This will ensure that contact be arranged with someone who has an awareness of what support involves. The Infant Welfare Sister could also ring the Foundation or Association for assistance in selecting an appropriate supporter if she prefers that option.

The following interview with an Infant Welfare Sister demonstrates clearly that each cot death is experienced as an individual event. It is not necessarily easier the second or third time the Infant Welfare Sister finds herself involved with the experience of cot death. This contributor called upon her inner resources of warmth and sensitivity to be there, to listen, and to acknowledge the reality of what was happening for the bereaved person:

'I have been involved with three cot deaths, and with all of them the initial shock was quite profound for me. How I handled each one was quite different.

'In the first instance . . . I had never seen the baby . . . . I had never met the mother, but I felt I had to visit. I was terribly nervous on two counts:

    (a) I was just getting back to infant welfare work, and
    (b) it was my first experience with cot death.

It was an education in treading carefully for me . . . . I really didn't know what I was doing . . . I can remember very clearly. The mother was very good in a sense because she showed me all the photographs of the baby. She explained what the baby had been on, she went through the night the baby died, and the reactions of the family and the other children. So I didn't have to say very much. I just sat there most of the time, listening, just a comment here and there.

'Looking back on it now, I think I was more worried about my own role, to be honest. I didn't know what was expected of me . . . . Subsequently I did get to know that mother when she had another baby, and I had that baby to care for. During those visits she really wanted to talk about the baby that died, so it turned out that I did get to know her quite well . . . over the years.

'With the second cot death it was really quite different. I knew the mother and I knew the baby – a beautiful baby . . . . I had said so to the mother several times. After he died the mother said "but you said he was so beautiful" and I didn't know whether she was blaming me, or reminding me that something beautiful had been taken.

'I can't remember exactly when I visited her, but I worried whether or not I would handle it the right way from the parent's point of view. Again all I could do was be there, listen, draw it all out in the open, and I spent about two hours there while there was just this spilling out of all the facets of the whole thing. I felt that my role was being there, listening and supporting in that way. I am never sure if that is enough. I really don't know *what* is expected.

'With the third cot death, I blamed myself. It was a different type of baby, and had a cold. I had seen that baby within the week. I was a little concerned, I know, when I learned of the death. I was sitting up in bed late one night – we had been out – and I was browsing through the death notices because we were expecting the death of an interstate friend from cancer – we knew it was coming. Then I saw the name of the baby and I was absolutely devastated.

'It was our little baby. It was stupid really, I was wandering around the house in the middle of the night in a daze. The funeral was to be the next day, and although I had a lot of things on that day I knew I would go. At some unearthly hour of the morning I was sorting through the wardrobe finding something to wear. It showed my state of mind because I could have gone in what I had been wearing. Instead here I was behaving as if it was my own baby, or someone very close to me. I did get a tremendous shock. I had seen the baby just a week before.

'I went to the funeral. I am glad I did. I opened the Centre at 1.30 p.m. and left at 2 p.m. to attend the funeral. I told all the mothers I was going. They knew about the death; it was in the papers. They were absolutely marvellous. Some dispersed and some stayed and waited. I said I wouldn't be long . . . . The funeral itself was beautiful. I really don't think it could have been better from the family's point of view, or for all the people there. I think everyone was very moved . . . . I was impressed with the eulogy. It was so personal . . . . When we came out of the church the coffin was placed in the car and the service continued around the car . . . . It seemed garish and irrelevant when everything else seemed so beautiful . . . . I think this was because I knew, and had handled the baby so often before . . . . I was having difficulty thinking about our beautiful baby inside the coffin . . . . The mother was clinging to the priest, her arms around his neck, and he was gently rubbing her back . . . .

'I went to visit the mother later. I left a note, as she wasn't home . . . I needed to see her . . . . She rang me as soon as she came in . . . . I made the visit . . . we looked at all the photos of the baby . . . she likes to talk things out and I didn't find that visit difficult.

'. . . I don't know how other Infant Welfare Sisters handle it, I really don't. With this mother I simply said: "We can't bring her back, but we can talk and try to do it together the best way we can". She has lots of support from family and friends too.

'Support for myself is not always easy to get . . . . Sometimes our own system is not supportive, but they do try: they *hear* about cot death, but they are not involved *in* it. I think our advisors are concerned about us and how we feel . . . that has been my experience. What else can they do if we don't tell them how we are feeling? It's not just cot death either. Babies die from other causes . . . .

'At an in-service course one Infant Welfare Nurse told me she was aiming to set up a support group for Infant Welfare Nurses in the region. I think that's a good idea because we're right in the middle of things all the time . . . . It is different to working in a hospital. There you might get support from the doctors. In these situations there is a "don't let's get involved syndrome". That is no use to us; we are involved right up to our necks.

'With doctors there is a problem with time . . . . It is time-consuming to listen to someone for an hour or more; and again counselling for problems other than cot death, like marriage breakdown, takes time. As Infant Welfare Sisters we are in the frontline . . . sometimes in isolation . . . caring for mothers and babies.'

Another contributor stated:

'My problem is to know how to support a mother who has had a subsequent baby. Very often she won't let the baby sleep on his tummy, and she checks him every two hours during the night'.

Susan Lurie continues:

Often the Infant Welfare Sister will be asked about the advisability of having another baby. This puts her in a very awkward position because having another baby is such a personal decision. The Infant Welfare Sister however, may be in an ideal position to help the parent explore her feelings about having another child. How the Infant Welfare Sister responds to the parent's anxiety and feelings of responsibility for the next child is very important for them both in their continuing relationship.

There is no doubt that a regular opportunity to discuss the baby's physical progress in detail with a childcare professional who encourages, in a good-humoured way, the airing of anxieties – no matter how trivial-seeming – is of great importance in coping with the subsequent child. The Infant Welfare Sister has an obviously important role to play here, as does the family doctor, and others in the chain of support. Parents may need to feel supported for many months. Recently in the United Kingdom it was found that regular visits by Health Visitors to help support, and record development of the baby, was experienced as being beneficial to parents and babies alike.

To monitor or not?

Most Infant Welfare Sisters find that a number of parents who are thinking about having another baby, or who have already given birth to their next baby, want to discuss the possibility of monitoring. However, the question of whether or not to monitor is not confined to parents who have had a baby die from S.I.D.S.

Again the Infant Welfare Sister is in an excellent position to help parents explore their thoughts and needs about monitoring. However, it is extremely important the Infant Welfare Sister is accurately informed about *all* aspects of monitoring a baby, which is not quite the simple process that some articles in the popular press would have people believe: for example:

- A monitor is not a household appliance. It is a piece of sophisticated medical equipment.

- They may register many false alarms.

- Decisions will have to be made about whether to monitor all the time or not. Will the parent monitor the baby in the car? In the supermarket or when she or he is awake as well as when asleep?

- Grandparents and friends may be uncomfortable with the monitor.

- It is not really known yet what the effects of monitoring may be on a baby's development.

The ultimate decision of whether to monitor or not must be the parents. There is an excellent article titled 'The Monitoring of the infant in the home', prepared by the Scientific Advisory Committee to the Canadian Foundation for the Study of Infant Deaths, which is most useful when parents are trying to make their decision. It is obtainable from S.I.D.R.F.

Caring for Yourself

All Infant Welfare Sisters contributing here agree that it is important at this time, as at other times of great emotion, that you acknowledge your own needs and find ways of taking care of yourself.

Any or all of the following options may be found helpful:

- talking to a colleague

- talking to a partner or friend
- writing about your feelings or the experience you have shared
- ringing an organisation such as the S.I.D.R.F. or its equivalent in your state to have someone *listen* to you.

It was suggested by some of our contributors that:

'When the second cot death occurred I felt like I was repeating the previous experience—it still brings tears to my eyes. I was able to talk to my colleagues, and discussed my experiences at length . . . still, it took a while to get over'.

'I went to a conference last year expecting to gain knowledge and reassurance: [instead] I was really surprised by the depth of feelings expressed, and the degree of sharing between parents and health professionals. I have never experienced childbirth; I felt cheated by nature; I felt cheated of the breast-feeding experience. I am sensitive . . . I was confused. It was such a maze, so complicated . . . it was raw . . . grieving . . . life . . . I got a taste of it . . . it wasn't like reading about it in a journal . . . . S.I.D.S. is a totally illogical thing!'

'I felt very isolated; I felt there was no support or backing. I needed some personal contact from colleagues, but there were none near by [country centre]. My husband was very understanding and let me talk.'

'. . . I saw the first mother fairly often, and we arranged a film and information afternoon. Mainly for the benefit of myself and the staff, although we invited parents too. That was important because we could talk about cot death. I'm sure it was great for the staff. Our only negative feeling was that there were so many people we wanted to reach and they didn't come. On the other hand, I planned it for the staff; that worked, and I felt good about that.'

'I spoke a lot with a girlfriend who is a bereavement counsellor in the U.S.A. We talked about the dangers of over-involvement (with the family) and how easy it is to become drained yourself. Although I felt nurtured and supported by my family, I could tell it was difficult for them to see me upset.'

'I can unload with colleagues. I understand death very well. I have been close to it.'

Reassurance can be offered by Infant Welfare Sisters

Susan Lurie suggests a common sense approach to cot death is often helpful and urges Infant Welfare Sisters to remind anxious parents of the following:

- cot death has been with us for hundreds of years
- its incidence is not increasing
- it is a rare event. There are 499 chances out of 500 it will not happen to you.

By practising good general child care we can ensure that babies do not die unnecessarily, but we do not believe we can prevent S.I.D.S. The Sudden Infant Death Research Foundation publishes a leaflet, *A Common Sense Approach to Cot Death*, which refers to practical child-care suggestions. Many mothers have found it reassuring. It seems too, that these babies cannot be resuscitated (they have been known to die in hospitals and in doctors' rooms and could not be revived).

There is a small group of babies (about 5 per cent of all S.I.D.S.) whose deaths were probably the result of an apnoea (stop breathing) attack. (The term 'near-miss S.I.D.S.' is now out of favour with most researchers). Any baby who has been found by his/her parents apparently not breathing should be seen by a doctor for medical assessment. Often a reason for the event will be found — for example, a fever.

In three out of four cases the event will not recur, and sometimes the reason for it is never known. Quite often a doctor will suggest that parents of such a baby might use a home respiration monitor for a time. It is unwise to undertake monitoring without the back-up of a doctor or hospital. Monitoring does not *prevent cot death*, but may be useful in cases of apnoea.

In Conclusion

Susan Lurie, nurse and mother of a baby who died of cot death, makes this valuable concluding contribution to this section:

Eighteen years ago I took my sons Nicholas aged four years and Timothy aged three months to my mother's house — she was to mind them while I went shopping.

I was to breast-feed Timothy before leaving, but as he was not ready for his feed my mother and I made a cup of tea. A few minutes later I went to pick him up from his basket and found him dead. Thus it was then I became a 'S.I.D.S. mother'.

I was a nurse, but never in my training or anywhere else, had I heard that sometimes babies died without an explanation being found. How I wished that I could meet and talk with someone else who had had a similar experience!

Many years and much pain passed. In time I had two lovely daughters, became divorced then later, re-married. At this time I was able to think of 'retiring' from the full-time nursing I had been doing. I had heard that a group existed to help families who had suffered a cot death, and felt I had something I could contribute, especially as I had had some training in counselling. I made enquiries and soon found myself participating in a programme to train parent-supporters. (One of the leaders of that group was Ruza Trivan, and another participant was Janet Deveson Lord).

Not long after I completed this training I was introduced to Lesley Maloney, then Community Education Coordinator at S.I.D.R.F. She asked if I would assist in this work. I did this at first in a voluntary capacity, then as the work grew, became a part-time staff member. When Lesley and her husband decided to live in Canada I became Community Education Coordinator. In this capacity I have had much contact with professional people.

I believe that while the tragedy of cot death is as great today as it was when Timothy died, far more effective help is available. This is due in no small part to the work of self-help organizations throughout the world. Most of these have been begun by bereaved parents and nurtured by caring professional people. *Among such people are Infant Welfare Sisers.*

PART II

THE AFTERMATH

The restless throbbings and burnings
That hope unsatisfied brings . . .

Adam Lindsay Gordon

CHAPTER FIVE

An Overview

The grief that follows the sudden, unexpected and unexplained death of an apparently healthy baby differs from that which follows an expected death in as much as there has been no emotional preparation. Likewise, there has been no exploration via fantasy of what it might be like for the family to be without the baby. For the parents and family, cot death is brutally sudden.

Through her books and field work, Dr Elizabeth Kubler-Ross has done much to assist the terminally ill prepare for their death. She also has shown families and friends of the dying person how to say goodbye while their loved one is still alive. Cot death parents have no such opportunity. Without preparation and without the comfort of being able to say goodbye to their baby, these parents must begin their journey through grief — the slow journey that moves through many stages and phases.

This journey through grief is also experienced by others associated with the experience of cot death — other family members, friends, the various responders to the emergency, and those concerned with the aftermath, clergymen, funeral directors, civil celebrants and infant welfare sisters. They too must move through certain stages of grief experience, although conceptually different experiences occur for those who are observing the bereavement and those who are bereaved.

To try to understand the aftermath of cot death, one must weave together the various stories of all those different people who have been variously touched by the event. Part II of this book endeavours to respond to this need.

It first explains the complexities of grief in relation to cot death, and that parents have individual responses to grief, for ultimately grief is an individual experience. Every endeavour is made in this section to show that individuals work in many ways with their grief, and in ways that suit them best. While there is a description of common experiences and thoughts, it must be remembered that not all parents experience all the thoughts and feelings described. The aftermath is felt and endured to larger and lesser degrees by each individual.

Part II also demonstrates that, contrary to popular belief, grief does not end after the first three months, that even though they appear to have survived these crucial months, parents are not really 'feeling better'. In fact, at about this time, parents are just beginning to realise their baby is dead. Most report feeling at their lowest ebb at around this time. It is shown that there are layers of grief in relation to cot death; that as the months drag on, from sharp jagged and intense feelings, anger and pain move on to become deeper anguish and more complicated anger. The shock-waves hit the parents with surprise and unexpected force as time, the supposed healer, passes.

The journey of grief in diagrammatic form at the end of this chapter is drawn to represent the first twelve months after the baby's death. Grief does not necessarily end there, however it does have a beginning, middle and an end.

Much of this next section reinforces the message contained in Part I, that is *to provide options*, and let the parents decide what they want. The basic message to be taken in this first chapter in the Aftermath section is that *it is imperative that parents move at their own pace*. Any attempt to shorten, sidestep or deny feelings that emerge, can lengthen the very difficult journey parents are now undertaking. This awareness is especially important for the second wave of emergency responders who become involved with the family, and for relatives and friends who may have been shocked and sometimes frightened by the sudden death of the baby. The clergy, funeral directors and sometimes the infant welfare sister have vital roles in laying the foundations for the individual's journey through grief. The first three days following the baby's death are important because *how* the foundations are laid has an effect on the parents' and siblings' recovery.

Laying the foundations is characterised by:

- allowing parents and children to feel the impact;
- acknowledging the parents' confused/complex reality; i.e. working with the parents from their standpoint and viewpoint;
- emergency responders and others 'standing still' to allow parents movement;

- providing options, thus encouraging parents to make decisions for themselves;
- listening empathically: *I have no ears—I make sensibility my ears.*

(Anon, *A Warriors Creed*, Old Samurai Verse.)

To grieve is hard work. It requires courage. Perseverance is needed during this often lonely travail. In sorrow and pain it is sometimes important to be private and alone. On the other hand, to be completely isolated, feeling no one cares or understands, can cause unnecessary pain, and many misunderstandings between the bereaved, their families and the wider community.

For the bereaved there is work to be done. Father Chalmers of Mater Mothers, Queensland, defines four tasks of grieving to be undertaken. Following cot death, they can be stated thus:

1 to allow feeling and expression of the pain, anger and hurt the death of the baby has caused;
2 to accept the reality as well as the fact that the baby is really dead, i.e. he or she can't come back;
3 to decide to step back into a world (family, home) where there is no baby;
4 to 'let go' the emotional tie to the baby and reinvest it in life (embrace life once more).

If recovery is to be holistic and ultimately completed, the tasks listed above will be completed in an unhurried and individual manner. Task one on the list above, the need for those bereaved by a cot death to express—and probably to continue to express—pain, anger and hurt, is an overlapping task. This factor remains relatively unique to the persons concerned, to their own characters, their particular circumstances and family and cultural makeup. For this reason it seems wise to pause at this point and focus upon the overlapping nature of the task of the bereaved in adequately exhausting their anger through different modes of expression over an unspecified period of time.

Anger

As suggested above, where to place the subject of anger in this treatise on S.I.D.S. presented difficulties for the author because anger can indeed be present in all the stages of grief and mourning, and may continue even when mourning is over. To isolate it is to give a false impression. To suggest it can be dealt with summarily is not the intention of this segment, but rather to explain that anger is likely to flow through all or many stages of the grief process.

To be true to the emotion, anger is one that has to find its individual means of expression. Not only do people experience anger as a result of a particular circumstance, they also express or suppress the emotion in highly individual ways. Thus individual expressions or suppressions of anger are present in the recorded accounts throughout the book.

The following words on anger are just words, no more or less. The reader, therefore, needs to be aware that as they turn the pages, various expressions of these words will be found as individuals relate their own experiences.

- Anger, sharp and jagged can be present initially, at the impact of the death.

- Anger can sneak up in the form of an apparently irrational outburst, at a time seemingly inappropriate to others.

- Anger can be present as a dull resentment which emerges from time to time over years.

- Anger can be expressed or supressed.

- Anger can be directed at others or at oneself.

- Anger can be felt by parents, extended families, children, police, health professionals, health care workers, funeral directors, and members of the community as a result of the untimely, 'unjust' death of a baby who is the victim of cot death.

- Anger is an emotion we are discouraged from expressing.

- Anger expressed — changes the *status quo*
  - discomforts others
  - can create by its release space inside the angry person for other emotions
  - can bring relief through release.

- Anger in relation to cot death: surfaces, hides deep inside, explodes, implodes, forces some people to justify their actions, or forces others to rage at those who could not prevent the death.

- Anger sets parents and extended families against each other, opens or closes lines of communication with God and others, makes some people afraid and strengthens others.
- Anger, *often*, is denied.

Anger, as expressed in the following pages (and those already read) is all or any one of these things.

Momentum of Grief

While the work of grieving after cot death can be seen to involve a certain number of clearly defined tasks for the bereaved, the whole process is a drawn out one. From the first moment of shock and disbelief the grief process begins, fanning out from this point in place and time to involve an ever widening range of emotions, reactions, attitudes, feelings and behaviour. At the same time there is renewed grief momentum — sometimes expected, sometimes unexpected — at intervals during the days, months or even years that follow. Although there may be a climax at the date of the first anniversary, the grief process does not usually end there. For some parents, however, it may signal a turning point in recovery.

To explain this more clearly, the second chapter of Part II is devoted to this 'journey through grief' and is prefaced by a diagrammatic interpretation that has been found useful to many. Developed by the Sudden Infant Death Research Foundation, it shows the ripple effect of the impact of a cot death. Chapter Six is one of the most important in this book, providing insight and rationale for almost every other aspect of the subject of cot death.

It would have been easy for the author to move on from here to some of the ways whereby bereaved parents and families can be assisted through the difficulties that seem to engulf their lives. However it would be overlooking one of the most crucial aspects for cot death parents if a chapter about the funeral was placed later in the book. The funeral signifies for parents and mourners alike that the baby's death is a reality. It is worth emphasising that even when parents have fully participated in the funeral rites, it may be a long time before the death is finally accepted.

For those reading this book with the purpose of supporting parents and other grieving friends and relatives in a cot death aftermath, chapters seven and eight are important. The latter deals in particular with the role of the celebrant of the funeral rite or ceremony. The clergy have a sensitive and important part to play when parents need to express their hurt and bewilderment. The bereaved's relationship with God and the clergy — and their public and private faith in both — can be sorely tested. A civil celebrant is sometimes called upon to officiate, and their role is also important.

The aftermath of cot death is probably improperly understood by most people. The fact that cot death itself cannot be properly explained may have a lot to do with this. Part II of this book endeavours to help people understand the aftermath of a cot death and appreciate why it is different in so many ways from other kinds of bereavement. The ultimate aim, of course, is to give people confidence and a degree of practical guidance so that they can give empathic support to the cot death family both at the time of the bereavement and throughout the long period of recovery.

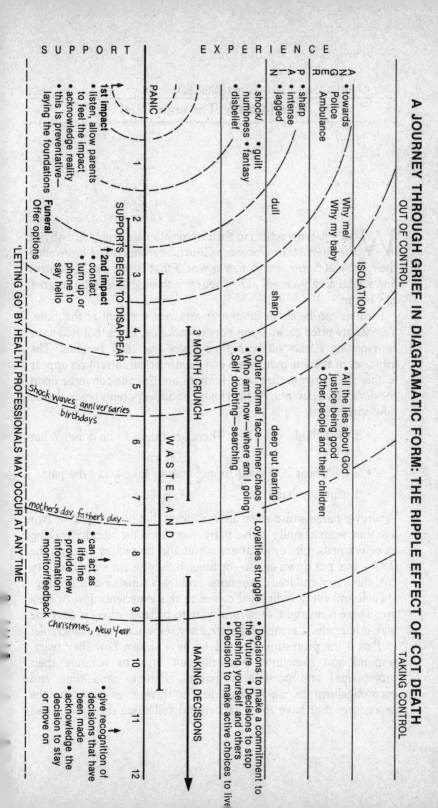

CHAPTER SIX

The Journey Through Grief

WHEN parents return to their home after leaving their baby at the Hospital or Coroner's Court, or from having farewelled their baby at home, they enter a world that is still out of control and frighteningly unreal. Their journey through the maze of grief has begun.

Feelings can be either intense or apparently absent at this time. Parents are often called upon now to make decisions that will have far-reaching effects on both themselves and their families. The attitudes of those around them can be influential. Strangers appear at this most private time, and families and friends converge upon the devastated parents. As the chaos continues parents try to decide how to proceed:

- 'I can't think, can't feel. There are things to be done. What are they?'

- 'I can't bear it. I want to die; please, take away the pain.'

- 'I want my baby'.

Wherever parents turn there are reminders that just an hour or two ago they were a family with a baby; nappies in the laundry waiting to be washed, soft toys that are automatically picked up from the floor – and put down again – or hugged tightly; the empty, empty cot; the other children's questions and tears flowing and flowing.

Each and every individual comes to this experience just as they are. There is no 'right' or 'wrong' way to behave – there is only the way it happens. Parents and emergency responders are vulnerable: In Part 1 the professionals involved have shown how they react, respond and sometimes how difficult it is to separate their professional and personal responses. Parents need time and encouragement to make decisions for themselves regarding the procedures that have to be carried out following the sudden and unexpected death of their infant. It has been shown that even in their traumatised state parents can make these decisions. If they are robbed of the opportunity, many will have bitter regrets about their lack of involvement, or their lack of clear recollection of the events. It has also been shown that their own welfare and that of existing and subsequent children can be affected by their comprehension of the events taking place during the first hours of their baby's death.

During the first three days shock is paramount. Also during this time numbness begins and the disorder and confusion that registered immediately continues. The parents, siblings, extended family and friends, the clergy, funeral director and infant welfare sister are all likely to be drawn into the tumult.

Explaining the death to the children may also be one of the difficulties in the first stage of the parents' journey through grief. In their shocked and disbelieving state, some parents may choose not to do this themselves—others may insist that only they should tell the other children.

As children too react and respond to death, it becomes important that they begin their grieving with as much accurate information as can reasonably be given. Whoever tells a child that their baby brother or sister has died can be encouraged to give, as gently as possible, an honest, truthful and simple explanation of the death. This may sound easy enough but is often very difficult to achieve. There are three points to remember:

1 The children very often are present when the baby is found, and know what they have seen with their own eyes.

2 The parents do not know themselves exactly what has caused their baby's death.

3 No one wants to believe what has happened.

Children may or may not have heard their mother's screams or observed their mother's or father's frantic dash to the telephone. If they were in the home they will have been part of the pandemonium surrounding the summoning of the ambulance, police, or doctor. Often they are bundled out of the way to be dealt with later when the situation is a little calmer.

As parents struggle to take in what is happening they cry out in their pain and anguish 'My baby is dead—I think she is *dead*!' It is very unlikely that any parent in this state will be able to calmly sit down with their children and explain that their brother or sister is dead, much less why she or he died.

In whichever way the child takes in the message, there would be little doubt that some strong impression would be imprinted on the child's memory, given the general state of panic and confusion. It does not automatically follow, however, that children are unable to adjust to the death of their brother or sister. Certainly they will be affected by the death, and experience feelings of loss and grief. If they are allowed to feel the impact, and are encouraged to work with their feelings, most children will survive this experience with little or no negative long-term effects. The outcome will probably depend also on pre-existing relationships between the parent and child, and the child and the baby.

The sibling response to the sudden and unexpected death of a brother or sister can be found in the writings of B. Raphael (1983), and J. Golding, et al (1985). J. de Frain, et al (1982), have also written an excellent chapter on telling the children about the death. (See bibliography at the end of this book).

In the literature available which deals with children's reactions to death, the authors generally concur that:

1 Children, of whatever age, feel a sense of separation and loss upon the death of a brother or sister.

2 Children, of whatever age, require a simple, truthful account of the circumstances surrounding the death (explanation of what caused the baby's death).

3 Children, of whatever age, can be included in the family mourning, viewing of the baby, and funeral.

4 Children, of whatever age, will react to the parent's response to the death.

5 Children handle the reality of death in ways that sometimes astonish their parents.

6 Children, in the absence of a factual explanation of the death, may invent a reason. This fantasy may well be worse than the reality.

7 Children, of whatever age, are helped by their parents towards an understanding of death, when parents give an explanation that they personally believe in, otherwise inconsistencies will eventually surface.

8 Children, of whatever age, may need assurance that their ambivalent feelings of jealousy, rivalry and wish fulfillment were not a factor in the death of the brother or sister.

9 Children, of whatever age, may respond with confusion, fear and anxiety if euphemisms are used instead of the word dead, e.g. 'gone to sleep', 'got sick and went to hospital'.

10 Children, of whatever age, will respond one way or another to the altered family strucutre.

11 Children, below the age of approximately five years, do not understand the permanence of death.

12 Children, below the age of approximately five years may need repeated assurances that she or he will not die too, i.e. they too will not disappear suddenly.

13 Children of pre-school and school age have to cope with their peers' responses to the death. They may seek or need guidance in how to reply to questions and awkward remarks.

The Journey Begins

From the moment of discovery of the dead baby, a shock-wave begins its journey; a wave of panic, disbelief, guilt and helplessness extends throughout the community. The impact that the death has had produces the shock-wave which can decrease in strength and velocity as it spreads. It is a 'ripple effect' as when a stone is dropped into a pond. At the point of impact the wave is violent enough to completely overwhelm. The further from the point of impact one is, the less one is buffeted by the wave. No matter who you are, or where you are placed in the sphere of influence of the shock-wave, you will feel its effects. In Part I, the emergency responders have already attested to the strength of the impact.

The diagram given above is an attempt to catalogue the common experiences of bereaved parents. These experiences were related to the S.I.D.R.F.'s Counselling Unit over a period of three to five years. The diagram covers only the first twelve months. It was through this period that the most frequent contact was made between the Counselling Unit and individual parents. As parents increasingly took up the threads of their lives, their contacts with the unit decreased. The exception to this general statement occurs when the parents become pregnant with the next child (see later chapter).

The funeral takes place in an atmosphere of shock and overwhelming grief. The cause of death will have been determined, but ripples of fear and uncertainty about what causes cot death will occupy the minds of many mourners at the baby's funeral. The small white coffin symbolises the disruption to the natural order of events that has taken place. The universally held belief that we die when we are old has been shattered.

Confronting the tiny white coffin reminds the mourners of their own mortality, and the mortality of those they love. Normal expressions of sympathy seem inadequate in the extreme. The probability of this funeral being a new experience for the young parents is high, strengthening the feeling 'this can't be happening'. For the baby's grandparents too this funeral is particularly difficult. Not only have their hopes and dreams for their grandchild been lost and their own sense of security badly shaken, but their grief has been experienced in double form. To mourn the death of their grandchild is painful; to witness the pain of their own child can elicit feelings of helplessness and heartache.

Funeral directors and the clergy also are affected. Some testify to feelings of awkwardness and embarrassment when they are called on to arrange an infant's funeral.

For many parents the funeral takes place in a dreamlike atmosphere, and when they wake from this state many report regrets about their lack of involvement or lack of clear recollection of what actually took place.

During the first fourteen weeks or so parents vacillate between a state of uncomprehending, paralyzing shock and an acceptance of the reality of their baby's death and the certain knowledge that the baby can't come back. This interval encompasses the physical letting-go of the baby and the fantasy that he/she might still return. In the first few weeks hallucinations are common. Seeing images of the baby and hearing its cry are familiar experiences. Rising from sleep in the middle of the night to prepare to feed the baby, as well as finding oneself in the laundry in the morning ready to wash the nappies, are all part of this confusing, painful and bewildering time. Many parents feel they are going crazy as they struggle towards acceptance of their baby's non-existence.

During this period parents cope, combining routine tasks and practical issues, such as what they want to do with the baby's room, nursery furniture, clothing and toys, etc., all the time with a desire to flee, to escape. Some in fact do take a holiday during the early weeks of bereavement. Often this suggestion is made by a relative or friend.

This was summed up by a parent who explained: 'We were trying to normalise life . . . but the crunch has got to come. There has to be something said about it. The grief process is so long.

The Second Impact

When the 'crunch' comes, there is a second powerful impact from the shock-wave and several factors come together. The issues themselves are common enough; the way in which they combine, however, is not commonly understood.

The issues of shock, numbness, collusion between parents health professionals, relatives and friends, the supports available, guilt, blame, anger and isolation are all part of the parents' experience. How they combine and the disparity between the parents' experience and the community's understanding of what is happening is the crux of the issue.

1   *The shock* that acts as a natural barrier to the pain of the death has been wearing off. This is usually replaced with numbed feelings and responses which can last for several weeks.

2   *This numbness* also protects parents from the pain and hurt acceptance of the death will bring. Numbness also allows parents to function in a seemingly normal manner. They will prepare meals, provide callers with refreshment, meet basic needs of their other children, and continue in jobs and careers. To those observing the family, it appears life is returning to normal. A query from friend or relative as to how the parent is feeling/coping can bring the response 'I'm fine' or 'We're okay'. The numbness parents are experiencing makes it difficult to reach them in a sensitive way.

Parents have difficulty in acknowledging they might not be feeling much at all. After all, their baby just died days or weeks ago. If on the other hand, they acknowledge they feel worse now than in the beginning, they may fear they can never recover.

As the numbness wears off it exposes parents, with increasing frequency and clarity to the reality of their baby's death. Parents are beginning to understand that the baby can't come back, and many give up looking in pushers and prams hoping for the magical return of the baby.

3   *Collusion* between parents and their health professionals, friends and families is common up to this point. Parties tacitly agree to take part in a charade in which they act the parts of 'you're doing well', 'you're so strong', and 'you're coping wonderfully'. In their desperate need to know survival is possible, parents want to believe what they are being told. While parents continue to function automatically, these clichéd responses to their grief sound plausible.

However, they take on a different meaning as the numbness wanes. As the parents sense the approach of the second impact, their world once more begins to crumble. (This seems to be a more common occurance for mothers than for fathers.) 'Lost' and 'dead' take on different meanings. Friends say 'I'm sorry you lost your baby'. The parents say 'I lost my baby eight weeks ago'. The parents who have been searching for their 'lost' baby, now begin to understand their baby can't come back. Their baby is dead. This is the reality. This hurts. This is terrifying. The shocking disparity between 'lost' and 'dead' is becoming clearer. The pain becomes insupportable. They ask 'Is this what is meant by coping?'

To give in now and allow expression of the hurt and pain brings collusion between parents and others to an end. If the pretence continues beyond this point parents enter the 'wasteland' with major conflicts between their innermost feelings; how they would like to be; what they would like to present to the world; what others see, what others expect, and what others imagine. Such pretence allows the possibility of unnecessarily prolonged grieving. Parents may have lived up to their own, and the community's expectations for several weeks, months (or years) before realising the second impact is upon them.

4   *Friends, relatives* and others who have supported the parents during the early months of grief may honestly believe that the family is coping well. The supporters are probably feeling tired, if not exhausted, from their efforts, for supporting a friend through the initial stages/phases of grief is exhausting work. Some respite is called for, so support from others begins to wane as time, the supposed healer, passes. If parents believe the common myth that simply because time passes grief eases, panic, followed by despair can set in.

5   *Isolation*: At this time of greatest need and understanding parents

may find themselves isolated within their community. The supports are disappearing, the parent's world is crumbling and the outside world is oblivious to the parent's dilemma. Again, this is most often true for the mother of the baby. The father has returned to work while still grieving. Often he has forced himself to cope because 'some-one has to'. In doing so he has had to take firm control of his own feelings. When he returns to his home each night he may be impatient with his tearful wife, untidy house and squabbling children. If communication between them is difficult, he may not understand why his wife is suddenly 'not coping'.

Isolation is brought about by misunderstandings, myths and misconceptions about mourning.

When the pretence ends, the dammed up pain, guilt and anger come flooding back. Faced with this onslaught, parents can do nothing but withdraw. As a consequence, the parent experiences a new degree of isolation.

6 *Guilt*: As shown in Part 1, guilty feelings over the baby's death are inescapable following cot death. From a study of fifty-one parents (twenty-eight females, twenty-three males) conducted by the Swinburne Institute of Technology Psychology students it was found:

As it would be expected, S.I.D.S. elicited profound guilt in many parents (73 per cent) immediately following the death of their child. To these parents, it seemed that their capabilities were called into question. In fact, 32 per cent of parents considered that they or their partners were [directly] responsible for the death, often believing that the child had suffocated due to parental neglect. Guilt was also indicated by a number of parents who felt that they could have prevented the death if they had only done something, such as finding the baby earlier in order to attempt resuscitation. Several parents also expressed regret for their past lack of involvement, and/or appreciation of their child, or for their impatience with the child's demands.

When parents cry out several weeks or months later, 'But I still feel guilty', it is important to encourage them to air those feelings for they last long after others have 'forgiven' them. Many parents take a long time to accept that they were unable to protect their baby from harm (death), or that in some way they let their baby die. Initially it is impossible to accept that the death was not *some-one's* fault.

7   *Blame and anger* that was at first focused on the police, a doctor, the ambulance officers or other emergency responder, may shift to the relatives and friends, the surviving children, spouse (again), a counsellor, a neighbour or to God, as parents ask again 'Why me? Why my baby?'

Having exhausted these avenues, the parents themselves may decide to accept the blame. If the parents can find no fault with their respective care-giving roles, they will probably examine the past for possible explanations. This normally leads to the death of their baby being seen as a punishment for past sins, real or imagined. The parents may now submit to the guilt for unexpiated past sins.

8   *Nightmares and dreams*: Dreams too at this time can be particularly distressing, and can take on a nightmare quality. Not all parents have this experience (some participate in active imagination or fantasy), but those that do describe, among others, images that relate to the decomposition of their baby's body, and/or a searching for their baby, or dreams that indicate to the parent that the baby is still alive.

While dreams are intensely personal, and cannot be interpreted other than in a personal way, the following examples are given to indicate the areas that may be explored in a counselling session with a parent who is reporting nightmares or disturbing dreams.

(a) *A 'lost' baby*:

A dream which shows the parent searching for the baby may be tied to the parent's inability to visit the grave and thus locate the baby in reality. Or a dream such as this may indicate that the parent has not yet accepted the reality that the baby is really dead and can't come back.

(b) *A dream in which the baby is alone*:
Dreams of this kind may have been precipitated by a real event such as a particularly cold day or night, and the parent's concern that their baby can still feel the cold or rain, i.e. the parent is still struggling with the need and longing to nurture and care for the baby.

(c) *A dream in which the baby's body is in a state of decomposition*:

A dream of this kind is probably the most horrifying a parent can experience, and may be linked to the previous examples, that is *the baby is gone, and the parent's role has disappeared as well.*

With this dream there is the added emphasis of the parent not being able to protect their baby from harm (death), or from the natural cycle of living and dying.

Nightmares and disturbing dreams usually reflect anxiety. In the examples given above intense grief and sadness accompany the parent's anxiety at not being able to fulfill their parenting role.

Disturbing dreams following cot death could be seen as an opportunity for the parent to acknowledge an aspect of their anxiety and grief that has not previously been heard, understood or acknowledged, and therefore could not be responded to in their waking hours. When the parent understands the message in the dream, and is able to address the issue, the dream will gradually fade.

9   *The 'crunch'—a milestone*: Parents who have struggled daily out of bed to attend to their family's needs, wake one morning to discover they can go on no longer. In a state of apprehension and anxiety the parent approaches the second impact. Pain, overwhelmingly sharp, jagged and intense, reemerges with terrifying intensity. Previously, numbness provided a thin dull coat as a covering. Utter despair results when a parent accepts the baby is dead.

Parents, who are so totally overwhelmed, are oblivious to the phase of grief that is passing, and the new one that is about to begin. What has passed is the death, the funeral, the shock and the numbness. This is the point of entry into many many months of profound personal struggle, often a lonely period during which a reappraisal of life values cannot be avoided, and grieving continues. Parents emerge from this 'wasteland' with changed views and values about themselves and the world in which they live.

It should be noted that the second impact overlaps the period from about six weeks after the death to beyond four months. Because the individual responds to his/her own needs, these times should only be seen as very approximate. For some parents this 'crunch' can occur a year or more later, but for a few, not at all. Recognition and acknowledgement of this experience is important *whenever* it occurs.

The Wasteland

The diagram shows the wasteland overlapping a period of months— from around three months to near the completion of the first twelve months of grief. Again it is important to stress that the dates themselves are used only as approximations. Individuals decide their own timing within which they work towards a resolution of their grief.

When parents accept the reality as well as the fact of their baby's death, the ravages of the catastrophe are laid bare. Often with an outer normal face, but inner chaos, the devastated family faces the future. The empty arms that still long to hold a baby may physically ache less often, but the emptiness inside brings an ache that seems impossible to assuage.

During this period in the wasteland, parents spend time feeling the pain and hurt that the death of the baby has brought. The hurt may show itself in anger. Anger that the world goes on in spite of them or perhaps to spite them. Anger deepens, may not be obvious, or it may be so visible that friends and relatives may be stunned by its force so long after the death. They may also wonder why the anger is directed at them. Parents' minds are increasingly occupied with profound concerns. Questions of loyalty arise, as well as deep philosophical issues.

Loyalty:

The accepted way of grieving followed by modern western society encourages and enforces the supression of the parent's inner dialogue; those voices inside that say:

But I'm not feeling better as time goes by . . . I'm keeping busy at work, but it isn't helping, and besides, work isn't as fulfilling as it was . . . But I know that having another baby isn't going to take away my feelings about Clare. If I have another baby what would she think? Would she think I have forgotten her so soon?

Parents feel a powerful loyalty to their dead baby. At the same time they feel a strong loyalty to their friends and relatives who have given support. These demands are often in opposition and lead to inner chaos. These conflicting loyalties can create immense inner tensions which compete for expression. This will often interfere with each person's need to grieve in their own individual way, and at their own pace.

Philosophical questions

Loyalty to previously held religious beliefs can also begin to be questioned. Parents are forced to examine the commonly held belief that reward and punishment is meted out according to some divine plan. The spectres of morality and justice rise from the ruins of previously unquestioned beliefs. Where do parents stand if they believe God is good and kind? When bad things happen to good people a different view of good and bad needs to be found. It is awesome to witness the parent's outraged attack on God when they demand of him 'Why me? Why my baby?' The energy and courage required to find the answers to these questions is often wrung out of exhausted parents.

One father, who was not speaking from a religious viewpoint, summed up the views of many when he said: 'It's not fair. It's just not fair'.

Self-esteem:

'Who am I now?' 'Where am I going?' 'Am I less than I was?' are questions that in each case relate to the parents' feelings of self-esteem. If it is the first-born child that dies, the loss of the parenting role is intensely felt. The mother has been robbed of her reason for being. The father has been cheated of his special role, so briefly experienced. Additionally for the father, feelings of failure to protect his family may be present. For all parents diminished feelings of self-worth are common. Doubts surface about 'good enough' parenting. This applies to surviving children, as well as to the baby that died.

The parents' very existence is penetrated by intense episodes of self-doubt. Fathers have reported fleeting thoughts of changing jobs and home. This father reflects his feelings of low self-esteem and his frustration at a missed opportunity: 'I was put up for a promotion. (In the public service where the appeals system operates). After the baby died I was in such a state of mind that I didn't appeal against the guy who appealed against me. I have been kicked in the guts twice now, and it is something you have to live with for a long time: not only the cot death of course, but realising I buggered the position I had.'

A mother whose first-born child died of cot death addressed the 'Who am I now? Where am I going? Am I less than I was?' syndrome when she said: 'I don't fit in with my friends any more. They all have babies still. I know when I am with them I am a reminder that babies can die. We are uncomfortable together. They try [and] I try to forget I am a mother without a baby. It doesn't work well. I feel lonely. All my family live overseas.'

Norma whose first child died of S.I.D.S., said: 'John's job had changed three weeks before Andrea died. It left me feeling confused because of the life-style change. John gave up his old friends who worked on the factory floor — the friends we played cards with and went on picnics with. When Andrea died I had no baby and a husband with a new job. I was not a mother any more, just the wife. Nothing was the same as before. I felt I had nothing to live for. I went back to work where I had some security, my old job. They understood I had to go back to work . . . they let me stay there.'

Relationships:

Husbands and wives usually express their grief quite differently. The mother may be preoccupied with painful memories of the baby, and trying to fill the empty days; the father occupied with stresses at his work place, and the difficulties associated with grieving while still performing at a level that will ensure continuing job satisfaction, and even continuing employment.

The husband often expresses concern at his wife's persistent sorrow, and can decide that her grief is too visible and too prolonged, that she 'is not getting over it'. The relationship may be stretched to breaking point, and separations are not uncommon at this time. Another way of dealing with the feelings of emptiness is to decide to have another baby. Either husband or wife can apply subtle pressures to the other in the hope or belief that the next child will ease the pain and perhaps provide a reason for living.

Mothers, fathers and children:

Children may still be trying to find ways of expressing their grief. If the child has been exhibiting withdrawn 'good' behaviour or has opted to be noisy, naughty and 'bad', parents may become increasingly concerned and frustrated by the child's altered behaviour. Many seek reassurance and guidance in their handling of the situation. With the combination of a strained marital relationship, and the disruption that can result from the child's different and often difficult behaviour, it is not uncommon to find the family facing much discord and pervading unhappiness.

Some difficulties can often be resolved by examining early explanations or questions. It is important to assure children that nothing they did caused the baby's death. They may be asked an innocent question: 'Was the baby awake when you went in this morning?' From this the child may believe that he in some way caused the baby's death. Many months after the death the whole family may need repeated assurance that cot death cannot be predicted or prevented.

Other people and their children:

Friends, neighbours and relatives can be perplexed and hurt by a parent's apparent lack of interest in their babies. This is often far from the case. For parents, the emotions of jealousy and pain and love and longing conflict with the desire to hold a baby again. The sight of another baby can be felt as a knife thrust and the 'Why me?' question asked again. Memories surge to the surface when grieving parents hold a baby in their arms. Sometimes the memories are overpoweringly sweet; at other times the memory of finding their baby dead causes overwhelming pain. A pain that cannot always be assuaged by holding someone else's baby.

Friends, neighbours, relatives and parents may be more comfortable with each other when they become aware of each other's position. When a bereaved parent and a friend or relative come face-to-face, the issues that stand between them often look like this:

Friend:
- I want to 'do something' to ease your pain.
- I will share my baby with you for a little while.
- Surely you're 'over it' by now — let's prove it.
- It's time you had another baby anyhow.
- I don't believe my baby will 'catch' cot death from you.
- I am glad my baby is alive — I want to say how grateful I am.

Parent:
- When I look at you with your baby I feel angry.
- Why did it have to be me/us?
- I feel jealous. I don't want your baby dead, but I want mine alive and in my arms.
- I am in so much pain, I want my baby back. Can't you understand? I need you to understand!

To summarise: There are parents for whom the sight of another baby causes pain and anger, and who will *not* want to show any interest. There are those for whom the sight of another baby causes a surge of love and longing for their baby, who will want to cuddle the baby and cry. There are parents for whom the sight of another baby causes both the above responses, a situation full of conflict for all concerned. More commonly, there are parents for whom the sight of a friend's baby elicits the response: '*Today* I want to hold your baby; tomorrow I might not want to. Please try to understand'.

This pain is sometimes deliberately hidden, for fear of being seen by friends, neighbours and relatives as 'not coping' or 'not getting over it'. Parents describe the pain as 'leaden', or 'a boulder pressing on the heart' or 'in the gut': the weight may cause a parent to cry out silently 'My heart is breaking'. The dead weight of the pain is juxtaposed against feelings of emptiness. These feelings are so oppressive that it seems no other feeling is possible, or ever will be.

Misconceptions: (Of the observers *and* the bereaved)

There are many misunderstandings between the bereaved and those observing the bereavement during this time in the 'wasteland'. During the first three months of grief, both the parents and the wider community expect that life will be grim for the parents who are mourning their baby.

However, there is still a common misconception that time, of itself, heals grief. There is little awareness of the depth and duration of grief. Surges of intense pain still claim the parent many months after the death. Parents attempt to maintain a normal countenance in their desire to believe and demonstrate that they are 'getting over it'. Conversely this display will sometimes be so convincing that a friend or relative may wonder, 'Does she think about her baby anymore?' A child is never forgotten — mourning for the baby ceases eventually, but the memories remain.

Anniversaries:

Observers may or may not be aware that during the first year, parents must confront many anniversaries, not just the anniversary of the baby's death. The baby's first birthday is an extremely emotional time for the family. Given that the occurrence of cot death is high for babies between the ages of two to five months, the first birthday often arrives before the anniversary of the death. In the western world we expect babies to survive their first year. A child's first birthday party is often imagined during pregnancy. It is a deep blow when the fantasy is not realised.

Mother's Day, Father's Day, Easter, Christmas, family birthdays, school holidays, any family gathering or celebration, weddings and engagements bring into sharp focus the absence of the baby. The grieving family can find these occasions extremely difficult. Loyalty to family members (wanting to be happy for them) and loyalty to their dead baby causes conflict. Gladness for family members is tinged with sadness for self. Many parents also attest to the guilt they feel when they 'laugh too early'.

The first Christmas without the baby is poignant. Celebrating Christmas is about celebrating the birth of a very special baby; the irony is difficult to bear.

Guilt and self-forgiveness:

Although friends, relatives and health professionals have given many assurances that the baby's death was not the fault of the parents, the parents are the only ones who can give themselves absolution from the guilt they take to themselves to a lesser and larger degree. *Self-forgiveness* following cot death means not only giving up the belief that 'I must have been able to do something to prevent the death', but also acknowledging 'it's alright for me to be alive even though my baby is dead'.

Guilt and punishment go hand-in-hand — so we have been taught. With the cot death experience, punishment is most likely to be self-imposed. The parents, or whomsoever had the care of the baby at the time of its death, are exhorted not to blame themselves, but as has been previously explained it is really impossible not to impose some degree of self-blame. Blaming themselves or someone else for the death is part of the process parents go through before they can forgive themselves or others, before finally accepting the fact that the causes of cot death are unknown, and that therefore blame cannot be apportioned anywhere. The death was not 'just'. It is this alleviation of guilt that parents deal with during the 'wasteland'.

Grief:

It is against this background that parents continue to mourn their baby. There are still intense bouts of pain and tears, but there are spaces between these overwhelming episodes when parents glimpse a future that can make some sense. There are surges of energy and hopefulness which are replaced all too quickly with feelings of despair and fear when a painful reminder of the baby surfaces unexpectedly. Parents are often frightened by the strength of their pain when it is felt many months after the death. There are still days when it is impossible to believe that the pain will ever go. In this state a parent can ask: 'Do I want to survive?' 'What does survival mean?' 'What kind of life can I have without my baby?'

The Turning Point – (Taking control)

On the diagram, the turning point overlaps the period from about eight months after the death to beyond the first anniversary of the death. Again, the dates only indicate that another change occurs – not when it happens. Again and again it needs to be stated that parents work to their own timing, and are often unaware themselves that a stage or phase is passing, or has passed, until long after the movement is completed.

Before parents reach the turning point, their experience could be likened to that of a wanderer, journeying through a strange and alien land, for the world they knew and experienced changed overnight, became frighteningly unreal and out of control.

When parents decide to take control of their world once more, they make an active choice to do so. A world that has been traumatically shattered takes an indeterminate time to restructure. The parents do not reconstruct their world easily. Parents may give up feeling guilty, and stop punishing themselves and others, but may need to struggle for months or years longer with their feelings of loyalty and their reevaluation of life. Some parts of the past are easier to leave behind than others.

It is not easy to describe this next movement because the timing is extremely individual, and taking control involves making active choices about the future – a future that can be shaped to an individual's needs, as well as each family's needs. This task is not easy: parents have learned that planning for the future involves taking risks. They have learned this in the most painful way. A great deal of courage is needed to step out into the abyss again – that measureless dimension called 'the future'.

This phase of determining the future also demands a 'letting go' of the punishment and the anger, the pain and the guilt, and parts of the past. These burdens can weigh heavily if taken into the future. Letting go means parents stop punishing themselves and others for their baby's death. They forgive the baby for dying and themselves for its death. Guilt is jettisoned. They renounce the pain, that emotional tie to the baby. They cease to look back for the person, or family they once were. Much will depend on how they have resolved loyalty and philosophical conflicts. A reappraisal of values and loyalties has brought them to the threshold of the future.

Before parents can let go, they 'hang on' tightly to what has been. One way or another they find ways to embrace their child one last time. In *Anatomy of Bereavement*, B. Raphael says: 'As there is a growing acceptance of the finality of the loss, there is an increasing preoccupation with memories and a review of the lost relationship'.

There is fear and uncertainty in those moments of last embrace. Letting go means giving the baby up to the past. Before there can be a future, one must deal with the present.

No one has mentioned his name for months. They have all forgotten him. If only they knew how much that hurts. It is as though he never existed. He did exist and he has a name. When I talk about him they all look uncomfortable. Do *I* have to forget him too? I won't! The pain isn't as bad any more, but they make me wonder about that. Should it be? Should I feel that pain forever? I don't want his memory to fade, but I don't want the pain any more either.

Since the baby's life is denied existence the parents will hang on to the hurt and pain to keep the baby's memory alive. When parents are encouraged to give expression to the life the child lived, his existence within the family is assured. It is the integration of the baby's life and death into the parent's emotional life that allows the baby to be given up.

Some mention needs to be made of the confusion between memories and mourning. Mourning is to grieve — be sorrowful; memory is a having, or keeping in the mind, a remembrance. Many parents, as well as the wider community, believe that when mourning is completed the baby is forgotten. This is simply not so. Parents do not want to forget their baby: Many fear they will when they cease sorrowing. The memory of the baby can be held fast, it is the mourning that is let go. Memories and mourning are not the same. Whenever the baby's name is mentioned, his place, his existence, is affirmed within the family. He is remembered. At the turning point, parents realise that they can begin to hang on to the memories without so much pain.

At the turning point there are changed, or changing values; values which have brought the parents this far in life. Although the future is uncertain, at the turning point, parents reclaim hope.

Diana Simpson gives this parent's account:

It was pointed out to me recently that it seems possible that when a baby dies from cot death, as many as fifty people may be drastically affected by this death. On reflection of our own circumstances when Donna died just over four years ago at the age of two months and two weeks, many of our relatives and friends were not only shaken by Donna's death, as we were, but so many of them also took it upon themselves to assess the situation on our behalf.

The unfortunate thing about general assessment in relation to grief is that not any two people grieve in exactly the same way. Trying to get this message across to our loved ones and those friends who cared about our loss was most difficult as we ran the risk of offending them, so most of the time we just kept quiet about our inner feelings.

As it was, Allen and I already had a great deal of difficulty in communicating with each other, and then there was the problem of communicating with our other three children. We had never had any direct contact with death before, and just didn't know how to go about guiding our children and ourselves through our pain.

In those very early days following Donna's death I can remember that Allen just did not want to talk about her death or anything to do with her. We initially did not grieve openly for her, and I found this very hard to take. I thought that he did not care that our daughter had died and this greatly increased the pain of her death for me. The children were at the time aged eight, seven and two and a half, and each of them were coping with her loss differently. At times I felt that I was having to share in the grief of four other people than myself, and after a short time I began to feel like I was in a vacuum type cylinder and just could not get out.

By going back to work two weeks after her death I thought that this would be an easy way for me to cut off the pain of Donna's death but really, this didn't work either because at 5 o'clock each day I had to make my way back home to face the whole mess all over again.

I soon realised that there was no easy way through the process of grief, and that there was no easy way of coping with our loss, especially when it came to my own family, other relatives and friends.

Having met many parents through group meetings, I found that I had a great need to talk about my daughter's death. This seemed to be the hardest thing for me following her death. No one I was close to really wanted to hear about Donna or her death, and I was forced to bottle up my feelings at home and in the company of friends. They all had this strange feeling that I was continuing to put myself through this great torture by talking about what had happened, but the need to talk about it was very intense for me.

There would be remarks like 'Don't put yourself through this', or 'You are only greatly increasing the pain for yourself if you continue to dwell on what has happened', or 'She was really very young and you hadn't formed a great attachment yet'. All very negative statements which most of the time made me angry, but also I knew that my need to talk about Donna and her loss was not decreasing.

As time went on, my thoughts about what was right and what was wrong when it came to talking about Donna became very clear to me, and I found myself having the courage to say to some people that I simply had to talk about her, and that I resented anyone of them 'pretending that she just didn't exist'.

I knew that I had given birth to a perfectly healthy baby girl in early January 1979 and that in mid-March 1979 she died from the Sudden Infant Death Syndrome. I became very determined not to allow anyone to stop me from talking about her whenever I wished, and I felt that if they could not handle my pain and loss *with* me, I just didn't care.

I guess the whole point of my putting all this down on paper is to try and let other parents appreciate that there is nothing wrong in wishing to speak about their lost child, *constantly* if they wish, as most of the time, this is our only way of breaking through the barrier of grief. Silence is *not* 'golden' when it comes to our own feelings, and even though I do realise that our remaining silent about our loss may at times decrease the pain for others, I feel that we, as the parents of the children who die from cot death have rights too. If we need to talk about our child and our loss of that child, relatives and friends need to be told right from the beginning that we may have the need to do this, and we must ask them to be patient with us.

I didn't do everything right when we lost Donna, but I have learned a great deal about myself and my family and friends following her loss, and for this I must thank her. 'You made me a more understanding and caring person. This is the good that has come from your loss.'

CHAPTER SEVEN

PREPARING FOR THE FUNERAL: THE PHYSICAL GOODBYE

In the words of Philippe Aries in *The Hour of Our Death* (1983):

There are two ways of not thinking about death: the way of our technological civilization, which denies death and refuses to talk about it, and the way of traditional civilizations, which is not denial but a recognition of the *impossibility of thinking about it directly or for very long* because death is too close and too much a part of daily life.

Arranging the Funeral

When a baby dies, a funeral of one kind or another has to be arranged. For many young parents the funeral of their baby will be the first they have attended. Many come to this situation unprepared by tradition or experience, unless it be the traditional conspiracy of silence that surrounds the making or arranging of a funeral. In the experience of this young family, at most there may have been overheard a whispered exchange among their parents and relatives about Great Aunt Maud's funeral: 'It was awful', 'It was beautiful', or 'Thank God it's over'.

In a death denying society it becomes very difficult to talk about dying and funerals before they become a reality. How then, when a death is sudden and unexpected, can there be any preparation for the kind of funeral that will meet the needs of bereaved parents? When the sudden death is that of an infant, another dimension is added. The overwhelming shock can paralyse the thoughts and feelings of the young parents. It is from this background that parents attempt to arrange their baby's funeral.

When a baby dies from cot death the parents, or care-givers, have absolutely no control over the death; to date there is no way the death can be predicted or prevented. The laws of the land dictate the events that immediately follow, i.e. police involvement, an autopsy, the pathologists report and the signing of the death certificate. In this situation it is extremely hard for parents to realise that now they can take charge. Also, the law of the land dictates that burial or cremation of a dead person must meet prescribed health regulations, that registration of the death has to follow State/Federal regulations but the parents have the ultimate choice over the *manner* in which their baby is buried or cremated.

When the formalities have been completed the parents *do* have time to pause, to think about the options they have in arranging a funeral. The roller-coaster ride towards a speedy funeral does not have to take place. If parents are unable to exercise this option to slow down the process, memories of their baby's funeral often contain feelings of frustration, anger and disappointment.

Arranging the funeral of their baby provides the last intimate physical connection parents can have *with* their child. While the erection of a memorial, planting a tree or shrub, placing flowers on the grave and other such acts can be performed, they all take place *after* the funeral, and are merely symbolic of the continuing love parents have and want to express for their child.

The Role of the Funeral Director

The role of the funeral director is a very important one. His or her background and response, emotional and practical, has a profound influence on the immediate well-being and later progress towards wholeness of the bereaved parents and family. Funeral directors, too, are under pressures to provide a speedy funeral. These pressures are both internally and externally imposed. A funeral director of many years experience described the background to this situation in the following way:

The trouble is, it is so ingrained in our cultural system that the faster we have the funeral the better it is. The first question anyone asks when they come to the home (of the bereaved person) is: 'When is the funeral?'

At the time of the funeral director's first intervention, you've got people in a stunned situation, and a number of people trying to render assistance at one level or another . . . and people trying to protect each other.

Speaking specifically about cot death parents, Lynda Brown, (past) Executive Director of the Australian Funernal Directors' Association had this to say:

The problems I pick up when listening to people talk on the subject of S.I.D.S. deaths, or the death of a toddler, is that so often the parents aren't even involved in the arrangements. You've got everyone else, who nine times out of ten will also be shocked, like grandparents or an aunt or uncle, who are feeling so distressed themselves they might not be aware of what the parents are (actually) saying. They try to protect people from pain — well meaning, but futile, because you can't stop the pain.

The funeral directors, too, may want to avoid the feelings in themselves, and they may want to get in and get out as fast as they can. Funeral directors say the most difficult funerals to arrange are those for infants, children or young people, because they are identifying with their own children, and that creates difficulties for them. The situation is uncomfortable; all of us have difficulty in witnessing another person's pain.

Another spokesperson, *Meredith*, said:

I purposely try not to. [Arrange a funeral for an infant.] I feel really, really low whenever I am confronted with having to. So I tend to try and steer away from doing it. I will actually ask if there is anyone else available who can do it. I really don't handle them very well at all . . . . I know I can hand it on to an older person in the Company who will do it, although reluctantly. I find it terribly difficult . . . I get too emotionally involved, and again, I'm not saying that's bad, just that I find it hard for me to get on with the work that actually has to be done. I have arranged three funerals for families who have had cot deaths, and one for a stillborn baby.

Lynda was prepared to add:

Funeral directors are not always able, nor do many want to pull down the blind on the window of their emotions. There are many things going on for that individual, who happens to be a funeral director.

Slowing down the process

It is possible, and very often very useful, to slow down the process of arranging and completing the baby's funeral.

The *experienced funeral director*, who made the earlier contribution, continued:

Over the top of that [the general confusion] comes this notion that the sooner we have the funeral the better. Parents are almost powerless to slow down the process; The very thing that ought to be happening. The funeral director has people breathing down his neck; get this over and done with and get out. The difficulties start at the beginning when the funeral director first arrives. A young father, a strong parent, aunt or doctor is there. It gets taken out of the hands of the mother. To say then: 'Hang on, what does the mother think of all this? To sit in there and bat on, takes a fair amount of courage.

We should think about slowing the process down by about 24 hours. People who can influence this are doctors, counsellors, ambulance officers etc. There are problems there too. Professionals resent interference from outside sources. [They say:] this social worker stuck her bib in, or this clergyman. Funeral director's are like that too—they get testy—'we know our job'. With so many professionals involved it might be better if there was a team approach and consultation between them.

You see it doesn't really matter for the funeral director if his first face-to-face contact with the parents is delayed. He could be notified by the family that there is a cot death and given the broad details.

That doesn't preclude him from contacting the Coroner, or collecting the baby and begin preparing for it. In fact, the agreement could be with the family, not to rush having this funeral. You know—you don't [even] have to call the funeral director on day one.

If someone insists at first that they want the funeral the day after the death, I would say well, that can be arranged, providing we can make the necessary arrangements with the cemetery and the priest. Having acknowledged the possibility it can be done tomorrow, I might say—I wonder if you would like to listen for a minute or two to another suggestion or alternative. Also we all need to be aware if we are going to slow the process down for the benefit and value of the parents, that giving them information/suggestions/alternatives will be difficult when they are shocked—they may not be receptive.

That first face-to-face contact need only be about:
- being present
- showing that I care
- that I am aware of the death
- I am here to provide some service, and
- perhaps leave with a few ideas floating around about the kind of funeral they can choose.

The funeral director's responsibility to his own business must also be taken into account. Although his profession lies in a slightly different field to that of many other professional people, he is nonetheless in business to succeed and must constantly observe his client's wishes, even to making sure the funeral proceeds quickly when, in fact, he realizes that a hurried sequence of events might later be regretted in one way and another.

The businessman in the funeral director and the dilemma that this sometimes produces is addressed in this further excerpt:

In slowing down the process, there is a fear for the funeral director that the bereaved family may take their business elsewhere. It is the same for any businessman — when a client says I want that job done today, or I want to buy that tape-recorder on the shelf, and if I can't take it away with me, I will go somewhere else. The business side is an element that's there.

When a family rings and says 'come and arrange the funeral' they are not necessarily saying 'come this instant', but many funeral directors have interpreted that to mean 'come at once'.

Different funeral directors have different responses.

Services Provided by the Funeral Director

The services provided by the funeral director are not always fully understood, especially by young parents without previous experience in this regard. Speaking out of long experience our spokesman explained:

A family sometimes wants to do the arranging of a funeral themselves. If a family takes over all the services the funeral director currently provides, the businessman in the funeral director directs that he would have to tailor his services accordingly . . . .

The consumer should be able to buy as much of the service as he requires, be charged accordingly, and that's that. It can be done, and is done. It is especially important for people with deep spiritual needs, and where there is a deep attachment to the deceased person. Some people need and want to remain closely connected to the body of that person. For example, when someone has nursed a loved one for a long time, has met their bodily needs on a daily basis, and needs to continue meeting that need one way or another after death. There is a concern displayed towards the deceased person that is very easy to see when you come across it.

The term 'funeral director' suggests someone has to take charge — direct the funeral — but the responsibility for the funeral lies with the client. The funeral director makes sure the kind of funeral asked for is delivered without hitches. Personally, I prefer the term funeral facilitator, because that suggests a coordinator . . . . That doesn't preclude him from giving direction to the clergyman, the grave-digger or the mourners.

The funeral director does so much behind the scenes that people often don't realise how much work has gone into what they witness and the part they play as mourners in any funeral service. For example, the mourning cars arriving at the right time at the right place. Timing is important in any funeral service . . . it looks easy, but the public only sees the public part of it.

Our contributing spokesperson had these further comments to offer:

Meredith:

The trouble with funerals, for adult *or* child, is that you are paying for something you don't want to pay for . . . . Afterwards all you've got is a horrible empty feeling, and not much else to see for all that money you have paid out. The funeral industry is a service industry . . . and an unwanted commodity at that.

Lynda:

It took me quite some time to realise just how much employees of the funeral company, and the funeral director, invest of themselves and their time when they arrange a funeral.

Certainly community attitudes and interests are changing. Consumerism has an influence. People ask questions about everything they buy, every commodity they purchase, and funerals are not exempt from that. I think that's okay.

In conclusion

In summing up the role of the funeral director, it was strongly emphasised by contributing spokespersons from the funeral industry that while the services provided and the general level of understanding and professionalism on the part of funeral directors and all their employees are of high standard, and continually being up-graded, there is still work to be done to change the public 'image' of the undertaker. They said:

It's no use trying to justify in economic terms what the funeral director provides . . . . Even when people can see the value for money spent . . . that is useless if the consumer is left saying 'but what was its purpose . . .? it was meaningless'. Furthermore 'undertaker' is a word that still brings images of Dickensian characters; somber face, dark clothes, and a remote event shrouded in mystery.

The funeral director is no longer the tall, gaunt figure; he no longer just gets information from the family to enable him to legally and efficiently cremate or bury the body. Once the functionary aspect was all there was . . . correct notices in the paper, the priest booked for the right time, the body to the church on time, a clean hearse, etc. Today the human aspect is present and important.

Des:

I see myself as a professional person who can provide something of value to the people through every facet of the funeral experience. I have more to offer than just being politely present. I can suggest ideas (for the funeral service) that reflect more on the person's life . . . can make the funeral memorable, and even a happy one when that's appropriate, and so make the funeral more meaningful. However, all the caring in the world won't help if we don't take care in doing all the things people pay us to do.

Lynda:

There have been changes in the last five years. [since 1980] I believe the Australian Funeral Directors Association has contributed to these changes. The industry is more accessible and it is seen to be more successful. This is reflected in the community by the numbers of people who look for someone from the industry to come and talk to school groups and Service Clubs. The demand for our involvement is increasing. Thirty years ago that was not happening.

Des (again):

The funeral industry has a responsibility to itself; to ensure the service it provides is relevant to the community it services . . . . If it doesn't do this, it may as well not bother opening its doors.

Ancillary Services

Another development in the industry has been the implementation of ancillary services. These *counselling and education services* are tangible evidence of the changing role of the funeral director.

Lynda explained:

There are probably two main reasons for the development of these ancillary services. The first is the rise of self-help groups. They came into being in a community when so many other support systems collapsed. The second is an educated, questioning community. The community is beginning to recognise and understand issues that have always been present, but not acknowledged. There is a growing knowledge about guilt, blame, anger and helplessness following the death of someone close. The community is confronting these issues and learning how to cope with them. Grief reactions were not recognised thirty years ago; the withdrawn, grumpy and irritable person was left in isolation to cope as best they could.

Meredith said:

I find it easier sometimes to talk to our bereavement counsellor. She's very understanding. More often than not it is helpful to have someone who is involved with the industry, because they know themselves what it is like; the pressures. It's like a self-support system — they understand what you've been through and can relate to it . . . you don't feel like you're talking to a brick wall so much.

Before the Funeral

The time between arranging the funeral of the cot death baby and the actual funeral itself is an important time for grieving parents and family, be it a matter of one day or several days. As mentioned earlier an intimate and physical connection with the baby can occur after death.

Viewing a baby again, and even dressing a child for burial need not always be as horrific as our fantasies dictate. Our reactions to seeing a dead body are governed to a large extent by the denial of death in our society today. The case studies presented in this chapter are included because they display courage shown by parents and families who had the strength to swim against the tide of current public opinion, and because they demonstrate that far from having a harmful effect, these families treasure the memory of their direct involvement.

Viewing:

In most cases of cot death the baby will have left the home within an hour or two from the time he or she is found dead. For some families this is sufficient time to have said a final farewell. Others may decide during the next two days to see their baby again. This can be important if the baby was disfigured or discoloured when found, if the other children were absent at the time of the death, and if the baby's father was away or at work. Grandparents especially, but friends and relatives also may wish for an opportunity to say goodbye privately.

Jenny and Gary took their five year old son Brett to the funeral parlour to say goodbye to Graham, his brother, who died aged seven months and seven days from asthma. When Brett was told by his parents they were going to visit Graham in his casket, he responded with 'I want to come too'. When Brett was two and a half years old, his then younger brother, Adam, died from cot death aged four months. The experience of having a baby die was not a new one for this family, but taking Brett to the funeral parlour and graveside ceremony was. This time they were 'handling things differently'.

Jenny commented that it was as though they were grieving for two babies this time, 'two babies worthy of hopes and dreams'. Graham lay in his casket 'as beautiful in death as when he was alive' with his rattle, squeaking duck, music box, his woofy dog and other momentos that were important to him and his family. His Christmas presents from Gary and Brett and family photos were tucked in as well. Jenny stated, 'I felt we were doing something for him and ourselves, not just burying him.' Brett touched then cuddled Graham, and checked that his toys were there. 'Oh good, he's got them all'. Jenny remarked on the naturalness with which Brett responded to Graham, and on how difficult it was for others to cope with his spontaneous reactions. Being 'seen and not heard' was not a dictate Brett adhered to. There was laughter in Jenny's voice as she recounted the following: 'Brett decided that the Minister matched his fantasy/reality of what God looked like. As the Minister stood at the graveside in his flowing robes, Brett took delight in pointing out to the mourners, 'There's God!' Mostly people were not sure how to respond.'

For this family, viewing the baby was a positive and warm experience, but seeing the baby again should always remain an individual choice. As a very experienced Civil Funeral Celebrant said:

Where there has been a sudden and traumatic death . . . psychologically there is a very sound basis for viewing . . . but it should never be an arm twisting sort of situation. Today there is a great emphasis on everybody viewing every body. Although I am pro-viewing . . . I don't agree with it in a total sense . . . . For some people it creates a memory that stays with them for the rest of their lives. (A memory they may not want to keep.) Most people are very clear on whether they want to view or not. The only reminder you can ever give to people is to think about this chance, that will not repeat itself, to see the person one last time. There is time to think about that decision, and some do change their minds when they know they don't have to decide this minute.'

Parents should be told what to expect and explanations given if appropriate

It is important that parents be given an accurate description of the child's condition before the viewing takes place, especially if the baby was badly disfigured or discoloured when found. Parents need to be told their baby will look more like the baby they put down to sleep and less like the baby they found. It is important that parents have the opportunity to retain a less horrific image of their baby. Sometimes people need guidance not only about what to expect, but also in coming to an agreement about the decision to view their child.

A young funeral director was involved in arranging a funeral for a baby where an ex-husband and wife expressed individual needs:

It was a broken marriage and the baby had died. It was a cot death. It was a terrible arrangement to be sitting in on because I really felt for the father. He was there on his own, and his ex-wife was there with her new boyfriend, and everything this father said was shouted down, and I was the arbitrator in the argument. It wasn't an arrangement, it was a fighting match. The father wanted some of the baby's own clothes on, his ex-wife didn't. He wanted the other children, two and three years old to say goodbye to their little sister, his ex-wife didn't. In fact, she was taking a very negative attitude because of the visible bitterness between them. The bitterness got in the way. They couldn't get on with thinking about the funeral of their baby. I shuddered.

I just let the father know separately that if he did want to see his daughter we could arrange that. As far as I was concerned he had every right to see her, and I told his ex-wife as much. The father wanted to have a viewing –

he brought the clothes. He viewed his baby just prior to the funeral, and in the end so did his ex-wife and the other children. They sort of followed him in. The little girls were fine. Parents have a natural instinct to protect their children, but very young children don't appear to have any innate fears about death. It's the adult who is afraid, not so much of the dead person, but of death itself.

The role of those who handle the dead child before the funeral:

The professionals in their various departments have it in their power not only to make viewing of a cot death baby possible, but something that can be held comfortingly in the parent's memory. The manager of a large Funeral Company states:

If the condition of the dead person is so bad that viewing is likely to be a horrifying experience for that person, say in the case of a bad accident, and the bereaved still insisted on viewing, I would first of all describe the condition of the body, and then insist they have someone with them at the viewing, and make sure there is time to talk about it afterwards. The embalmer has tremendous skills, and he can make an enormous difference to the appearance of a person, or an infant who has been autopsied. The person who has done the autopsy also has a responsibility. Care needs to be taken. Often the difference between being able to view or not rests on the skill of the embalmer.

The Embalmer decribes his work this way:

I pick up the body from the hospital or home and I treat the body for viewing and burial. I have been an embalmer for seven years.

Embalming is not a job for everybody. I was asked if I wanted to do it, and I said yes. To me a dead body is still a human being. I know they are a person, but when I am treating them I become involved in what I am doing. It is easier if I have a photo, because make-up is important . . . .

Hair styling is important too – it must be parted on the correct side. It is pretty hard sometimes; usually I don't have direct contact with the bereaved, so I have to go by what the funeral director says.

The term Mortuary Care is usually used rather than embalming. Embalming frightens people I think. Most people don't know what that means. They think you just close their mouths and eyes, put on a bit of make-up and that's it. There is more to it than that. Quite simply, we put a liquid through the blood system, and that brings back the person's natural colour, preserves the body, and kills any other germs.

A lot of people view their friends or relatives, and some embalming is done in each case. Viewing is encouraged in this Funeral Parlour. I believe in that, and in my own case when my wife's father died, my three year old son viewed his grandpa. My son kept talking about how grandpa had gone crook at him just before he died. So I said, 'Well you can see grandpa, you can talk to him, but he won't be able to talk back'. He talked to grandpa, and was just matter-of-fact about it, and no longer shows concern that grandpa went crook at him.

Kids affect me when I'm treating them. It is very hard when you have a son of your own. I manage to do the job okay, and it feels good when the parents respond with 'he looks lovely'. But later when I am home I think about it – when I'm going to sleep. Little things affect me. One lady said she was really happy, and I nearly cried on the spot. I think it was a cot death baby; she said she was so grateful I had dressed him in the clothes just the way she wanted them. She wanted the nappy put on a certain way, and things like that. It's hard; and difficult because they are so little. I didn't want her to dress her baby because it had been post-mortemed, and I was worried about how she would react to that, and the lifeless body. I think I try to shelter them from the realities. It's a very touchy situation because of the autopsy.

Dressing:

For some parents the opportunity to dress their infant is a loving ritual that can bring comfort. Parents who undertake this task will almost always need some preparation. They should be prepared for the suture marks present from the autopsy, and for the physical difficulty of dressing a lifeless little body which they may not have thought about.

Parents who have elected to dress their own child report having to overcome resistance from those professionally and personally involved. This is perhaps understandable when we reflect on how far removed we are today from a personal involvement with death.

A couple who included themselves in this final preparation for the burial of their baby stated it was a beautiful and intimate experience. Warwick had died at home aged two years. The death was sudden and unexpected, resulting from an asthmatic seizure. This is Diane and Michael's story:

After he left home – I felt as though he had gone somewhere for a holiday – I finished making the tapestry for him. His grandmother finished knitting his jumper. I washed his best clothes and polished his shoes. I think I knew then I was going to dress him for his burial; like sending him on a trip. I don't know what made me want to do it, I only knew I did. It seemed natural to me. I didn't want strangers to dress him.

The Clergyman didn't want me to do it, and the Undertaker was resistant at first. When we first went in and saw him, I was sick to my stomach, horrified by the smell, a sort of antiseptic smell, and he was stone cold. I adjusted to that — to the shock of it, and after a while it just didn't matter. I realised he was my son. I was so glad to see him; it was Warwick.

When the Undertaker saw we were determined to dress him, and we could in fact handle it, it was wonderful. He helped us a lot and was very supportive.

I knew what I didn't want to see. I didn't want to see the suture marks, and I didn't want to look at the back of his head. I knew there was seepage and I didn't want to see it. The Undertaker assisted us in every way with these requests. I asked him to take Warwick's old singlet off and put on his new 'thermo' singlet. This singlet was to keep out the cold. When that was done, I put on his favourite red underpants, and Michael put on his trousers, shoes and socks.

Warwick had his head on the Undertaker's lap, and then I put on his shirt. The Undertaker propped Warwick up and showed us how to dress him. On with his jumper (finished in time) and his duffle coat.

We had told the Funeral Director in advance that we would need a coffin larger than Warwick, as we had planned to bring some favourite toys, rather a lot actually, to place in the coffin with him. His old sheepskin, teddy, some cars and his favourite book: the frieze he liked best — from his bedroom wall — his lunch-box and bottle. All he would need for a trip. He had photographs of the family and his cousins, and locks of hair and Humphrey Bear. We laid him in the coffin and placed everything around him, with one hand touching teddy's ear and the other hand on his favourite book. We put a rose bud in his hand.

Before the Undertaker left us alone with Warwick, he pulled the hood of his duffle coat up, because he knew my fear. When we were alone we held him — I wanted to make him warm — and we talked to him. It started to rain outside. Michael said 'This means puddles Warwick, making a mess in the puddles.' At that moment rain started coming through the roof. It formed a puddle near Michael's feet, and that meant a lot to Michael. He felt then that Warwick was okay. I wanted to laugh — it seemed so funny — like made to order. Later I actually asked the Undertaker was it part of the service they offered. Had he stood on the roof with a watering can for us? He was horrified, for several reasons I think. Later the Undertaker said because of the experience he shared with us, he would never again attempt to prevent parents from becoming involved.

I wanted to take in every minute detail of Warwick, and I did. I was relieved to have done what we did. When we made those decisions I remembered a counsellor's words: 'He is your child, you can make whatever decisions you want about him'. When I look back now I see him with everything he loved. He looked so handsome.

In this account solid foundations were laid for the mourning that followed. The parents were active, made decisions for themselves, and were listened to. The reality of the situation was acknowledged, and the professionals worked with the parents.

A funeral director's view:
As much information as possible should be given to the parents prior to their actual involvement in dressing the infant. Suture marks need to be covered. I would want to check the baby first, because the size and condition of the baby makes a difference. If the funeral director is going to suggest they ought not dress the baby, he needs to do it as gently, and with as much care as he can, but ultimately leaving the parent with the decision.

Our practice is to say to parents, 'Give us the under garments, let us commence the dressing. If we put on the singlet and nappy it is less distressing.' From that stage, if the parents want to be involved I would never discourage them. Over the years I would have been involved with about 6 babies where in each case there has been the dressing of a very small infant, and in some of those circumstances I've said to parents, let us take it part of the way, I've never had anyone say 'No – I want to do the whole thing totally and utterly'. Other people tell me that has been said to them, but I believe it is in the manner that the information is presented. You're not saying, look you can't dress your baby; what you are saying is – let us help you; we think it's better for us to start the process. They could witness that if they wanted to, but let the funeral director do that bit.

If the parent senses cooperation and not resistance I believe they will be guided by the Funeral Director, and learn to trust the professional involvement.

Another Funeral Director responded this way:
I have offered the parents the opportunity to dress their baby themselves, but no one has wanted to. Obviously that would be a very difficult thing to do, and a very individual choice to make.

If a parent wanted to dress their baby I would make sure I was there with them, and try to prepare them for what it would be like. Because last time they did that (dressed their baby), their baby was alive, warm and breathing, and now they will find their baby is cold. I think that would be a frightening sensation. It is frightening for anyone to feel someone who is dead because they are so cold, and they don't have that natural limpness that a live baby has. I always ask the parents for a bonnet. If they ask why a bonnet, I explain about the marks from the autopsy . . . . If they want to hold their baby again—well—parents know how to hold their baby, they have done it often. Nevertheless you have to let parents know what to expect, because if you don't it will be frightening and upsetting.

The funeral director's story that appears below, demonstrates the warm and caring attitudes that were prevalent among the funeral directors interviewed for this section of the book.

George:

'I am rigid and unbending in one respect . . . which annoys the Company a little bit. Once I've seen a family, once I have conducted an interview, I am the person who will look after them at the funeral. By hook or by crook I will be the person there for them. I believe it is comforting for them to see a face they know. I know this because I see their faces relax. People come and say "What do we do?" and I tell them. If I say, "I'll just be over there . . . checking those papers", they might say, "No, don't go, stay with me", so you feel it—the bond that was created during the interview. It is important to me that I'm at the funeral. I become involved and I stay involved for the whole time.

'I have been involved with too many children's funerals. I wish there was one child's funeral that could be prevented. I don't like doing them—but if two funerals are booked for the same time, I will choose the child's because I believe that family needs the most support. Sometimes they are passed to me from others who are uncomfortable doing them. I just try to do them as well as I can.

The hardest bit of all is the first contact with the family after having spoken to them on the 'phone. It is hard going through the events that have led to the death, and in so doing help them to face what has happened. That is a time obviously for tears and upset and this affects me too because I am only human.

'I always ask permission to use the child's name, or a pet name if I notice that. People respond to that because we are talking about someone they love and identify with. It is very important to use the name of the child. During this visit, which lasts about two hours, we talk about many things.

'If the death has been expected, we talk about how the child came to terms with knowing he was dying, or if he knew. When people begin to trust you they may share inner feelings. I listen. I listen to any desires they may have had for the child's future – hoping he wouldn't die and knowing he would. I listen to the dreams they had.

'If the death is sudden and unexpected there are different things to talk about: "Who first got the news and how? Was the parent alone? Did they seek immediate help from a neighbour, husband or wife?" When people start to retrace how and when the death occurred they begin to see things more clearly. For example, "The policeman came to our home. It was such a shock – he was a lovely man – he was helpful". From the blurred beginning they begin to see the policeman clearly doing a job he didn't want to do – he didn't want to be there either.

'There is guilt after a death. If a child has run across the road and been knocked down I would say, let's not forget what children are, and what they do. I mean a child can be sitting there one minute and out the door the next – they will take off, and you just can't stop them. I try to get communication between a husband and wife as early as possible because I have learned that marriages are shaky after a child's death. It only takes one or the other to ask; "Were you holding his hand?; Were you watching? Were you talking to someone?" for blame to be felt.

'In the case of cot death, if the mother was at home by herself, she is particularly vulnerable. She might say, "I should have checked one more time", and if the father replies, "Did you really look? You were very quick", somehow they need to understand that if they checked one more time it wouldn't have changed anything. Sometimes, but not always, I might explore that with them. It depends on how trust between us has been building. I have asked, "Had you been there at that moment, what *would* you have done, what *could* you have done?" I would try to help them become aware that even if a doctor was at the scene, in the case of cot death there is nothing anyone can do. That baby, at that particular moment, and for reasons we don't understand, died.

'Sometimes the wife may resent her husband's absence at the time of the death. If I notice that, and if it feels right, I will explore that a little bit. Through questions and answers it is possible to help the wife see that her husband was always at work at that time, or that he was doing something he normally did at that time, and that if he had been present they would have handled things together. I would point out that even together they could not have prevented the death. That can be a comfort for the wife if she was on her own.

'It is a worry to me that the counsel they receive from me may be the only counsel they get. I like to keep it low key, and I like to round it off in some way. In two hours I come across two strangers and have an intimate discussion with them about their child that has died; how they feel about that; how it is going to affect their lives, and the lives of the other children, I try to assure them in some way that it wasn't their fault.

'I have to hope I'm not just meeting my own needs in there. Perhaps I am in that I feel I have done something for them; I have to be aware of that. Sometimes I try to make them aware — and this is risky, so I don't do it every time — that there will be troubled times ahead; this is a new experience charged with emotions, and an important part of their life is missing. Their lives are going to change because everything they did around that child they no longer will be doing. Something as simple as Dad taking Brian for his traditional Saturday afternoon walk. All those things will be difficult. I would then mention resources that might be available to them; give them the brochures of the self-help groups. That then breaks the interview. I reassure them I am available, and I know that sounds corny.

'Most people don't ring back before the funeral. Sometimes I might ring them and ask: "Are you prepared for today?" or "Are you aware the car is calling for you at such and such a time?" I don't always ring, because I don't always feel quite right about it. I want to do something to help, but the humanness in me is uncomfortable — I don't want to be hurt and I don't want to hurt anyone. So it is a "sometimes" thing.

'On the day of the funeral I involve myself with the family, beginning with the mourning car. For instance, a family might decide to drive themselves to the funeral. We are concerned about that, just from a caring point of view. Families often don't realise the costs are the same whether the car goes to the house to pick them up or not. I like to be either at the home or parlour to receive the family. This is a time I feel uncomfortable being in my morning suit. It doesn't seem appropriate for a baby — so harsh and black. I do offer to wear a grey suit because I feel better in it.

'I always open the car door and greet them in as gentle a way as I can, avoiding the cliche because they are feeling dreadful. I've heard people say "At least you've got a nice day" or "Isn't it good it's not raining"; in other words, be grateful for that. Sometimes I just touch them and say come inside out of the cold, or heat. They are just low-key words to get them away from the car and into the Church. Reality is coming — this is no bad dream from which they can wake.

'For a chapel service I would indicate the viewing room: "Do you still wish to see . . .?" I tell the parents I'll leave them in private, and come back for them to help them take the next steps. It's now time to go into the chapel. They have to go into a space that is filled with people, and they can feel as though they are on stage; everyone seems to be, or is, looking at them. With children's funerals the parents are really hurting; they have just said goodbye. The coffin is still in another room. Then comes a blow: I have to ask them if I can seal the coffin because they have to give permission. Sometimes then I ask them would they like to see their child one more time — there is the opportunity still. On a couple of occasions the parents have literally jumped up and gone to their child again.

'When the coffin is brought in I step well back, for this is intensely private. It is the time for the mourners to come forward and place things on or around the coffin. I am becoming sensitive to flowers: a flower is so significant because it can be pressed and kept. For the parents one flower from their posy to keep, if they want it; for the mourners an opportunity at the graveside to approach the coffin and drop a flower into the grave. It brings them all together. People come forward and say goodbye. Participation is important.

'There is one baby's funeral that I still feel guilty about. It still hurts.

'A young couple came into the Chapel, a navy man and his wife, and said their baby had died from cot death. There were only three staff members present. Myself, our receptionist and my Group Manager. I had another appointment to go to, my Group Manager said he couldn't see the couple, and the receptionist wouldn't because it was an infant's funeral. That left me with only twenty minutes, and the knowledge I couldn't get back to this young couple later in the day. In that time you don't make an arrangement, you only take details. I took a few details, listened to a bit of a story, said goodbye and off they went. I said to my staff, "I feel really terrible; I feel I have done them a disservice, and we are supposed to be giving service." They tried to reassure me, but it didn't help me, and it couldn't help the parents. I imagined them in the carpark saying "What's going on? What happened in there?" I felt very guilty about that and thought I should have tried to change the other appointment to give them more time. I didn't, and I'm stuck with that.

'On the day of the funeral I had a choice: the funeral of that baby or another one. I chose the other one because I felt so guilty. I did not want to see the young couple. When that family rang up with a query about the plaque, I again avoided speaking to them. Nearly a year later I am still stuck with that guilty feeling and the things I should have done. It's like the "if only's", and it hurts. It's an occupational hazard.

'I haven't shut the experience away and I have tried to deal with it. You can't make the clock go back and you can't make it go away. I have to forgive myself though, no one else can. Maybe one day I will: maybe I never will.'

CHAPTER EIGHT

The Funeral, The Clergy, and Civil Celebrant

Like the marriage ceremony, baptism, bar mitzvah or graduation ceremonies, the funeral ceremony is a passage rite. It is a ceremony which proclaims, in a way enacts, an individual's passing from one stage of life to another. Many see it in the religious sense of assisting the spiritual transition of the departed soul or spirit from an earthly existence to a new life beyond the veil of death. For others, its importance is for those who are mourning to become witness to the reality that the loved child or adult, who can no longer exist with them as he or she did before, is now passing into a new existence within their memories.

Every known society in every age has evolved certain passage rites, none more revered, precious and necessary to society's well-being than the funeral rite. It helps not only to confirm the change in status of the loved person, but it affirms and confirms the solidarity of the family, social group or congregation and the community in general. It proclaims the love of those within these frameworks, for one another and for the child or adult, who has died. It reminds people that the human condition is naturally a caring one and it can generate strength which helps those mourners afflicted by grief, comforting them and easing their stress.

The funeral ceremony can represent something well-done by the bereaved for the person they love, and something accomplished for themselves. For the cot death parent who is left with so short a life to remember, the funeral is just as important as a funeral for someone who had lived long or contributed greatly to society.

Every ceremonial rite must have its celebrant. This person may be of the clergy or a civil celebrant, or even someone especially elected from a group or small community. The officiating person thus takes upon themselves certain responsibilities that represent the group, church or society which they represent. At the same time they have an immediate responsibility to the family whom they are serving. When a child has died, or a baby has died suddenly, the celebrant's task takes on a heightened responsibility and because of this is sometimes more difficult. But his or her way of performing this difficult role is all the more important. Harriet Sarnoff Shiff, in her book The Bereaved Parent (1977) gave this warning: 'Although customs vary according to belief and religion and country, the imperative for the funeral is that it *not* become a further source of pain for the grieving parents.'

Usually the officiating person is well-trained and experienced. They may not be experienced, however, in officiating at the funeral of a cot death infant. The rite or formula may be fairly much the same as other funerals, but the circumstances of this bereavement are so extraordinary that in many respects it will seem very different both to the person officiating and to the witnesses.

Funerals, by their very nature, are personalised ceremonies. Each funeral demands a certain degree of individual planning and a sensitive attention to the needs of the occasion. Even more care must be exercised in the case of a child who has died suddenly. The effectiveness of the ceremony is governed by many things. Serving the particular wishes of the parents is one of them. Things may be asked for that seem trivial, or sometimes odd, but they may be very important to the family and could be a vital contribution to their ultimate recovery.

Some pre-funeral contact with the parents on the part of the officiating celebrant may prepare them and lead them into a much richer experience. The setting for this last ceremony, while still being held at a traditional venue of church, funeral chapel, etc., can be changed slightly to suit different circumstances. The scene need not seem as formal for a baby's funeral as for an adult. The baby's funeral can be arranged to express the joy the parents and family found in the baby's life. The ultimate well-being of the family can be made the aim of this passage rite. The music, arrangements of floral and whatever other tributes, the words spoken, readings and order of things don't have to pay respect to anything else but the fact that this baby that was so recently physically alive and loved and part of the family, is now passing into a new existence within the hearts, minds and memories of the family members.

Sometimes a very important moment occurs immediately after the funeral ceremonies when the officiating clergyman or celebrant speaks momentarily, but spontaneously and privately, with the grieving parents. It is a very intimate moment. The parents have already laid their trust in this person so that brief opportunity to give further comfort, friendship and counsel can be very effective. If the celebrant is the family's regular priest, minister or rabbi there will be opportunity to give on going help. This is not beyond the scope of the civil celebrant, especially in smaller communities.

As the American psychiatrist, Elliot Luby, said, 'when a parent dies the family suffers the loss of its past. When a child dies the family loses part of its future.' This, in fact, is what makes the task confronting the family of a cot death baby so awesome. How can the future make any sense when the baby that represented 'future' has died? The funeral and the part played by the clergy or civil celebrant constitute some of the first building blocks in the bridgework to follow.

In writing this book, the author turned to some of those who have officiated at the funeral of a cot death baby. Their words uphold the importance and the difficulties of the task. They offer them in hope that they will give help and encouragement to others yet to face the occasion.

The Clergy

Father Grant Edgcumbe, Anglican Priest, presented a discussion paper to the National S.I.D.S. Workshop in April, 1985. With his permission this excerpt is quoted from the paper titled *Death, Grief, Life and Faith:*

Part of living includes death. All around us we are surrounded by death. Autumn trees lose their leaves, seeds appear to be dead but yield after being planted, older people die after having lived their lives. In every one of these instances, and I venture to say that in all cases where we encounter death in our world, there has been a sense of purpose and continuum. The dying of leaves on a tree has the purpose of allowing the tree to rest so we can enjoy the beauty of spring; the apparent death of a seed exists so that it can be planted and so we can enjoy whatever grows.

When we are confronted by the death of a person who has lived only a short time . . . our creative impulse is immediately triggered, bringing to birth memories of the deceased. We invoke again the continuum, and although that line may have been interrupted when we did not expect it, we still can back-track over the line that does exist, and create in our minds and hearts impressions of those whom we have lost. This is a very important part of the grieving process. Achievements are extolled, and we find something to hold onto. We can easily, in most cases, find something we are going to miss. The grief we feel has a very concrete basis and is not too difficult to identify. We can affirm too that we are better for having shared in the life of the person, and we can pledge that we will carry on some of the good they tried to achieve.

. . . The sudden death of a child means that the creative process has been interrupted. Parents in this instance are seen as responsible for this process of creation. . . . The parents also fulfill the function of creating on behalf of the rest of us, and are involved in the very nature of God himself: in the very first line of the very first book of the bible, *Genesis*, we read 'In the beginning God created'. When this process is interrupted then *all* of us are affected, even if only in the most mild psychological manner.

One of our ways of coping with this situation is to run. The death of an infant, especially when it is sudden and unexplained, threatens our very being and social structure, so we do what is natural to us — we run. In trying to assist people in coming to terms with this great tragedy . . . we need to acknowledge the death, and the pain that surrounds the coming to terms with the realisation of that death. We have to struggle with this (realisation) in ourselves first, before we can take it to others.

In the beginning, and in the book of *Genesis*, 'God's spirit moved over the waters when there was chaos over the deep'. When we come to those in chaos we often respond with a flurry of verbiage and action. Words and actions are sometimes helpful, but if we are to be the agents of creation, creating new relationships and order out of the chaos, we need first to 'sit in the shit' with people. That's spirit stuff: making ourselves, our essence, available to the pain.

We cannot stand on the edge of the pit and throw a lifeline. When people are in chaos they are vulnerable — they hand us power on a plate. In protecting ourselves, it is all too easy to misuse that power.

We need to be unleashed and involved with those who feel so alone and isolated. Faith can lead us to that involvement of spirit, and it can lead us to overcome some of the prejudices, fears and misunderstandings that are so common.'

For the clergy, the baby that dies from cot death brings them face-to-face with the strength of their beliefs. While men and women appointed to the Church are confronted with death often, and are regularly called upon to perform funeral services for the elderly, the impact upon them when death comes suddenly and unexpectedly to a tiny baby, can throw them into confusion. In times past, when the death of at least one infant per family was expected, it could be argued that the clergy was more comfortable in conducting these funerals, as they were an anticipated part of life. Also, the fact that there was usually a recognisable cause of death of the infant, for example, diptheria, small pox, typhoid and penumonia, gave the clergy an anchor. Cause and effect was obvious to all.

Despite the advances of science and technology, Sudden Infant Death Syndrome continues to challenge the medical and research fraternity. The causes remain unknown, and this fact places the clergy in a situation which is not to be envied. In the absence of a medical explanation, parents often look to God for a reason for their baby's death, and His representative, the clergyman, or female cleric or rabbi faces difficult questions from the parents. No less difficult can be the questions they must ask of themselves — and of their faith.

When a member of the clergy finds themselves in this situation they, like many others, can rush into an explanation of why the baby died. They may be anxious to offer comfort to the bereaved, and in so doing may find themselves offering words that make little sense to the parents. For example: 'It is God's will', 'God needed another flower for his garden'. Anger or bewilderment from the parents is the most common response to phrases of this kind. An overt display of anger by the parents may leave the man or woman of God wondering what went wrong. If the parent pushes the anger down out of sight, the clergyman or clergywoman may never know the impact of those words, nor the situation in which they placed the parents. They may never understand that it is permissible, perhaps even vital to the parents' spiritual growth to question and test their own beliefs.

The path of the clergy can be smoother if the person tries to gauge whether the family is looking/seeking for spiritual guidance before offering it. If the member of the clergy responsible offers only as much as the parents want at the time and leaves the rest — maybe for years — they lay solid foundations for spiritual growth; a phase or stage of growth parents will make when they are ready.

The Reverend Grant Edgcumbe had taken four funerals for babies who died from cot death in just two years. He said in an interview with *Church Scene*, in July, 1984: 'Your priesthood is called into question. You find yourself asking just what you are doing'.

Father said that the first cot death funeral rocked him. Even the course now available to the clergy on death and dying had not prepared him for his experience.

I had heard of cot death, but knew nothing about it. I hadn't even heard about the association that provides counselling and support for the parents. I wonder how many clergy know that advice is available until they are confronted with their first such funeral.

It was only after that first harrowing funeral that a member of his congregation pointed him in the right direction. As bereaved parents do, he also turned to them for help. Father Edgcumbe says the parents suffer 'the torments of hell'. A parent's account supports this:

I had been bought up in a Christian home. I had even taught Sunday School when I was younger. I believed in 'good' and 'bad', and had been taught that if you did not set out to harm anyone, and performed acts of kindness and charity when they presented themselves, that 'bad' things would not happen in your life. When my daughter died from cot death I had to find a 'bad' reason for her death. I was in conflict and torment for a year as I raked over the coals of my past searching for the 'bad' act that had caused her death. I made myself very ill in the process. During that time I did not, could not, go near my Church.

My Vicar, as was his wont, continued to visit me at home on a monthly basis. He had done this for years. We did not talk about God or my daughter's death. We talked about other things; events in the town, the other children. I'm sure now that he knew something of my struggle. He told me years later that he felt guilty; guilty because he had been on leave at the time of my daughter's funeral, and did not even know of her death until he returned. I wish we had been able to talk about it at the time, because I was feeling so guilty too.

Eventually my anger surfaced. I realised I was angry at God; angry at the teachings of the Church; angry at the myth that God dispenses justice; angry at my parents for perpetuating that myth; angry that my daughter was dead, and that her dying was something over which I had no control. One morning I woke and knew it was time; time to let God know just how I felt. I went to the Church at a time I knew it would be empty. I asked the Vicar not to come in, told him I was going to 'have it out with God'. And I did.

I can laugh now at the things I did that afternoon, but not then. I picked up all the cushions from the pews and hurled them all around the Church; prayer books flew and I beat my hands on the altar rails, all the while telling

God just what I thought of Him. I was an exhausted, tear-sodden mess by the time I had finished. I felt better, but then began to worry about retribution.

Well, the sky didn't fall in on me, and I wasn't struck by lightning. Nothing much happened except that I continued to feel better and better. In the end I realised that not only could God take my anger, but that maybe He even understood it. Years later I read *When bad things happen to good people* by Rabbi Harold Kushner (1981). It helped me make sense of the non-sense I struggled with following my daughter's death, and have no hesitation in recommending it to anyone who finds their faith tested in this harrowing way.

Father Edgcumbe says:

I try to tell parents that perhaps one day we'll understand why this has happened, even though none of us, including me, understands now. I never pretend I know what's going on; I don't. I tell them it is healthy for them to be angry with God, to abuse Him all they like, and that they must not feel guilty for doing so.

Clergymen admit that conducting the funeral of a baby who had died from cot death or in other tragic circumstances is supremely difficult. At the funeral of an old person, the eulogy usually includes details of that person's full life, and as the congregation listens they can draw comfort from the memories and experiences related. With the death of a baby, life has barely begun. How much more difficult then the task of the officiating clergy.

When parents become pregnant they fantasise the life ahead for their child. When the baby dies, it is not only life that is ended but the expectations, hopes and dreams the parents had. Almost anything the Priest, Minister or Rabbi may say will seem inadequate when so tiny and innocent a life is ended. It is a heartbreaking experience to put to death those hopes, dreams and expectations. Saying goodbye to the hopes and dreams is a long and difficult task, and the funeral is often the first realisation for parents, family and friends that this task lies ahead.

Even the youngest life contains experiences that can be drawn upon. While the act of describing to the congregation the simple daily routine of the family may produce tears, it affirms the existence and the impact the baby's life had. Parents do make the statement 'I sometimes wonder whether he lived at all, whether I really ever gave birth to him, or if he had lived before he died'. Parents will affirm too, that even though it is painful to talk about the baby, they feel better for doing so. Parents express this need, the need to talk about their baby, time and time again.

In the eulogy the person officiating has the opportunity to talk about the relationship that was developing between siblings and the baby, and in this way ensures the other children are included in the service. Grandparents too have a special relationship with the baby whether they were actively involved or not, and can be included in the service.

The funeral is no less easy for the friends and family who attend. The sight of a tiny white coffin is devastating. There may be other young mothers and fathers present who are terribly afraid. To be part of a society that largely denies death altogether, and then faced with the reality of the tiny coffin, can be overwhelming. Some clergymen have been able to ease this trauma by suggesting that the coffin be open during the service. By encouraging the congregation to become active he helps the mourners to say goodbye. The simple act of approaching the coffin, and seeing the baby lying peacefully inside can do much to lessen the fears most of us have about coming face-to-face with death.

Parents who have a religious inclination usually plan to have their baby baptised. If the death occurs before this event has taken place, some parents fear for their child's soul. Some may heap guilt on themselves for not ensuring their child's spiritual welfare. There have also been cases reported where a minister has refused baptism after death, and so 'punished' the parents for their lack of adherence to a particular Church's dogma. In the light of the sudden and unexpected nature of cot death this action seems cruel, and causes some parents much pain. Parents who are not particularly religious have also tortured themselves with the thought of their baby being designated to some nebulous limbo.

Father Edgcumbe recounts this experience:

The baby was only two months old when he died and had not been baptised. That traumatised the parents. They wanted to know if I could baptise the baby after death. They feared he would go to hell. I was faced then with explaining what baptism is about, and assuring them that Jesus accepted all the children when their mothers brought them to Him. Unfortunately the parents can fear you are just saying it to ease their minds: that it is not true.

The Service

For many parents a religious service is important.

Warwick's mother wrote:

We had put so much time and effort into deciding the kind of funeral service we wanted for Warwick. We spent a lot of time with the minister explaining what we wanted and why we wanted it that way. We had carefully selected some poems we thought appropriate. Poems that referred to lost youth, and hymns too that meant something to us. We went to the Bible and chose verses from *Corinthians* (1-13 selected verses), verses about love. During the days between his death and the funeral, these tasks kept us going. We felt we were doing something worthwhile.

When we arrived at the church we were overwhelmed by the number of friends and relatives gathered. The service that followed was a shock. It was changed, altered. Anger kept me going. I just couldn't believe the service. I was so angry. I can hardly remember the beautiful verses we had chosen from *Corinthians*, because the minister also read something about fire and brimstone. Relatives tried to placate me. 'He (Minister) is upset for you'. I felt he was upset for himself. He didn't know how to handle it. We asked especially that he not mention God and religion; he went against our wishes. We spent hours planning the service. It hurt when he didn't do it our way.

Caroline contributed this:

I think the hardest decision we had to make was to go against the traditional way people had their funerals arranged. Coming from a Catholic family myself, the very few times I did come into contact with a death, the funeral service was conducted in a very traditional way.

It wasn't until our daughter Kylie's death that we were faced with the decision of how to arrange a funeral. We wanted to do it the best way we could because it was our way of saying goodbye for the last time. We didn't really know you could have a say in it until our friends told us it's really up to you to have the kind of funeral you want, and then to find someone who will do it that way. The religious side of it was important and so was the involvement of people we knew. We didn't want strangers saying things at her funeral; it made more sense to have people who knew her.

Mick and I had Kylie before we were married, but had planned to marry. The date was set and arrangements made. Kylie died a month and seven days before the ceremony. We were having counselling at the Bayside Unemployed Self-Help Organisation with Father Bruce Waldron, an Anglican Priest, and we asked him to perform the service. He knew us, knew Kylie and our friends. We had the greatest support possible from our friends and family which helped us. Our friends and the priest conducted the service, which we had at our home. The funeral director we used went along with our wishes and helped us immensely.

Kylie died on a Sunday, and it wasn't until the following Friday that we had the service. During those days we were really amazed at how many things you can do. We didn't want to rush into anything, and had several talks with our friends, family and the priest about how it could be arranged. It all took a bit longer to organise by doing it this way. Our friends knew us really well, and we trusted them and the way the decisions were being made.

On the Wednesday Mick and I went and looked at the cemetery. We chose one that was a bit further away from home because they had a special children's section where there were little graves.

We were all involved in planning the service: it was a mixture of religion and other things that were important to us. Before we had to think about a funeral we were like most people I guess, and thought it was up to the funeral director to make the decisions, but the funeral director, too, made it clear to us that we should do whatever made us feel comfortable.

We had the option to dress Kylie ourselves, and to hold her again, but we declined the offer. We had her dressed in her own clothes and brought to our home in an open coffin on the morning of the funeral. My fiance played a large part in our baby's funeral. He carried the coffin from the car to the front room and to the graveside. This made me feel better and helped him because he knew it was his last chance to do something for her. His friends were right next to him to give support or to take over if it all got a bit too much.

When it came time in the service, our friends talked about Kylie and their memories of her. Our friends knew her — it gave their words meaning. With the help of the Priest, as well as everyone else, we were able to say goodbye the way we wanted.

As can be seen from the two accounts above, one at least combined a religious ceremony with other needs determined by the parents. For a clergyman to conduct a service without reference to God or religion would present a tremendous challenge, but with closer communication between the parents who made that request and the minister, there may have been a way of discovering what the parents really required. Choosing a service that included some spiritual aspect appears to have been important for those parents.

Providing as many options as possible for parents is obviously helpful when arranging the funeral service. If the baby is very young, it may not have an identification in the wider community, and some parents may feel more comfortable, and indeed the funeral may be more meaningful, if the service *is* conducted at home. When the clergyman discusses the life of the baby he not only meets the parents' need to talk about their child, he also puts himself in a better position to arrange a service that meets the needs of that particular family.

The Civil Celebrant

Not every family wants a religious funeral service when their baby dies.

The reason may be very simple or complex. In this quote from *In the Midst of Life . . . the Australian Response to Death*, by G. M. Griffin and D. Tobin (1982), the authors offer this suggestion:

Australians, on the whole, have never earned a reputation as particularly religious people. There were no religious ceremonials to mark the occasion when the first settlers, convicts and marines stepped ashore at Sydney Cove. Indeed it was over a week before any service of worship was held and years before a church was erected, only to be burned down immediately. That seems to have set the national style . . . . When, in time, migration became a stronger force than transportation in the Eastern States, and the churches played a larger part in the life of the developing nation, as many Australians stayed away from public worship as attended it. A recent survey has suggested that the situation has not altered. Fewer than one-third of the Australians studied claimed to be more than 'slightly' religious.

Whether or not this is the basis for parents chosing a civil ceremony for burial, the fact remains that for an increasing number of people a non-religious ceremony meets their needs when a child dies.

Di Storey, a mother of two children has been a practising Civil Celebrant for eight years. Her warm approach, her careful exploration of a family's needs, and her thoughtful appraisal of the needs of surviving children are all clearly demonstrated in the account below:

So that I don't frighten an elderly or ill person, I always make sure I am talking to the right family. To ensure I have not dialled an incorrect digit . . . I always ask is that the family of the late?

My objective in that first call is to establish a suitable, mutually agreeable time to meet. I don't put a great emphasis on crisis intervention at that time. Once I asked someone how they were feeling, and they said 'How would you expect me to be feeling under these circumstances?' I thought, fair enough. That was a fair retort, and Di you really ought to know better! The better question is probably 'Is someone there with you?'

I always provide an option for the first visit: this time or that. When they have decided, I ask them to check the time with other family members; a decision made with consultation is better than one made just to appease me, meet my needs, or to get me off the phone.

When we meet for the first time, I let them set the tone. Some people need distance; the last thing they might need is the lady who is going to bury their child coming too close. On the other hand, especially when we have had previous contact, there can be warmth in the greeting. When I have worked with a family before, a hug can be the appropriate greeting, and always is if the Mum reaches for me. I shake hands with the father, because I like to make contact one way or another under these conditions.

It is important now that I just be present for them. I am there to write a funeral service that meets the unique needs of *that* family as they are expressed by them. This is a critical time in the interview, because apart from getting a clear understanding of what the parents want, we need to reach a state of mutual trust. I do a lot of listening. I put my pad on the floor and dump everything that says 'this is work' while we explore what happened. Parents have a *huge* need to empty out those areas of how the baby died and from what cause, and I use the words 'dead' and 'death' in our conversations. When a cot death occurs I get precise recall of what happened prior to the discovery. It is important to get a real feel for what has happened if the funeral service is to be unique and meaningful for the family.

We explore the baby's life from the moment of birth, or if the baby is very young, from conception. This is significant because so many of us take our pregnancies for granted. When you have had a child for only six to eight weeks, you need to look at the whole process. This is one way to include the father. I remember one Dad who set up a crayfish dinner. A romantic husband setting the scene to create. Their recollections were a moving experience; they reached for each other and held hands while remembering this planned pregnancy.

I try to move forward with the family at their pace, and this often happens when photos are produced. The photos create all kinds of memory responses, and I see the history of the child. From surgical scars to a child holding his Dad's hand, and both in gumboots — a memory from the day they planted spuds or something. It's really important to work with the father too, because he may have fewer memories; not less poignant, but less numerically. The funeral service becomes special or unique for that family when you are able to draw from experiences like that.

In planning the kind of service the family want, there is a great need to really hear what they are saying. For example: the first thing one family said to me was, 'Di, please don't make it morbid. He was such a happy little boy, he would not want that'. Not only are the parents saying he wouldn't want that, they are also saying, 'We don't want it to be morbid'. So, I'm mindful of that. I always read the service back to the family before I give it. I check for sensitivity and awareness, and that I have interpreted their needs accurately. It is critical.

The needs of surviving children should not be forgotten when the service is planned. I remember one family: A funeral director rang me and said 'there has been a cot death, the much-longed-for child of a second marriage'.

There were siblings of fourteen years, nine years and two and a half years. The mother was too distressed to speak with me on the first day, and the father made an appointment for me to visit them both the next day. The paternal grandfather was the only member of the extended family within the suburban area, and he was present too. Although subdued and withdrawn, he wanted to be helpful. The elder boy had absented himself — disappeared. 'I'm going Mum. I've got friends to see, I'll see you when I see you'. The daughter had a commitment to a sporting event, and the toddler was at home and reacting to the changed mood of the environment, although there was a roaring fire and cosy atmosphere in the home.

After hearing what happened, and tracing the baby's life up to the death, we began to make the actual arrangements for the funeral. And specifically, in this case, how to meet the needs of the absent son. The mother said 'I'm really worried; he really adored his little brother — I don't know what to do'.

One of the things I found very effective in my own grieving many years ago, was to write a letter to express some of the feeling I had that was unspoken. I've used that technique for a lot of years now, and recommend it to anyone of any age. Even very young children can make a drawing if they are not old enough to write a letter. This suggestion should be given when the child is relaxed and not under pressure. Parents often respond to this with 'But they're not even going to the funeral', and I tell them that's fine, the service will be recorded. Later, maybe twenty years later, that child can hear his letter mentioned, realise he really did matter, and was important in the family unit that day.

This was the suggestion I made to that mother. I explained the letter could be placed in the coffin, or on top of it. I also suggested she ask the children if they would like to go into the garden and pick fresh flowers and herbs. That is another way of letting the children know their feelings mattered on this day, and that they were very much a part of the spirit of the service. They are involved then whether they come to the funeral or not.

Sometimes I have direct contact with the children: One said 'he used to come into my bed in the mornings' and I included that child in the service that way. I do try to find a phrase for each individual that will help them to identify, in the long term, with the life of the baby. That baby will always matter to the individuals within the family. It helps everyone come to grips with the fact that the baby did exist. I believe this is critical.

Decisions made at the first interview are rarely changed, other than the one relating to spending more time with the baby. The viewing issue I urge people to take time over, and especially where children are involved. Having explored the issue thoroughly with the parents, I then leave them to discuss the subject with their children. I will point out gently, but straightforwardly, that it is easy to make decisions for our children, perhaps to protect them. If the issue is explored sensitively, and the option given without pressure, invariably most children plan to view. Certainly when they've written a letter, made a drawing, or picked flowers and herbs, they want to place them as a final act. The four year old boy and his nine year old sister saw their brother again, and they brought their letters and flowers to the funeral. They told their mother they were so glad they had.

The service I write is personal. It relates to the baby, the mum and dad, the siblings, the grandparents and maybe favourite aunts and uncles. But really we talk about the baby and the difference that baby's life has made, irrespective of the length of time it lived. We explore realistically the things that have happened within that family that evokes memory, because memory is the thing that heals. Time does not heal; time helps you to adjust to a new and often harsh reality. Memory has a warming, a consoling affect. I believe expression of memory is vital to the healing process, and I stress this at the funeral service. Talk about your baby; laugh; cry; he was, and always will be a significant part of your life.

The community needs to be helped towards an understanding that the bereaved parent needs to be able to talk freely and openly about their baby. For example: I believe a baby's birthday is a time of deep remembrance for as long as a mother and father live. Most people ignore the parents on that significant day, and say 'I can't go around to Jan today — it's the baby's birthday!' I mean, we avoid Jan on that day in the belief she may have forgotten what day it is. How extraordinary!

Finally, it is an extraordinary realisation to discover the many things a child or baby has done in its short life – and that's not a matter of deifying the dead in retrospect. It's rather an understanding of the impact their lives have had.

You know, you can become gushing, sad and tragic, but really people want you to be effective. On the other hand, I think it is important to seek a meaningful involvement with the family. It is all too easy to be just a functionary and miss the other role of care-giver. I do care.

The Baby's Grave

Parents today are becoming increasingly insistent that their baby be buried in a single marked grave. This has not always been the case, and it is necessary to take a very brief glance at the social conditions of the late 19th and early 20th century to understand why this is so.

During that period large families were common, and there was an expectation that at least one or more babies would die at birth, in early infancy, or childhood. Often these large families experienced poverty and deprivation at many levels. Lack of sanitation helped to spread infectious diseases which claimed the lives of so many infants.

In Australia during the early days of settlement, and particularly the goldrush period, 'life was cheap and little was sacred on the goldfields'. [Griffin and Tobin (1982)]. Under these circumstances the practice of 'public' or 'share graves' developed with as many as eighty to one hundred infants being buried in the one grave. Stillborn babies have always been susceptible to this treatment, and unhappily it persists today.

From the beginning of the 20th century, social conditions were changing. Since about the middle of the century the numbers of births per family began to fall, and the improved medical and health services were lowering the rate of infant mortality resulting from infectious diseases. With the advances in science and technology since, we have moved a long way from the expectation that one or more babies will die at birth or in the neo-natal period. When parents plan to have only one or two children, and one dies, the constellation of the family is severely disrupted. Contraception in its more permanent form of tubal ligation and vasectomy, adds to the difficulties for families when their family planning suddenly and unexpectedly goes awry. In the 1980s the parents' perspective is different from those parents who brought children into the world in the 19th and early 20th century. Now, no one *expects* their baby to die, even though deaths do still occur.

It is advisable to keep these changing attitudes in mind while looking at burial practices, lest blame be apportioned indiscriminately when parents' needs have not been met in recent years.

Phillipe Aries states in *'The Hour of our Death'* that 'changes in man's attitude toward death either take place very slowly, or else occur between long periods of immobility'. If the historian looks only at a small time span, he 'runs the risk of attributing originality to phenomena that are really much older'.

In this period of seemingly rapid change in our attitudes toward death, the contemporary observer can only report what seems to be an awakening of consciousness to the needs and sensibilities of the time. For example:

A parent's account:

When my daughter died I was so shocked and distressed I allowed other people to make all the funeral arrangements. I went to the church service, but did not accompany her to the crematorium because 'women don't go to funerals'. I want to stress here my own acquiescence. I just let it all happen. When her ashes were returned to us for scattering, my husband took that task to himself to protect me from the pain, then refused to tell me exactly where they were, and I still don't know. Six years later I decided to do something about it.

I was fortunate enough to be taken to the crematorium by a funeral director who understood my need to complete my daughter's funeral rites, and to mark a special place for her in the cemetery. Up till that time, whenever I thought of her, my mind wandered off into the never-never. I could not locate her.

The manager of the cemetery was puzzled by my need. 'Why so long after her death?' I doubt my reply made any sense to either of us; I could only say over and over — 'I need to'.

He too has my heartfelt gratitude, because although he could not understand, he assisted the funeral director and myself every step or the way. Finally I wandered through the cemetery until I found a place that met my particular need. I claimed a place where there were gum trees, a small pond, rocks, rushes, birds flitting to and fro and the sun was shining.

I sat in that place for some time. By the time I left I had met my need; she had a place of her own and I was at peace.

A baby's grave is not only a reminder that the baby is dead. Visiting the graveside is also a way of facilitating the memories of the baby's life. It is a clear reminder of both. Parents sometimes report they are unable to visit the cemetery during the first three months or so, but for others there is both comfort and pain in visiting the grave frequently during the early months.

It is important that whenever parents decide to visit the cemetery, they have a specific grave or part of the cemetery that belongs just to them and their baby. During the first two months parents are shocked and numb. When the numbness begins to fade, a parent's first visit to the cemetery can herald the realisation that their child is really dead. Parents sense when they are ready to accept the reality of the death, and may seek a focus for it. To be confronted then with an area of lawn 100 m by 100 m and told 'your baby is somewhere in there' is devastating. The parent is truly bereft in these circumstances.

Multiple burials of babies in unmarked graves have brought heartache to parents in recent years. So extreme were the feelings of some parents, that requests for exhumation were made in some cases; requests that could not be met.

Where multiple burials take place, it is not possible to either mark the site with an individual plaque, headstone, tree or shrub.
Ian Mountford, Necropolis manager, reflects on the needs of bereaved parents today:

In the past there were many reasons for multiple burials. Because social attitudes changed slowly, it was difficult to foresee the situation that arose in the late 1970s and early 1980s when parents began to speak out and demand better conditions for the burial of their child. A few cemeteries did have a children's section; other cemetery trusts have recognised this need and are allocating sections specifically for children's graves. Fortunately, more are doing so all the time. Today, single burial in a marked grave is of the utmost importance to parents.

Multiple burials occur for other reasons: sometimes through a lack of awareness on the part of the parents that there are alternatives, particularly in the case of stillborn babies. A further and harsh reality is the cost of burials. When they come on top of the expenses of setting up a home and the expense of having a baby, the cost of a private grave is prohibitive for some.

There have been cases where parents have taken out a loan to bury their baby in the manner of their choice. In an endeavour to overome the problems of cost, some cemeteries are providing graves for children which are smaller and less expensive. If a parent buries their baby in an adult sized grave, the costs are the same as for an adult burial. On the other hand, parents are often comforted at this time by buying a family plot which ensures the baby will remain close to them.

Where cemetery trusts have responded sensitively to the needs of bereaved parents, their actions are to be applauded and encouraged.

Although not strictly the role of clergy or civil celebrant, it is within their scope to help parents, most of whom have no prior experience of 'buying a grave' or deciding upon burial or cremation for their infant, to make a decision that is compatible with their own needs now and later, and their own innermost feelings and aspirations — even intuitions about what is right for them.

PART III

The People Touched by Cot Death

For some, gates are for closing.
For others, gates are for opening . . .
For all people, they allow time to pause and take
bearings.

Anon

CHAPTER NINE

The Complexity of Women's Grief

In chapter five, the bereaved family's journey through grief was put into perspective by describing the ripple effect that goes out from that first moment of shock and disbelief. This same moment begins another phenomenon associated with cot death. It is the chain reaction which first affects the parents and immediate family and continues to eventually touch many people, some who may not have even known the family personally.

So important is this chain of reactions, and so necessary is a proper appreciation of it, that a whole book section, Part III, has been devoted to the people affected and their at first individual, and later interlaced, reactions. The first people to be affected by a cot death are, of course, the parents. They are affected as individuals and as a couple. It it in this second respect that they are likely to endure the more complex reactions. But before examining these it is important to take account of the way grief may affect the individuals concerned.

Women, of course, are those usually most immediately affected as it is commonly the mother who finds her baby dead. Her grief is also very complex for a number of reasons. It is in the context of the complexity of her grieving that this first chapter in the section devoted to those people affected by cot death is written.

The depth of a woman's grief, as well as evidence that her grieving for her baby that has died lasts much longer than the customary three to six months allowed by her partner, extended family and the wider community, is to be found on almost every page of this book. In this chapter, therefore, it only seems necessary to remark on the few aspects that are not covered elsewhere.

One of the things I wish to restate is that men and women grieve differently to each other, and I emphasise this point by focusing on women. Chapter Ten addresses the way men grieve, and I do not want to imply in either chapter that there is some kind of competition between the sexes as to who grieves 'better'. However, since a marked difference in male and female grieving patterns is evident throughout most cot death case histories, and since this is not always fully understood or sensitively appreciated, it would seem important to shed a little light on the subject. For both men and women, their learned roles will influence the way they grieve, as will individual personality and character traits.

Acknowledging that Women Grieve Differently to Men

Acknowledging that there are differences in the way men and women grieve may open up new areas to be explored, but for those assisting cot death parents along the path of healing it is of much more immediate value. Acceptance that there is a difference in the grieving behaviour of the sexes is of utmost importance to those supporting cot death families and the parents themselves. An understanding of this difference, and acceptance that it is quite normal and natural, can prevent or defuse misunderstandings between couples. It may avoid hesitancy on the part of individuals to follow through a certain grief response, thus allowing them to take their individual road to recovery.

If each parent understands that the sudden and inexplicable death of a baby son or daughter puts them in a distinctly personal kind of maze that they need to find their way out of, they will more easily move forward, released from having to think about anyone but themselves for the time being.

Mourning following cot death is likely to alter an individual's image of themselves, and of those around them. Women in particular are likely to have their self-image changed by a cot death. They may emerge from their grieving, and all its rippling shock effects, with a new perception of themselves. Many will have plumbed their own strengths and weaknesses during their necessarily lonely travail. They may be astonished at their ability to rise from these depths by their own force. They may have exercised will-power and experienced self-mastery and self-victory for the first time in life.

These new self-realisations can be bewildering. A measure of preparedness and some understanding that her perceptions may change could empower a woman to eventually integrate the changes in a positive way. It could equip her to balance the gains and losses that may be involved. She may be able to see her altered perceptions to the advantage of her family and lifestyle. She may also be able to use them constructively upon her marriage relationship and within friendships. These changes can occur despite her learned role behaviours and her past adherence to them. Her partner may need to be sensitively informed of the likelihood of some changes, and reassured that they may signal a new maturity on which she can begin to rebuild her future. It is important for both a man and a woman to know what is happening to the other. Some will intuitively understand. Many will not, especially in the light of their own intense emotions. They may not be able to work it out for themselves. Both can be spared unnecessary bewilderment, anger, resentfulness and even envy if they really know what is going on. This can do much to improve the quality of the healing taking place in each of the parents.

History's Contribution

Twentieth century men and women are the product of both cultural and biological evolution. They have learned to behave, react and perform in certain ways from the countless generations before them. How women grieve is a case in point. Women's grieving, especially for a child that has died, has always had within it certain undertones of guilt — a feeling that they should in some way have protected the child better and ensured its survival.

Athough sparse in its deliberations on the subject, literature is sprinkled with references to the sudden deaths of infants. In the light of present day knowledge and statistics many of these can be recognised as possible 'cot deaths'. It has always seemed necessary to attribute a cause to every death, including the seemingly inexplicable sudden deaths of babies.

Only in very recent times has the unexplainable aspect of these all too frequent sudden infant deaths been given due emphasis. This has served to encourage research rather than fully exorcise 'old wives tales' or totally exonerate women's guilt for 'allowing' babies to continue to die.

Just as history had been wont to give a cause to sudden infant deaths, it chose to implicate women, undoubtedly because of their traditional mothering and caretaker roles. The mothers of infants, along with nurses, nannies and wet nurses have long been held responsible for babies dying suddenly in their beds or their wrappings. Changes in styles, trends and methods of mothering have further compounded the issue of guilt and blame, particularly in respect to 'overlaying' or suffocation of an infant. For many a mother who took her baby into the adult or family bed, and whose baby was subsequently found dead, death by 'overlaying' was the usual pronouncement.

It is small wonder that women bear a deep, instinctive guilt feeling along with their grieving. At conscious level many feel a need to blame themselves. If they can begin to understand that this instinctive 'blaming' is almost a part of women's race-memory, they may also begin to understand why, when another person says in relation to cot death, 'you are not to blame', initially the statement brings little relief.

Throughout history there have been recorded accounts of babies dying suddenly and unexpectedly. D. L. Russel-Jones, of St. Thomas' Hospital Medical School in London, in his article 'Sudden Death in History and Literature' gives this quote from Virgil's *Aeneid* (circa 20 B.C.):

> At once were voices heard, a sound of mewling and wailing.
> Ghosts of infants' sobbing there at the threshold, infants,
> From whom a dark day stole their share of delicious life,
> Snatched them away from the breast, gave them sour death to drink.

The ancient Greeks also knew the experience of infant death sufficiently well to account it in poetic form. Russell-Jones recounts, too, the judgement of Solomon in relation to the 'laying over' of a baby, and the experience of mothers in Egypt (1st Century B.C.), who were held responsible for overlaying their babies. These mothers were condemned to hug their offspring continually for three days and nights in lieu of execution – the usual sentence for murder – to ensure 'the mother would experience her full deserts of remorse and horror'.

In the year 1291, according to Russell-Jones, German mothers were issued a decree forbidding them to take infants under three years into their beds at night. A similar law existed in Britain, and still remains in the statute book under the *Children and Young Persons Act* whereby it is a criminal offence to 'go to bed in a drunken condition with an infant which is later found dead'. One wonders how many mothers and nurses may have been punished under this law for deaths which today might have been determined as 'cot deaths'?

In his *Bills of Morality for the City of London* in 1625, again according to research done by Russell-Jones, John Gaunt used 'overlaid' and 'starved-at-nurse' as causes of death categories for infants. In the literature available, not much effort is made to absolve mothers or nurses or servants from feelings of guilt or blame, and there was little exploration of the fullness of a mother's grief. (For example see W. D. Yeats' 'Ballad of Moll Magee' (Collected Poems, 1906)).

It would seem that grief and guilt were expected to be coincidentally experienced in the case of a sudden infant death – a sort of combined emotion of grief and great regret. It could be supposed that men too experienced an emotion of regret at the death of a child – perhaps a much looked forward to heir. But there was not the same sting there. It was always the woman who bore the double brunt of mourning inwardly and outwardly for her baby and at the same time wondering if she could have prevented the death.

Women, then, have always known the grief that follows the death of a child, and the attendant feelings of guilt and blame for somehow allowing her baby to die. Even as late as the early 1960s, when some research had begun to try and explain some infant deaths that had been acknowledged as 'unascertainable', there was an inclination to see causes such as 'allergic responses to foreign protein' (cows milk) where the mother, again, could have felt loaded down by guilt at not having breastfed her baby (or not being able to breastfeed) or having given her child the wrong kind of substitute.

As she mourns her cot death baby, the 1980s mother is left with a more positive attitude from science, for it has now been firmly stated that 'there is no reliable way to predict or prevent sudden infant death'. However, centuries or perhaps milleniums of guilt cannot be washed out of the veins of womankind with one or two scientific pronouncements. It will probably take many generations before women can free themselves of uncourted and unwanted guilt feelings when their baby dies suddenly and unexpectedly. While mothers may need time to free themselves from this extra burden, those who support them through their grieving are in a position to 'loosen the chains'.

Instinctive responses and behaviours

In the light of the foregoing, it is interesting to speculate upon the observation that women, on the whole, seem to respond to the death of their infants from some deep instinctual part of themselves.

Largely, they seem to know what they need to do for themselves if they are allowed full expression of their grief, that is, if they are not denied by a well-meaning community the rights/rites their collective (unconscious) experience has provided.

It has been reported by young women who have had no prior close contact with death, and while in a deep state of shock, that they 'knew' they had to provide their (dead) baby with toys, books, a feeding implement, etc. for the journey their baby was about to undertake. Or that they 'knew' they had to see and touch their baby again, even sometimes to dress their baby for the last time. They have told of the resistance they encountered from concerned people around them when they attempted to meet their needs in this way. Another way of stating the above is that women seem to be flexible and sometimes creative in their mourning. Usually they will give vent to their feelings, and make their needs known even though they may make others uncomfortable. It is the extra responsibility of the supporting persons to allow this expression. Not all supporting people understand what is going on, but if they are experienced enough to recognise the gains of the mother, indeed to the whole family in the long run, they can support the mother in her instinctive needs and her individual means of expression.

If, for the funeral of her baby, the mother insists upon an open coffin or some variation in the procedure, if she instinctively senses a need for her other children to be there, or to say goodbye to their baby brother or sister at the funeral parlour, or if she exhibits any other strong wish in these first stages of her journey through her grief, she can be encouraged to respond to her need. She may be fulfilling a deep basic need for herself — and possibly for her children whom she knows she must continue to care for even during her own ordeal.

Experience has shown that children, far from being harmed by the experience of attending a sibling's funeral, gain from participation. They can become aware that they are taking part in a ritual that says this baby that was very important to them, has died, and that they are now saying a final goodbye to this loved little brother or sister by having a special ceremony. Mothers who have prepared other ceremonies to mark important occasions for each of their children — their christenings, birthdays, etc. — will known how important it is to make the intangible tangible so that they can understand and appreciate what event is being marked. She may know instinctively also that her family, momentarily fragmented by the immediate crisis of the cot death, needs to be rebonded in this common expression of love for the baby.

She may know too, at some inner level, that if the other children are to accept that their brother or sister has died they may need to take part in this formal expression of its death. The hopes and fantasies that the baby might return are often shared by mothers and children, and the mother's intuitive response may be to include all the family in the funeral ceremony, thus allowing them an opportunity to absorb the reality of the death.

It has been observed that women who previously took their lead from a spouse in almost all facets of their relationship will sometimes, at the beginning of their grief and later in the process of grieving, assume a new sense of responsibility. It is as if, through their grieving, they have found their capacity to break new ground, psychologically, emotionally and socially. This does not happen to all women, but it occurs in a number of cases. It is as if the death of their baby has somehow stripped them bare and exposed value and belief systems they had not previously examined.

If nothing in their previous experience has prepared them for this event, how do women know what to do for themselves and their children? It would seem that some women can and do draw their own blueprint when faced with an extreme emergency, that many do find their own way through the maze when there is no roadmap. Woman may know herself better than she thinks, or be drawing from the well of collective experience.

Cultural Factors

It must not be forgotten that women in grief are very responsive to their cultural backgrounds. Even in times when there were less varied backgrounds among the women of this nation, they mourned their infants who died in different ways. An Irish Catholic 'Mass of the Angels' in place of an adult requiem was a very different ritual to the short Kirk and/or graveside service for a Scottish baby, or the sung service of the Welsh. In the day-to-day living routines in the home, the baby would be mourned in different ways. The Irish family would include the baby in family prayers. The Scottish family would be more stoic and less inclined to talk about the baby, each family member keeping its memory privately in their hearts.

In the rich cultural mix of present day Australia, the grieving process of families will naturally be coloured by different traditions and backgrounds. In so many cultures it is the role of the women and of the family to maintain customs, and it is at times of crisis and mourning that special rituals become important. They serve as acts of remembrance for a loved child, act to maintain family cohesion, and build both spiritual and practical strengths. Sometimes too it is the grandmother who will be the 'chief mourner'. In some cultures her senior position will make her the focal point of the sorrowing.

The Ripple . . .

How parents tell their children of the death of a brother or sister has been covered elsewhere, but how children explain the death to other children has not. Assisting her children to explain to their peers the sudden disappearance of a brother or sister, may be a task a mother, grandmother, aunty or close friend has thrust upon them.

In a social environment it is usually the woman who confronts the pre-school or primary teacher and who is most likely to suggest ways in which the other children of the class or group can be told of the baby's death. There would be others beyond the school to be considered because a family moves in a fairly wide circle with children attending scouts, ballet classes, sporting groups etc. It often falls upon the mother to deal with these announcements, even when her inclination may be to avoid this difficult task.

Neither the mother nor the teacher may have had any experience in handling such a task, but handle it they must. In the account that follows there is flexibility in the way the baby's death was reported, and the decisions made could have resulted from close communication between mother and father.

In a family of four children, ranging in age from ten years to a few months, the youngest, a baby boy, died from cot death. Each surviving child was asked how they wanted their classmates to be told of the death of their brother. Each child chose a different way and this information was passed on to the respective teachers. One headmaster found himself announcing the death over the school's public address system; another child wanted the grade teacher to tell the class, but did not want any questions asked afterwards; and the pre-school child decided to relay the news through the 'show and tell' segment in the morning's activities.

While the mother concerned here had her own flexibility challenged in meeting the needs of her family, another might have to plumb her own creativity in making decisions best suited to the needs of her children, teachers, and classmates of the children. How she deals with the needs of these others along with her own may have profound, far-reaching effects.

Others beyond the immediate family may be affected by a cot death. In a chapter that focuses on women, grandmothers and babysitters require a special mention.

Grandmothers

Occasionally the grandmother of the baby is the first to find the child dead in his or her cot, pram, car-seat, etc. The mother may have handed over an apparently perfectly healthy, lively baby to the care of its grandmother while she worked, shopped, went to the dentist, hairdresser, or cinema, or picked up other school children. Half-an-hour, or half-a-day later she may be called home to find her baby dead. In this case the crisis has a double impact. Not only will there be two women distraught with grief over the child they both loved dearly, but each will be feeling mixed emotions in regard to the other, and the ripple effect of the experience can be felt when another grandchild is born.

Some grandmothers have explained that the announcement of another grandchild on the way, whether to the same son or daughter whose child died through cot death, or to another member of the family, brings a rush of fear along with joy. Once a cot death has been experienced in the family circle, even if the grandmother was not present at the time, there is on-going trepidation on behalf of every grandchild under a certain age.

Grandmothers may not show these fears. Many will keep them very much under control and to themselves. Obviously a grandmother can be subject to fears, anxieties and uncertainties when she is called upon to babysit the next, or another grandchild.

Babysitters

Those who babysit, whether professionally or as an act of grace for a friend or relative, are vulnerable to the effects of cot death. The effects on them can be as profound as those on the baby's mother. They need the same assurances, i.e, they were not to blame, and that to date cot death cannot be predicted or prevented. As the primary care-giver at the time of the death, they should be offered support, understanding and information about the syndrome.

If the death occurs at a creche or childminding centre, there are added responsibilities for those in charge. Other infants and very young children can sense what is going on around them, as will the parents who arrive to collect their offspring. Fear and confusion result if the death is not truthfully explained. This point is particularly important to the child-care worker who found the baby dead. If the cause of death is not carefully and clearly explained to others, a cloud of uncertainty can surround her professional capacities, as well as compounding feelings of guilt and blame. Professional babysitters have been known to refuse to mind babies under two following a cot death experience.

Relatives of a cot death baby, in many cases, *won't* be asked to mind babies in the family, this in respect of their feelings. However a friend may ask a cot death mother to care for a baby without knowing of her earlier experience, and be perplexed by a refusal. If a blank refusal is given, or repeated excuses are made, a wrongful inference may be given. Babysitters, and those likely to be asked to be babysitters for an infant, if they feel uncomfortable about the task, can be open about their cot death experience. In this way they can maintain good relationships with clients and friends, and receive some acknowledgement of the experience they are endeavouring to come to terms with.

Babysitters are very often teenagers. It is especially important that if they experience a cot death while 'on duty', they are encouraged to seek help from counsellors who are informed about the effects of sudden infant death syndrome. To seek support may prevent retained or suppressed emotions exploding sometime later in life, perhaps during their own motherhood years.

In Conclusion

All women who are touched by cot death find themselves deeply affected by the event. Something imbedded in the female psyche seems touched by these deaths which they feel, somehow, should not have occurred. Women express a deep regret with a funny kind of guilty feeling to it'—something they can't fully explain.

Finally women do grieve differently—differently to men,

differently according to their beliefs and cultures, differently in relation to their role and relationship to the baby. In addition, women do seem to grieve differently to one another in almost every individual case; such is the many faceted, infinitely wrought condition of womanhood. In the face of a cot death the differences manifest visibly.

CHAPTER TEN

Men I Have Known Who Have Grieved

There is a popular notion that men don't talk about their grief, or do not *want* to talk about it. The further I explored this myth the more and more frustrated and uneasy I became as I discovered that most men *were* willing to talk about their grief and as I noted the *ways* in which men grieve.

Something seemed very out of balance. The men I have met who have grieved told me how they felt in every way they knew. The men interviewed needed no persuasion to talk — the reverse was the case. I was in no doubt about the depth of their pain. It also became increasingly obvious that men grieve differently to women.

They talked about viewing their dead baby, the funeral, going back to work, their isolation, the misunderstanding of their silence; they also talked about their sense of anger, frustration and powerlessness, and their feeling of somehow having failed to protect their family, first from the tragedy itself and then from the sorrow that pervaded their home.

They spoke of their longing to share with their wife and children the feeling of emptiness the death of the baby had brought, and the reasons they did *not*. They talked about their need to restructure their shattered world, and to feel as a family once more. They spoke of their need for a mate or friend who could allow them to act and be 'as they were feeling' at any given time.

They told of their pain and distress when, three, four or five months later, they would return from work to find their wife again in tears. They spoke of their fears when confronted with this situation so many months after the death.

Some told of their resentment that their wife was seemingly still being given permission by relatives and friends and society in general to cry, and in other ways bewail their fate, while they, the husband and father, were apparently not afforded similar expressions of their grief. Somehow, they felt, it was unfair that these ways of grieving were not open to them. They seemed to wonder why *they* had to keep a stiff upper lip all of the time when, in fact, their sorrow was just as deep.

Others were able to talk about their need for real, physical human comfort. They expressed a need to be held, to be touched and allowed communication in a tactile sense. They revealed how they were unable to ask for this most basic need to be met by their loved ones while hoping all the while that their wife, friends and relatives would recognise it. The arm of a friend upon their shoulder, their hand covered by that of a relative while they spoke of other things, and the close embrace of a wife were forms of communication they sorely needed at this time.

Many men were puzzled by the way grief had seemed to destroy their sexual relationship. While understanding the shattering experience the cot death had been for their wife, some saw sexual embrace as an expression of comfort for them both and certainly a way of fulfilling their own real need for human contact. When this need for intimacy was suddenly seemingly unshared by their wife some felt rejected and even wounded by their partner's reaction.

All the time these men were talking, they were expressing their feelings and sharing their grief. So much for the perception that the conditioning of men would prevent such expression! These twelve men were not having the slightest difficulty in talking about their experiences. Why? They were from different backgrounds— culturally, socially, educationally and geographically; they were of different ages and had experienced cot death from as recently as three weeks prior to the discussions to as long as three years before.

At this point, my writing of this chapter came to a full stop. I read everything I could lay my hands on, talked to colleagues, (badgered them endlessly would be more truthful), argued with them—wondered aloud if I had got men's grieving all wrong. I was a woman, what could I possibly know of how a man really felt? I questioned my motives for wanting to write this section (my own marriage had ended in divorce three years after the death of Clare). I decided I should leave it out, but *couldn't*.

I wondered if men affected by cot death were catapulted, perhaps, into a premature mid-life crisis, and would that explain what I perceived to be happening? These men certainly were, or had been, weighted down with grief and burdened with extra responsibilities.

They were questioning their roles within their families, and in the workplace. They also were questioning values and moral systems. They certainly were subject to loyalty conflicts and were responding to messages from the community that they set aside their own needs in order to protect, comfort and provide for their families. Their role not only weighed heavily upon them, the emphasis within that role seemed to veer from one point to another.

A brief look at these roles help us to understand the position men do find themselves in. Peter Dunn, drawing on William Schatz's experiences in *Healing A Fathers Grief* (1984), offers the following comments which are general and may apply to individuals in varying ways and varying degrees.

Strong-man role

When the bereaved father feels sad, what outlets does he have? Does he surrender to the lump in this throat, or the tears in his eyes? Probably not, unless he is by himself in a private place. Society accepts men crying at the time of the death and at the funeral, but not long afterwards. Friends 'help' the father to maintain this strong-man role by comments like 'You are doing well', 'Someone has to be strong enough through this whole thing'. Women who are also subjected to the same conditioning hold similar expectations of themselves and their men.

Protector role

Said to be the 'natural' role of the father. Because his child has died the man feels he's a failure in this role. His sense of failure is further reinforced when he can't protect the rest of his family from the pain or grief, nor shield them from the effects of his own grief. He is regularly reminded of his protector role by comments such as 'How's the wife doing?'

Self-sufficient man role

This is a well established role that serves to prevent men from reaching out to others. During his lifetime, he has probably been urged to 'stand on your own feet', 'learn to do it by yourself' which reinforces his need to be seen as self-sufficient. This makes it difficult for this same man to seek professional help and often creates a reluctance to come to meetings with other bereaved fathers. He is left to struggle through with his own feelings and emotions, and how to express them. He has had little experience in sharing this kind of emotion with his wife and has learned that he doesn't share feelings with other men. The result is that he denies himself the opportunity to explore his own feelings.

Provider role

The bereaved father returns to work to find that his workmates treat him differently. They often avoid him, or they may protect him from the normal stress and challenge of the work which, in effect, tends to reinforce his sense of failure and his low self-worth. He feels isolated. He may throw himself into his work, but each evening he returns home where there is the reality of the recent death and grief. At this time, he may start working overtime, drinking at the club or pub, becoming more involved in service club activities. Such behavioural patterns are judged as the man trying to forget his grief-filled reality of home, to avoid the pain of grief.

But a man *has* to provide. Is he really avoiding his grief? He has been told (directly and indirectly) that this is not the best way to deal with things. On the other hand, when the mother spends all her time weeding the garden or is not able to do more than physically keep the rest of the family going, people are understanding. 'It's quite a common reaction', they will say. Her behaviour is not labelled as avoiding grief, but her husband's is. With such negative value placed on this so called avoidance behaviour when *he* resorts to it, the man often comes to feel 'not okay' himself, nor about what he is doing. He feels isolated and misunderstood.

Open displays of grief may be helpful and necessary for some people, but to expect such behaviour of all or even any man may be counter-productive to their own way of grieving. Every man is different, as is every woman.

Would men feel robbed of their masculinity if we simply said 'grieve like women do?' I felt this was so, and was uneasy.

Finally, I sat down one day and quietly called to mind again the men I had met who had grieved. Mentally I threw away the books, the tapes, the typescript of interviews and let these men speak. They said:

'We are talking to you — are you listening?'
'We are sharing our grief with you — do you feel it?'
'Can you lighten our load — not add to its weight?'
'Do you understand the language we are using?'

As they sat in this circle in my mind's eye I came to understand that men do show they are grieving; they demonstrate their grief and they express it eloquently. It is the wife, friend, counsellor, relative or workmate who doesn't acknowledge what they are seeing, feeling and hearing.

Many men interviewed had been thrown into further conflict by grief workers and others urging them to 'look after yourself'; 'cry'; 'don't be strong'; 'show your feelings, express them'. They were told that if only they grieved differently all would be well.

My inner voice yelled 'but they *are* doing it differently! *That's* what you're trying to write about'. What did it all mean then — that men should grieve as women do? Surely not, even if only for very practical reasons. Grief lasts a very long time. Who was going to provide for the family if the man refused to go to work, let the mortgage fall due, etc. The answer could not be a simple: 'why can't a man be more like a woman?'

I reflected upon those women who had assumed the mantle of masculinity, some of whom paid a price for laying over themselves those parts of aggression and competitiveness that they believed were essential to making it in a 'man's world'. It seemed to me that women had to let go an essential facet of feminity to survive in the business world in the ways they chose, or had thrust upon them. So, in what ways then do men grieve? What *is* their language? Like most people they use body language, verbal communication and escapist language.

Body Language

Immediately I noticed the father sitting with his hand on his stomach. His hand strayed to that place each time he was moved to speak, or was visibly moved. That was where the knot was — the pain. Some of these men were heavy and slow in their movements; others vague in their motions. Some slouched in chairs, others sat uptight on the edge. Some showed anger and irritability in their movements and some smoked a lot.

The community does not respond to these signs with the words that can bring release. Sentences like:

'The frustration of not being able to save him must be almost too much to bear'.

'To feel so powerless; to know there was nothing you could have done would leave me feeling so angry'.

'It must be hard to get up enough energy to think, let alone do anything — or even know what to do'.

The man who is grieving may avoid making eye contact. At this time one can only conclude that this is sensible for he knows what

he will see in your eyes—fear first, avoidance second. If you hold
the gaze of a man in grief for ten seconds you will respond. Most
of us are terribly afraid of our own and others responses to the death
of a child.

***The men I have known who have grieved spoke of the rejection and
isolation they felt:***

'Well I felt rejected. Greg died on the Thursday night. I didn't get
home until Saturday lunchtime. [This father was in hospital at the
time of his son's death] All the family were there. Some of *my* family
were there, and no one seemed to want to talk about it. I never had
that real chance to talk to people about it and get it out . . .; as
everyone else has been saying, they would just talk about anything
rather than Greg, and some of our neighbours and friends had come
in—I don't know—they just seemed to walk straight past me and
go up to K— and wrap their arms around her, and have a good old
cry, talk to her for about half an hour or so and say goodbye to
me on the way out.'

*Others talked about their sense of isolation affecting them in different
ways:*

'I went bush . . . just because of the people that were in the house.
I just wanted to be by myself . . . . I knew H— was being looked
after . . . it was a plastic sort of atmosphere at the house I
wanted peace, just peace.'

'J— rang the other night. She introduced herself and said, "Do you
want to talk to me?" I just couldn't believe it. You want to talk to
me? I said. 'Yeah. How are you going? 'Who—me?.'

'A— was getting the support and understanding . . . [I wasn't] I
always liked the thought that [I might have got it] at a barbecue,
somewhere men can get together . . . where the whole family can
share these things around . . . someone might be there who is
experiencing some of these things.'

'I thought I was alone.'

'Yeah, the isolation was real.'

'This is, I think, where we were helped. We did have that immediate
contact where people knew what was going on. I think that was such
a great help. You were saying T— that you just started getting

newsletters, that was your only first contact . . . . We had a lot more contact than that in the early stages . . . so important because that is when you don't know what the hell is going on.'

Some told of their anger:

'When I got the phone call at work it was just shock and disbelief . . . . I walked in to tell the boss the daughter had died, and I felt it [anger] starting to come on. I was just about to go and he slammed a bit of whiskey into me. Well, that slowed me down a bit. I walked to the lift . . . I had an umbrella in my hand . . . I was [so] angry, and in an initial outburst of a sort of violence I broke it rather than cry. In the car I started to wonder how A— (my wife) was, and from that stage on my grief was just subdued, and I didn't cry at the funeral or viewing . . . I couldn't kiss the baby; but from that time it was just subdued, and it was only after time that bits and pieces would come out . . . .'

They expressed their frustrations:

'I felt absolute frustration. Frustration. My immediate thought was she had gone and I wouldn't see her again. Frustrated because I was at work; that was it, she was asleep when I left in the morning so I hadn't seen her since the night before.'

'I painted the garage . . . and the car, inside and out, all the doors.'

'I didn't know [that she was dead] until I arrived. There were two ambulances there and I knew it was very serious. I thought she had been scalded. I should have been told [at work]. It was a frustrating journey home—I spun out in the car.'

And they told of their powerlessness:

'You can't do anything when you're not there.'

'Plus you feel totally incompetent. It seems to me that everything takes its course; like the ambulance comes and they appear to know what they are doing; the policemen come and they tend to know what they are doing, and the doctor comes and he seems to know what he is doing. You tend to be sitting there and thinking 'what the hell is going on? This is my property. It's not theirs—what's going on?' Totally helpless.'

'My sense was how could you leave me without saying goodbye?'

'I found it [the next day after the cot death] seemed to be a game with a format or a programme, and you had to go through it. Like ring friends and relatives . . . I found it very hard to do. At that stage of the game you don't know too much about cot death. You have experienced it, but you still really can't comprehend . . . letting people know seems to be the male role. It was in my case.'

'When Keryn was at work (I was at home and found Kelly dead) and the police told her, she reacted violently with anger and started to kick and punch the policeman — and he said "It's okay; it's all right; go ahead, let it out". What I am drawing here is that Keryn's reaction, being the one away from home is like what the other guys have described here. It is almost like the powerlessness in that situation. You can't do anything.'

Verbal Communication

The men I have met who have grieved tell of their attempts to communicate to others the intensity of their grief, and the difficulties they experienced in doing so. Their verbal communication is punctuated with other indicators of their grief:

- the language of choking
- the lump in the throat; trying to swallow the pain
- and the tears

'You analyse yourself in the terms of somebody's got to be strong. Somebody's got to prop up the family; . . . but an important thing for men is how many actually walk into the room and see the baby after it has died. I think that would probably change the way we see things . . . . I came home; the baby had been taken away and there was just a realisation that the baby was dead. It wasn't there, it wasn't anywhere, but I'm sure that if I had been the one to walk into that room my reaction would have been pretty swift I think. I would probably have been pretty distraught like A— was . . . she was a bit of a wreck when I got home, so the immediate thing was to comfort her. That became the primary concern rather than me becoming a bumbling wreck sort of thing.'

'I couldn't really break down in front of anyone myself. I might have had just a couple of little tears, but that was with my wife. Then I had to wipe the eyes and forget it. Just carry on and look after her. But I really felt — I never got it — but I really felt I just wanted to wrap my arms around someone and just really cry my heart out. I have never been able to. Just what I felt like. I really wanted it. It was up to about six months after he died that I still felt that need.'

And one spoke representing those who didn't find it so difficult:

'I was fortunate that in the first couple of days I was able to really gush — which I did — and I was oblivious to whoever was there; that didn't really concern me, my mind was ticking over and I felt what I felt. Personally I think it helped, although I am still very emotional about it [three weeks after the death]. I think I am beyond tears, although I find solace in that sort of thing. I have got a hell of a knot in my stomach, but I think it helped.'

The Language of the Work Place:

'That was the hardest, talking to the blokes at work . . . it didn't ease my load. A lot of them just didn't understand at all. A heap of them had never heard of it. The questions they asked: "Well, what did he die of?" Cot death. "He must have had something else surely". That was the hardest.'

'I went back to work four or five days later. They're firing questions at me, and I work with five, six hundred blokes. Every lunch time there would be fifty, sixty different blokes standing around me wanting to know why . . . I still didn't know.'

'I am an outside broadcaster for television. I work with small crews of people . . . . I sort of move around a lot and I can go three months without seeing a particular cameraman, so with changing crews I didn't have a set lot of blokes to work with . . . there were only one or two who actually spoke to me about it . . . . I got all the usual "sorry to hear about it", but a lot of people tried to sidestep the issue ; . . [some] hung back and didn't say anything. I think the ideal circumstances would be to sit down with a dozen blokes and discuss it with them, if they wanted to know. Go through it once and then, as time goes by, they could come to see you individually.'

'It was two weeks before I was ready to talk to any of the blokes. They were asking. I am a plumber with the Board of Works. There are only two of us that look after this side of Melbourne. The other bloke was off crook; well, then I lost my young bloke. If anyone called for a plumber they said "John's lost his young bloke". That was over the P.A. and the radio. Well, everybody knew about it. People asking me . . . who I wouldn't know from a piece of chalk . . . bloody stupid.'

'I work with an offsider and he is number one as far as I'm concerned. He just told half of them to go and don't bother us. The blokes who really knew me he took aside and told them what Mark had died of; then they came and asked me, just slowly during the day, which helped me a lot. He made everything roll into place; he took all the rough edges off. That was one reason I wanted to get back (to work). Until about three months I didn't even talk to my wife about it. I could talk to my offsider, but I couldn't talk to my wife.'

'It took me six months before I broke down. I actually cried about it. It was at a Christmas function. It was hard. Everybody was getting presents. There was a few for my young bloke . . . when they called out his name, that set the ball rolling. It would have been his first Christmas.'

'Unfortunately I work with a couple of guys that drive me up the wall. There is no problem unless it happens to themselves. One guy eventually had a divorce and described it as the most damaging thing that could happen to a person. He is self-centred in that regard and it shows through at work because, given a week I was expected to be back into the throw without any obvious sort of problem, and it was not talked about . . . I would have liked, you know, to be asked, "how are you feeling?" To have been shown a bit of compassion in the [work] relationship between us . . . that certainly wasn't apparent.'

'I am finding it extremely difficult to concentrate. I have done about a third of what I normally do . . . there are five people in my office, and all bar one [person] has almost totally ignored me. She is a woman of about 40 years who has two children of her own . . . . For the rest everything is back to normal. Life goes on . . . . The thing I think I appreciated about that one woman was that she simply said to me "If you need to talk, come and get me".'

'That is similar to my case too. I work in an office with about fifteen people. I walked in and the receptionist said "Hi! How are you?" As if I had been on a holiday . . . nothing was said. In the end I just thought this is bloody ridiculous, so I went to a chap I knew and sat down and said, "Well, this is what happened . . . ." He said "Thank Christ you have approached me because I just didn't know how to go about approaching you." He didn't know whether I was going to break down [and become] a screaming wreck or whatever.'

The Language of Silence:

How we ignore this deafening sign of grief. We do not respond to this silence. We are relieved. We cannot find the words to say 'Is the pain so great today that you cannot say his name?' or 'Hold on to your bitter sweet memories — they are just as precious', sentences that acknowledge the silence and perhaps the pain, sentences that can encourage release through talking, if that is what is wanted. It isn't *always* wanted.

'The next morning . . . sitting and staring into space, that is all. I was there for about five hours. Sitting there. People falling apart, talking, running in and out. Just in a land of your own'.

'(after the phone call at work) I had two guys driving me home, and of course they were deadly silent. After a while I was talking about the weather just to get somebody talking . . . I started to feel weird . . . and then I started on the general philosophy of death. I was trying to find some middle-of-the-road explanation that we all have to go sometime . . . that is all I spoke about on the way home. That was interspersed with long periods of silence.'

Escapist Language

- Staying away from home
- Drinking
- Finding someone 'outside' to touch, or be touched by
- Heightened activity

We ignore these signs and signals of a man's grief; we do not seem to be able to say:

'Do you bring your pain to work with you, or leave it behind — at home?'
'Working yourself to death won't bring your baby back'.
'Does it help to drink away the pain?'
'Can I put my arms around you — hold you?'
'Can you hate that ball enough as you thump it?'
'Does it help to cut the grass three times a week?'

The language of escape is here in these excerpts:

'I thought about it — throwing in the job, starting again somewhere different — and knew I would never do it . . . [a] fleeting moment sort of thought. The injustice of it all. I think it's more an emotional cry than anything else. It came in and went out the other side.'

'Well, a lot of people said to us, you should get together, go on a holiday, get away from it all. But that is the last thing I wanted to do in actual fact. I didn't even want to leave the house because I was waiting for the knock on the door; for somebody to open it and say: "Look, here's the baby back, bit of a joke you know". . . . an unrealistic concept.'

'From six months onwards I drank more . . . . I was getting to the stage of feeling that, apart from this fellow [whom I drank with], I had nobody to talk to. It was after this stage that I found another fellow at one of the hospital seminars . . . and we just clicked. We had them over for tea and A — got on well with his wife. I was able to sit down with him and it was terrific.'

I cannot escape the feeling that we do men a double disservice when they are grieving. Firstly, we tell them they must grieve differently to the way they do, having already ignored the way in which they *are* grieving. We are guilty of having:

- ignored their need for acknowledgement
- carefully ignored the pain they are expressing through their bodies, and their verbal and escapist language
- ignored their need for understanding in the work place
- ignored their need to work too hard, or not at all
- ignored their need to be comforted quietly (without the right to overt displays we more naturally bestow on women)
- ignored their need to be quiet, introspective, quite alone, even withdrawn for a time
  and
- ignored their need to play frenetically, or give up outside activities for a while.

Secondly, having ignored their grief we compound their distress by telling them they have, at best, done it all wrong anyway, or, at worst, that they are denying their grief. My question is: *Who is denying grief?*

The men I have met who have grieved are not denying their grief, at least not disproportionately to women. The men I have met who have grieved tell me it is those around them who deny the reality of their baby's death — those of us who, unwittingly perhaps, cut off or cut short the signs of grief we do not wish to share, see expressed, or recognise.

We read the signs of grief in women, whatever they are, and encourage their expression. Why don't we do the same for men? If we were able first to become aware of, and then acknowledge the signs men exhibit, we could encourage further talking and expression of what they are feeling now, today, at this moment.

Grief counsellors, friends, workmates all need to work *with* what is happening rather than direct the way men should begin.

Human beings are social animals. They tend to gather together; even at the time of the funeral of the baby this social aspect is expressed. The men I have met who have grieved speak of their need to be acknowledged by the community for as long as their grief is working through them. There will be times when a man wants to be alone, be private in his grieving. If we are going to be helpers, comforters, counsellors, we are going to have to learn to *listen* to the ways men talk about their grief, without ears, making sensitivity our ears.

We are going to need to use our eyes to see what is happening to our friend, spouse, relative or client and listen with all our senses to what he is expressing; learn to acknowledge his pain and grief; not avoid his eyes because of the pain or plea we see there. Can we not share ten seconds of our lives with men who are grieving?

Michael Yosef Morawetz was born on 4 March 1985 and died of unknown causes (Sudden Infant Death Syndrome) on 18 April 1985. These fragments, among others, were written during the first three months after the funeral by David Morawetz. The selected verses show very clearly that men long for acknowledgement of their grief, and recognition of the anger and pain they are experiencing. (It is recommended that the very long poem from which these were selected be read in its entirety. Unabridged copies available from S.I.D.R.F.)

Michael

You there in that wooden box —
Can you hear me?
I want to talk to you.

Why did you have to die?
I don't want you to be dead!
I want you to be back here right now!

I miss you.

I miss holding you and singing you your special song,
The one I dedicated to you when you were half an hour old,
And I held you to my chest.

I miss rocking your chair with my foot
In a vain attempt to calm you while I write.

Most of all, I miss each day the you who might have been:
Not another Deborah,
Not another Ben —
But Michael.

I am angry.
Bitterly, violently angry.
How dare they take you away!
It is not fair!
I want to pound the earth till it trembles,
Till everyone stops, fearfully,
Searching the face of his neighbour
To find out what has happened.
Then they will all stand there in silence,
For a moment,
For a year,
For the rest of time,
In honour of you.

Hey, you out there —
I am angry at *you!*
How dare you go on with your lives as if nothing had happened!
My boy just died, do you hear?
I want you to *stop right there!*
Look at me!
Listen to me!
Tell me that you love me.
Show me that you care.

Most of my tears are private ones.
I sometimes wonder what people think when they see me apparently coping quite well:
That I am heartless and unfeeling?
Then I say to myself:
The ones who know me know that it is not true;
The ones who don't can think what they like.

Driving back from Taggerty on the day that you died,
Through the rain and the tears,
I was so aware of the previous cargo I had with me:
Two *live* children.
I have never driven more carefully in my life.

Then to see and feel your body there in the cradle,
Your skin like wax,
Your face icy, icy cold,
Your arm half stiff . . .
I had never seen or touched a dead body before,
Never realized that body and life force are so separate.
Your body was there in the cradle but you had already gone.
How fragile is life!

Your death has been harder for your mama than for me.
She is the one who carried you around inside her,
Who fed you from her body,
Who spent hour upon hour with you.
She is the one who is haunted by the image of that moment
When she picked you up, trustingly, to feed you,
And found you blue, misshapen, a rag doll, dead.

Knowing all this, I sometimes have to tell myself:
'It is true, it *is* harder for her;
Yet you were his father,
It is hard for you too'.
Fortunately, sometimes I listen.

I feel these days as if some awful monster with a grip like a jackhammer has grabbed
    me,
Lifted me,
Shaken me,
From head to toe, for days.
Now that it has finally put me down, I must tread warily, cautiously, one foot at a time,
Watchful of the dangers and hurts that lurk around every corner.
I must go gently, like a person recuperating from a life-threatening illness.

Ben misses you too.
He was always protective of you.
You only had to give the beginning of a cry
And he would come running, a picture of concern,
Shouting: 'Baby 'ry', over and over.

Deborah seems to have understood from the start that you are not coming back.
She told the children at kinder all about you in life and in death.
She sometimes has periods of great sadness when she thinks about you.
She is collecting stones for you.

Some people give me advice:
'You must have another'.
'You must talk a lot about it; you can grow through this'.
I am angry.

Some try to make it better:
'It could have been worse'.
Some try desperately to avoid the subject:
I feel disappointed, disconnected.

Then there are those, the blessed ones,
Who say in so many individual ways the only thing I need to hear.
'I am so sorry, David',
'I am with you David'.
The ones who, even five weeks later,
Ask gently, as if for the first time:
'How are you today?'
These bring tears to my eyes.
Someone called to ask me, the counsellor, if I am ready to start seeing clients again.
No, I am not.
I am sure that I would sit there and think: 'Don't tell me your troubles'; I've got troubles
    of my own'.
This helps me to realize that I am not just making it up,
That I do need this time with my family,
And with you,
Before I move on.

CHAPTER ELEVEN

Relationships

Sometimes the effect of a cot death upon a relationship is extraordinarily complicated and profound. Because it is urgent that the parents of the child who has died — and those around them — understand that their relationship must undergo some degree of change, it seems important that a chapter be devoted to this subject.

I have attempted in this chapter to highlight some of the patterns that have been observed in the development of the marital relationship following a cot death. To become aware of patterns takes time, and ideally more than one observer. This therefore is the result of over three and a half years of collaborative effort between myself and Ruža Trivan when we worked together for the Sudden Infant Death Research Foundation. During this period new ground was broken. Many people had listened to S.I.D.S. parents before, but the processes had not been labeled in such a way as to provide new insights.

Although we have spoken of roles and communication, endeavouring to examine them in the contexts of breakdown and renewal, it needs to be remembered that they are all inter-dependent. The individual roles affect the way couples communicate. *How* they communicate influences the degrees of breakdown and renewal. Conversely, communication between partners can affect roles, i.e. the wife may go back to work in order to have someone to talk to, or to block out pain that she may not be able to share with her husband.

The one uniform pattern which emerges is that the outcome of any relationship depends largely on pre-existing styles of communication, the degree to which couples are prepared to examine and take up new styles or methods of communicating, and the degree of flexibility couples can allow themselves in redefining their individual roles and individual needs when their baby suddenly dies.

Our hope is that the way in which we describe the patterns of communication and the process of breakdown and renewal will bring aid and understanding to both the workers in this difficult area, and the bereaved parents themselves.

It is important to know that while relationships are always affected, that is, altered in some way, the change does not necessarily have an adverse effect upon the relationship, especially if there was good, free communication between the parents beforehand. In the previous chapter we have used David Morawetz's expression of his grief for his son Michael as an example of how one man felt his son's cot death. David's wife, Evi, expressed her grief in her own way in the excerpt that follows. The messages conveyed by this couple in their individual expressions of grief demonstrate an effective communication within the relationship.

For Michael Sheli

It is nearly five months since the dreadful Thursday morning when I found you in your little cradle. Yes I found you, but you were not really there any more. The moment I touched you it felt as if my blood, too, had stopped running through my body. Then I turned you around . . . and I *knew*. I felt like paralysed for a few seconds, then raced into the street. I needed a telephone to contact your daddy, Deborah and Ben.

The night before, it was the most natural thing on earth to hold you, cuddle you, stroke your little head, talk and sing with you, feel your lips sucking. Then your life force, your soul, *you* Michael had gone and I barely dared to touch you any more. The shock, the terrible fear, the confusion, the bewilderment kept me away from you. I touched your little face with my finger. You looked so strange and felt so icy cold. 'What have I done to my baby? Oh God what have I done?' was all I could think of that day. They put your little body into a miniature suitcase and I can still hear Ben say 'Bye bye Maakul'. I have never felt the finality of a situation as deeply as then.

I 'saw' you one more time, this time covered in the little wooden box. I felt the presence of our friends who came to say goodbye to you. But I allowed myself to just be with you, my little boy; it was the last time.

You are still with me, Michael Sheli. I so often think of you, and I miss you. I guess I am a rather private crier. My tears flow easiest at night or when I am alone, alone with all the memories passing by and with my imagination of the Michael that will never be.

I remember looking at you, one or two minutes old. I saw your big nose, your wide neck, your fluffy fine hair, thinking how grateful I was to be a mother of another healthy boy. I felt so confident, with a wealth of experience around babies. Still, I wondered at times how we would all cope with three children. What if you cried a lot . . .?

Now I wish you would cry. It is so painful to learn to accept your silence. The visual traces have all disappeared: your little clothes, blankets, the cradle, the baby bath, the pusher, the snuggli; my breasts are dry. But the streets are full of prams, pushers, mothers with babies in their arms, the sound of crying babies. I then wonder what you would look like today and the pain takes over again, my tears rolling down my cheeks, my hands feeling so empty.

'How is the baby?' Such an innocent question; yet it used to tear open my deep wound. I still do not know what to answer if someone asks me how many children we have got. Often I tend to say 'two', because the interactions are very short and the answer is not of importance to the person who asked. So I don't explain anything; instead I let my thoughts wander off to you my silent little boy.

Michael,

I may one day forget the sounds, the tone of your voice as you cried, the funny noises you made when I tried to burp you.

I may one day forget the expression on your little face as you looked up at me, staring at me while sucking; how you used to squeeze my breasts in order to get the milk to flow faster.

I may one day forget the weight of my arm as I carried you around, your head leaning back over my arm.

I may one day forget the little mark on your right ear lobe, your funny little feet with toes almost all the same length; the little dimple on your left cheek as you tried your first smiles.

I may one day forget how I always used to rush home in order to be back in time for your feeds, the guilt feelings for having come back too late. There was your daddy, trying to keep you quiet by rocking you with one foot while working at his desk, or carrying you around.

I may one day forget Ben's concerned face calling 'Baby 'ry — mama chum' when you cried, or Deborah's proud face, carrying 'the new baby' around — even on an uncarpeted floor.

but

I will never forget your tiny body put into that little miniature suitcase. I will never forget your icy waxen face.

I will never forget the tiny wooden box, covered with a black cloth.

I will never forget the sound of the earth that fell onto you, down there in the wooden box.

I will never forget the last words that I kept on saying while all that earth was thrown on top of your box . . . .

Michael Sheli, you have taught me to become more aware of precious relationships. They feel at times like crystal: fragile and breakable, yet strong, precious and beautiful. Sharing the grief with your daddy has eased a lot of my pain. Our grieving did not always go in the same direction, but we are both your parents.

By the end of our three and a half years working together with couples whose babies had died suddenly and unexpectedly, Ruža and I had observed that:

- Some live on a surface level and separate
- Some live on a surface level and stay together

- Some struggle honestly and openly and separate
- Some struggle honestly and openly and stay together

- Some battle it out and separate
- Some battle it out and stay together.

Most couples struggle to find the right combination for them. It is not possible to gauge the outcome simply on a daily basis. Mostly relationships will survive, but how they survive is largely dependent on the strength and integrity that existed in the relationship *before* the baby died. This is true of relationships in general when confronted by a major crisis.

During a couple's child bearing years, their relationship is likely to be broadly based on one of them being the primary care-giver, and the other being the 'bread-winner', although variations on this theme will occur. As well as this there are several processes taking place. Each person is moving along their individual pathway through life (individual process); as each person is doing this it could be said there are parallel processes between partners. Further, it can be stated that roles within the relationship are being defined or subjected to analysis resulting in constant movement and subtle pressures which result in change.

Therefore, when a baby dies, working through the issues confronting couples occurs on multi-levels. There are not only individual issues, but also relationship issues, family issues, social, community, and universal religious issues – the latter touching them even if individuals do not adhere to religious dogma.

Amidst this confusion, what each individual is trying hard to do is to hang on to themselves. This is not that easy because, when grappling with many different issues at various levels, it is all too easy for confusion to increase.

Roles

In crisis, people tend to adhere to established lines of conduct and communication. The wife/mother and husband/father have separate ways of being. Inside and outside roles and realities are expressed through individual patterns of behaviour. Examining the differences between men and women requires taking into account those behavioural differences. Their roles are usually pre-defined through tacit agreement, and generally there is a balance and an unrecognised complementarity.

It is important to look closely at the roles men have traditionally held in bereavement situations, and to the neglect suffered by them in areas of emotional expression and unfilled needs. This is done in chapter ten. However, for the purposes of this chapter the following words from Peter Dunn suffice. They were written when he was a counsellor at S.I.D.R.F.

'Men since childhood have been exposed to a social conditioning process that establishes roles, expectations and conventions which often serve as barriers. These often subtle barriers may rob them of the opportunity to grieve in an open public way – an opportunity traditionally given to women. Whether they are also effective in hindering men's grieving privately is difficult to determine'.

During her work with the S.I.D.S. Foundation Ruža Trivan observed that:

'The father gets a chance at one level to physically move away from the walls of the home, and is forced to make contact with the outside world. He has to. He has no choice about it. Sometimes he escapes to it willingly, and sometimes he leaves for the public side of his life reluctantly. Nonetheless, very soon after the death the father is forced to face the reality of the outside world.

'The father's role remains intact to some degree. He remains the breadwinner of the family. He remains the protector of the family. He remains the person who keeps the family's cogs turning, and works to make sure the family survives.

'His role is not as fundamentally challenged as is the wife/mother's role. He still has a house with a mortgage, another child or two and his wife to support. He still has a boss to be responsible to, or a client, or whomsoever else he has to function for. At least that part of his role has remained more or less intact. Certainly he is affected, certainly a significant part of him has been blown away, but overall he is intact.'

The mother is thrust into a different reality. She is at home on her own (unless she too escapes to a job). She is continually confronted with the reality of a ruined family, a ruined house and emptiness. She has to listen to the silence all day. The husband/father faces it when he returns home, and endures it for that period when he is home. She has to live in the death-filled ruins.

Also, the roles of the mother and the father concerning the baby were very different. The mother's interactions were so interlocked, so connected with the baby at that early stage of life. Even if she has another child eighteen to twenty months old, she doesn't see her role at that moment as being as critical for the twenty month old as it was for the tiny baby. The mother was highly involved with her baby. She fed, bathed, changed, entertained and burped the baby; she fitted the twenty month old into the time in between. Her role was much more focused on the baby, and the baby was totally dependent on her.

The father's role tended by tradition to be one which had to oversee the well-being of the baby and family; often with a new baby the father might take up some of the demands, needs and care of other and older children in the family.

Differences in the ways men and women respond to the death, and the different pathways followed, may become evident as early as the day of the death. Arranging the funeral is a good example, and can demonstrate the mixture of roles, relationship and communication used by couples.

Where a relationship is based on good communication and respect for each other's needs, the baby's funeral is more likely to be arranged to meet the needs of both parents. Mother and father are likely to explore and express their individual needs allowing compromise and choice.

If, on the other hand, the couple's relationship is firmly based on pre-determined roles whereby the husband makes major decisions on behalf of his wife, the funeral arrangements are more likely to be made to suit his belief of what is best for his wife and himself now and in the future. For example: when a father suggests the mother doesn't go in and see their dead baby again, he may be exhibiting signs of his protector role as well as displaying a difference in individual need. Some fathers have described how this task confronted them:

'It was the natural course of events, rather than − "Oh gee, have I got to do this?"'

'The general arrangements were concluded by midday on the day of the death. I just felt I had to get things organised − probably something to do'.

'I felt like doing it . . . other things are completely out of your control . . . this was something I could do for my son . . . something distracting, if you want to put it that way, or concrete.'

The father is functioning at a *doing* level.

By contrast the mother is functioning at a *feeling* level. Her emotions are confused and in turmoil. In that stage of bewilderment it is difficult to make decisions; therefore she is more likely to rely on the pre-determined roles on which their relationship has been used. More importantly she no longer trusts her own judgement. Therefore she is unlikely to challenge any decisions made.

This difference may be further seen when, on some occasions, a father decides to call in a relative to clear the baby's room to save his wife that agony. He may not check with her first, or give her time to decide if that's what she wants.

Ruža:

There are many decisions to be made and somebody must make them. Because men and women grieve differently, a decision made by one can run counter to the needs or wishes of the other. It may be that the father decided his wife is in so much pain, and is so distraught, that it would be better if she didn't go down to the funeral parlour; he desperately wants to spare her further pain. She often doesn't have the strength, the energy, or the togetherness to question his decision. Often she is unable to be clear about what she does or does not want at this time, so she may decide that he's probably right.

You have two people in the same situation, but looking at it from different angles. So the differences can be there early, although I don't think they begin to strain the relationship until a couple of weeks have passed after the death.

For at least a few weeks after the death people are too numb, too devastated by the whole event, to give any more of themselves to anything; they just try to hold onto the fragments that remain in their world. There is not the intellectual, emotional or physical energy to deal with any of the differences. A few weeks along, when other people are beginning to say 'don't cry', and the father/husband has gone back to work, is when some energy is released for the questioning.

This questioning is the first step to exploring and expressing their individual needs and wants, but they still may not have the energy or will power to challenge the situation.

Two fathers in a discussion group who noticed differences stated:

I went back to work where, to a certain extent you can forget it. When I came home to the crunch situation, I found my wife still in a state of depression — it's hard to explain; after a while it tends to get . . . tedious. You think, there has to be a cut off point sooner or later . . . . I felt I had to say something; I felt she had been through the grief pattern and that we had to kind of get together again and start life . . . as it was before. A normal type of life in actual fact. You just don't know how long you should let that grief go on for — a few months is healthy, [at] four months you start to get a little bit worried, and [at] six months you think, Well gee — maybe there is something wrong.

About four to six weeks after . . . instead of coming home about 6 p.m. I would go out with the boys, and then when I got home it (grief) would start to gush a bit. It wasn't related to the way A— grieved because she was able to continually pour it out; [in that situation] you find yourself sitting and saying yeh, yeh, and you become the listener rather than the participant . . . . [Alone] I could sit and remember . . . maybe a tune on the radio would start it . . . then you pick yourself up and away you go.

Back to work. Back to the everyday situation, and after a while it would build up again. I would just slowly let it out. After a while it came . . . I let it pour out. You can only guess whether it would have been easier [to do that] just after it happened.

Another father in a discussion group wondered aloud: '. . . Is the difference [the fact] that men are concerned with *what* is going on, rather than *feeling* what is going on?'

The man/father is confronted by worldly demands of a social-economic nature. In other words, it is the outer world demands that occupy his mind. A mother's issues and realities are very different. Often she has more freedom to avoid the outer world demands, but finds herself facing instead the silence and isolation. She has lost the intimacy of mothering the baby that died.

Ruža

They must deal with different sorts of struggles I think. She with an inner, he with an outer struggle. He has managed to keep himself turning up to work every day, and she is progressively feeling the intensity of the silence and loss of her role. These different struggles often result in a further strain.

There is a critical time around three months. How the parents cope then, what sort of freedom to have individual responses they give to each other at that time can indicate the direction they will go. The issues they will be struggling with often become manifest at this time. The father has gone back to work at two to three weeks and faced the world; by two to three months he has been at work for some time. He has had to cope, function, and deal with the often brutal day-to-day realities.

When he comes home one day and finds the house not cleaned, or his wife perhaps not even out of her dressing gown, in tears, and saying 'I can still remember how the baby looked on the first day', the way he responds to that would probably be a good indication of what's likely to happen further down the line.

If his response to this is: 'It's time you pulled yourself together' and gets angry about it because *he* has to face the world, then chances are she's not likely to feel very understood. She is, in fact, going to feel he's a million miles from her. His internal response may be 'You've got to try harder and not let yourself feel low like that'. Her interpretation of his comment is likely to be: 'He doesn't care, he's got over it; he doesn't know how I feel. It wasn't him who played with the baby all the time'.

That is only one example. A very different scenario might be: If he comes home, and she's in her dressing gown and crying, she hasn't cooked dinner, and he puts his arm around her and says: 'It's hard I know, but you can't let yourself get too far down. Come on, let's make some dinner and go round to Mum and Dads or something', then you are likely to have a very different outcome in terms of their relationship.

The second example suggests a situation wherein there is much less likely to be serious friction between the couple than the situation suggested in the first example. In the first example the couple are clearly unable to share with each other at that point. He is unable to say: 'How come you get to sit and cry all day. I have to face a cold, hard world out there, and I am trying. I have to drag myself to work and it's hard for me too'.

She is unable to say: 'The silence is driving me insane. I can't live with the silence any more. My arms are aching for my baby'. Neither are able to clearly hear the message from the other. Communication between them is very unclear and may have broken down.

At the beginning they often assume and expect they will be there for each other. At least, they think: 'I have somebody to share this burden with', but three months later this expectation and assumption has been cruelly challenged.

Visitors are not calling around so much, the house has been cleaned out of all things belonging to or referring to the baby and the silence is deafening. Additionally mothers and fathers at that point are becoming aware of just how close they are to each other in reality, and beginning to discover how supported or understood they really feel. The fantasy, 'I am in this with my spouse and being supported all the way through' may begin to crack up.

It is not uncommon to see partners putting pressure on each other, often in subtle ways, to bring their spouse closer into line with what they believe is the better way to grieve. They do this to maintain the belief that they can share their grief and survive together. Their unconscious reasoning runs along the line of:

Ruža

I am terrified that I may not survive.

I need a guarantee that I will. Society has taught me that if I do it right I will be rewarded.

In my grief I translate this to:

If I grieve right I will survive. But, how do I know what's right?

I will know from what you tell me.

I will know I am doing it right if what I am doing is the same as what you are doing.

And so is born my powerful need to grieve the same way as you. This can mean:

  —going at it at about the same pace as you;
  —feeling and/or thinking similarly to you;
  —needing similar comforts as you.

If you do it differently to me it may mean that I am doing it wrong.

This may lead to me getting lost and not surviving; or you may survive without me.

Therefore when the difference is too great I may put pressure on you, and you on me, so that we do it the same way.

That way I can be sure we are doing it right and will survive together.

What is little understood is the reality that each must deal with his/her own grief, and that there needs to be at least an acceptance of the way the loss is being felt and experienced by their partner. This difficult and often painful truth is sometimes learned too late.

Grief is so overwhelming that people often believe they can't survive it on their own. The reality is that, one way or another, each person will have to find individual solutions and a resolution of their grief.

Very occasionally we have seen the wife sharing more in the decision making, thus taking some of the responsibility which usually lies heavily on the husband. This allows the husband to share his feelings more. She may give him more freedom to express his pain, thus lifting the emotional burden that she may have felt she was carrying alone. In this way they need not become role bound, i.e. when she does the feeling/showing, and he the protecting/organising.

Having the feeling that 'she (or he) doesn't understand what it's like for me' increases the experience and fear of being alone, and may result in a tightening of the roles that have been established, rather than a freeing of them.

Couples need to trust each other, and allow their partner to put the pieces of his/her shattered world together in the way that feels right for them. They need to assure each other of continued support, even if they are unable at times to fully understand.

Communication

It may be important to explore some of the differences and similarities between partners, and the reasons for communication difficulties. Following the death, these difficulties can result in expressions of:

'He doesn't understand how I feel'; 'He doesn't seem to care'; 'He seems to have forgotten him (or her) already', *and*

'She doesn't seem to be coping'; 'It's time she pulled herself together'; or 'I can't take much more of this'.

Ruža:

On the basis of the language people use to express their distress, it is easy to make the assumption that the same thing is happening for them. I doubt whether this is true. Mothers and fathers are saying similar things: 'Why my baby?' 'What happened?' and 'Why did it happen?' They may cling to each other and assume that their thoughts and agonies are the same in every way amidst the chaos and acute distress.

On the surface and to many outsiders their reactions may appear similar, but I think mothers and fathers tend to grieve in a personal way, and each has their own uniquely individual response. Certainly the questions 'What did I do wrong?' and 'Why our baby?' are the same, but I think there are *different* questions, too, and *different* needs beneath these questions.

Fathers may be thinking: 'Our baby is a member of this family. The family is not the same anymore: how does this affect what I can do; how does this influence what I do?'

Mothers often think more along the lines of: 'This is my baby, part of my body; how can she/he not be part of my body anymore?'

At the start I think outsiders can pick up signs and signals that there are differences, for example, the mother clearly demonstrating a need to talk, and the father questioning whether it is a good thing for her to do. He may demonstrate that at the door when greeting visitors. He may even go to the lengths of saying something like: 'She's pretty upset' – indicating in an indirect way that perhaps it would be better if she didn't see anyone because it may upset her more.

Within these expressions lies grief that is felt deeply by both parents. It is important to encourage each parent to understand what the other is feeling, and to help them find mutually acceptable ways of communicating these feelings.

Mothers report that their most common reaction is to scream when they find their baby dead. They also cry, and sometimes sob uncontrolledly. They express their shock and distress in these ways.

Men say they feel angry and shocked, and that they feel like crying when they are told their baby is dead, or when they find their baby dead, but most do not express their immediate feelings in the ways that women do. Many men react by protecting and comforting those around them. There ought to be no suggestion that to scream, to cry, and to sob is 'right', or that to comfort, protect and to become active is 'wrong'.

Initially, many men need to be active or task oriented while a woman's first reaction may be more an expression of her feelings and emotions. The comforter/protector role of men usually asserts itself in the crisis to meet the woman's need to be aided in her helplessness, and to help the man compensate for his feelings of utter powerlessness. These feelings of helplessness, frustration and powerlessness are experienced by fathers, but are often not appropriately acknowledged, and sometimes even ignored by those around them.

L. Ernst, J. de Frain and J. Taylor (1982) say: 'Some professionals working with families who have experienced S.I.D.S. guess the divorce rate to be 40 to 70 percent', but no one, to date, has been able to provide accurate figures. Families are often difficult to locate following cot death, as many succumb to the need to move away from the scene of such intense unhappiness, either immediately following the death or sometime later. However, it is certain that when a baby suddenly dies, the feelings and thoughts a couple communicate to each other, and how they communicate them, can have far-reaching effects in their relationship.

Cot death and divorce as cause and effect stand in uneasy alliance here, as the outcome following cot death rests on many factors. Individuals, with varying personal histories, and differing degrees of resources and skills, are thrust into the experience of cot death. How couples individually relate to this crisis, and to each other, depends not only on their individual life experiences, but also upon the strength of the foundations of their relationship, i.e. what drew them together in the first place, and their hopes, dreams and expectations of each other and of the family they hoped to become. All too frequently these things are not clearly understood and therefore cannot be fully expressed at the time of a cot death. Furthermore, it may be too painful for them to express such things at this time. What is certain is the fact that relationships are sorely tested.

Ruža

A couple's relationship can be based on mutual respect and an ability to communicate their needs to each other, or it can have a less secure basis, i.e. a relationship without the same commitment to learn to live together, to communicate, and to come to terms with each other's needs and wants. This will have a direct bearing on how a couple struggles through the crisis of cot death and its aftermath.

When cot death occurs, many couples are in the early stages of their relationship, and haven't yet had time to firmly establish their alliance. Cot death occurs at a very vulnerable time—at a very early stage of learning about relationship. On the other hand, if the couple have been married for ten or more years and struggled through their relationship and what it means to them, and are clearer about their bonds, then there may be a firmer basis from which to work.

J. de Frain, et al (1982) note that the death of an infant presents a crisis not only individually devastating but also capable of being 'totally destructive to a marriage'. It is true that some couples will move even closer together through adversity, but even those will undergo severe testing. As each individual deals with their grief, their marriage may sustain many almost fatal strikes upon its strengths and capacity to spring back.

Couples often feel that if they are not moving closer together through their bereavement, then it must mean they are moving apart; that their marriage is in danger of failing. After a cot death, the fear of another parting—through divorce—can complicate further a relationship which is struggling to survive.

From the impact of the death, through the first few weeks to the second impact ('crunch') at approximately three months, through the often lonely 'wasteland' which brings a couple towards the first anniversary, mothers and fathers experience the great *sense of loss* the death of their baby brings, in a personal, private and unique way.

Ruža

It is important that couples understand that their partner cannot do their grieving *for* them, and that this may mean times of aloneness and loneliness—a spiritual, emotional, physical and psychological separateness. A lack of understanding that this separateness is a part of the process of grieving may lead to breakdown in communication and relationship between parents whose baby has died.

J. de Frain, et al (1982) note: 'Grief and the process of mourning is a series of small steps taken when the individual is ready, and the marriage often takes second place to individual recovery . They agree also that for the individual survival on a daily basis can use up that individual's store of energy, leaving nothing at the time for the spouse.

Breakdown and Renewal

Within this context, *breakdown* refers to the inability of individuals to continue to act and behave in a way that is expected of them or, indeed, in a way they expect of themselves. This form of breakdown is necessarily a part of the change that is forced upon a couple by the cot death. Breakdown occurs because the many and complex parts that make up the individual, couple, and family, can no longer hold together or exist in the form they did prior to the cot death.

Renewal requires a time of self-evaluation and self-restructuring which may necessitate a withdrawal from the demands of the relationship for a time. While this can be frightening to the spouse, and may be seen as a further threat, it is nevertheless the first step to forming a new and different alliance. From this point, a reevaluation of the partnership can allow a restructuring of the marriage. Inevitably the quality of the relationship will change.

Ruža:

There are many degrees of breakdown. When I use that word I don't mean necessarily that the relationship dissolves or totally breaks down. For example: If a husband and wife cannot communicate with each other and they realise they are doing much of their grieving on their own, they can become fearful that the relationship may have broken down.

This inability to communicate may be only temporary if the couple work towards finding new ways to talk to each other. This is one very common form of breakdown and renewal.

A more serious form of breakdown occurs when couples begin to feel angry toward each other, whether they express that anger or not. They may become bitter and hostile toward each other because of real or perceived neglect.

A father said: 'Before, I would have sat down and played with the kids, then after the little bloke died, for about two months, I just sat there in front of the T.V. Just staring at the T.V. Just watching any garbage that was on. I didn't seem to take much notice of what my wife was saying. She would just yap away to herself. Then we had big fights about it because she reckoned I should have started talking to her'.

They may talk about separation, but to lose the baby and the marriage within such a short space of time would be too overwhelming. Sometimes they secretly admit to themselves that their marriage has always been empty.

Time and energy is needed to work out new ways of being with each other, yet they are already putting in so much effort just trying to keep going. It's one thing to know what's happening inside you, another to articulate it, and yet another to be heard.

Frequently breakdowns occur within the partner's sexual relationship. At the surface level, she may say, 'I don't want to become pregnant', while he may say, 'I need you close and need to know we're okay'. At a far deeper level she may be experiencing, perhaps unconsciously, the sexual embrace as a disloyalty to her dead baby. She may recognise an inner dilemma without understanding it: to whom will she be loyal – her husband who needs her close, or her baby to whom she still feels so close? The embrace holds the potential of another baby, and here lies the difficulty and difference of need.

It is important to look at the couple's sexual relationship as it existed before the baby's death. On what was it based? What was its purpose in the relationship? Was it procreation, power, duty, communication, pleasure? It could have been any or all of these.

In whatever way the sexual embrace was important before the cot death, it may have a heightened significance following the baby's death. Some women have reported they are puzzled by their partner's sexual needs in the first few weeks. Some are shocked. Others find warmth and solace in the closeness of sexual intimacy. Perhaps the man is able to forget for a moment, through their embrace, the pain he is feeling. Perhaps he is wanting closeness; perhaps he is seeking some nurturing from his wife; perhaps he is asking her 'Have I failed?, Do you blame *me*?'. Perhaps he is saying 'Trust me – I need you to trust me'. Perhaps, 'Our baby has died, so I need to know our *relationship* is alive'.

When a baby dies a woman's nurturing remains incomplete and unfilled. However, she can work towards completing her nurturing cycle through memory and active imagination, (and at the same time continue to mourn her baby's death). Another baby will not provide her with a solution to the incomplete nuturing, because her immediate need is to nurture that baby that has died. Even subtle pressure from her partner at this point, or her own belief that another baby will assuage her pain, can arouse inner feelings of disloyalty.

On the surface it may appear to her that he is rushing their lives along too quickly (she cannot reinvest herself in life again just now).

On the other hand, he may feel he must provide hope for himself and his family. The baby's death threatens to destroy his (yet unlived/partially lived) dreams, and he may need to restate his desire to continue the direction of his life as quickly as possible. Many men express their mourning in this way.

If we examine the parallel process involved, it is possible to see that the woman has an additional dimension to her grief.

For a woman the process looks like this:

(a) To complete her nurturing cycle through memory and active imagination. (Even though she knows her baby is dead, she continues for some time to respond as though the baby is alive.)

(b) To mourn her baby by exploring and expressing grieving, sadness, guilt, loneliness and emptiness. (She remembers moments of the relationship she had with her baby and relives the baby's life).

(c) To reinvest her emotions in life.

For a man the process is:

(a) To mourn his baby's death.

(b) To stabilise and reestablish life for himself and his family (as quickly as possible) while continuing to grieve.

Predominately: *his role is to*:

- mourn the death of his baby while continuing and furthering the life of the family

    her role is to:

- complete her nurturing cycle of the dead baby
- mourn for her dead baby
  then
- reinvest her emotions in life (continue/further) their lives.

These disparities may explain, in part, the differences expressed by men and women for example at around three to four months:
'He seems to have forgotten him/her'
'She doesn't seem to be coping'.

In other words, she has a need to suspend life while she mourns; he has a need to thrust forward, continue the direction, or redirect, his family towards the future. It is her suspension of life that runs counter to his sense of urgency. Herein lies a paradox for the couple.

If the couple are unable to express their inner fears and concerns, if either partner is unable or unwilling to understand and acknowledge the plight of the other, then feelings of resentment and rejection are likely to follow.

At times of great emotional turmoil it is difficult to express our inner chaos. Very often feelings are experienced without any clear conscious recognition. At these times it becomes even more difficult to communicate them to another.

Many couples become frightened when they allow themselves to become aware that all is not well in the marriage; the strain between them is increasing, the irritation levels are becoming higher.

Ruža:

Parents fear that the relationship may be disintegrating, and that fear can stop them from allowing themselves to acknowledge they have different needs; that they experience things in a different way; that it is a very lonely journey for them both; that they can only 'do it hard' and on their own. The parents' awareness that they have to work through this, and suffer and struggle through on their own, without anybody really understanding what it's like for them inside, is a very frightening, lonely and isolating realisation.

To live in that sort of desolation is fairly unbearable. The outward appearance of the relationship may continue, but underneath there can be a great deal of loneliness. The couple may make the effort to talk to each other about everyday matters. They talk to their kids about their homework or bicycle, or whatever they talk about normally. 'What's for dinner tonight?' 'Would you mind planting that tree in that corner of the garden because that's where I've always wanted it'; but another conversation is going on in their heads. They are both living their own double life. When they are unable to talk, they keep up the routine. This could be called the camouflaged breakdown.

Individuals need to be encouraged to explore and express their innermost feelings and thus remain loyal to their own needs. At the same time they need to remain sensitive to the needs of their partner.

Relationships Do Survive

The emotional chaos following cot death forces individuals to look inward, to reorganise, to rethink, to reevaluate so many aspects of their lives, and it is this that creates change, in spite of themselves at times.

This extensive reevaluation can provide a new direction for the family and its individual members. They will never be the same again. Individuals discover new attitudes in themselves and each other. Their world view is altered and values change. Marriage and relationship takes on a new meaning and the quality of the union may be enriched.

Cot death threatens the structures on which life was built, but it also provides the opportunity to reorganise by evaluating meanings, values, life skills, wishes, desires and hopes. In evaluating these, the individuals achieve a solidness, a confidence and strength they may not have had before, and the relationship a solidarity it may not have had before.

Evaluation

Once the baby has died, a couple can collude that it is all too horrible, and they can come to the agreement that this is something they will try to ride over. They will have to struggle through, individually, but try to do it less consciously and try very hard not to think too much or too long about any of it. They can agree that they will hold on and avoid confronting the many issues. They may fear they do not have the strength or support to survive if they look too close. They dare not ask for help because this would be stating the reality out loud. They hang on because they fear they will be destroyed and they know that it is possible to hang on forever. They may grow old together, or the futility of it all could catch up, and they could separate.

On the other hand, once the baby has died, a couple can communicate freely and openly, and in doing so, remain aware and in touch with each other; and accept each other without trying to force change, without trying to demand that the other be different. They can do their own individual sorting through (they must anyway, while acknowledging and accepting the other's pace.) They can have faith in each other and trust that the other is doing the best they are able. This couple have a chance of not only surviving with support, but surviving with understanding.

CHAPTER TWELVE

Children and Their Responses

Parents choose many different ways of telling their children that their brother or sister has died. Sometimes children in the same family will be given different explanations, simply because of their different ages.

There is little to write in preamble to this chapter. The parents' own examples of how they tell their children and how they respond is sufficient:

'We very carefully explained the death to him. He was five years old and we lived in the country. We explained 'dead' was like the dead birds we sometimes found; 'dead' was when one morning we found the rabbit in his hutch not moving, stiff, not breathing and we had to bury him. We were more distressed than he appeared to be. It didn't seem to worry him that his sister was dead and wouldn't be coming back. I remember being shocked, because using the word 'dead' reverberated through me each time I used it; she won't be coming back was the echo I heard each time.

'Our other son was three years old, and I honestly don't remember what I told him. I know I thought he was too young to understand. Looking back I realise how difficult and frightening the sudden disappearance of his sister must have been because he was the one who fetched and carried for her. He was the one who sat and played with her, who responded with delight when she smiled and laughed with him, and he was the one who was given nothing—no explanation that I remember.'

Other examples include:

'She died near Christmas time. I said Father Christmas had taken her.'

'We explained he was sick. We took him to the hospital, and that he had died.'

'I put him to bed. He went to sleep and didn't wake up.'

'She has gone to heaven; she is with God.'

'T— is in heaven. If you are very good, one day when you're much older, grown up, you will go to Heaven too. God only has good people in Heaven. T— was not in pain, he died when he was asleep. His body is in the ground—his spirit is in Heaven.'

'John is dead. He died from cot death. Only little babies die this way. It won't happen to you.'

'I didn't say anything. She's too young to understand.' [Twenty month old sibling].

'Jesus took her away; the box [coffin] is filled with flowers.' Sibling replied: 'I don't want to go with Jesus'. Parents said: 'That's okay— you're not dead'

When giving an explanation to their children of the baby's sudden disappearance, most parents agree that using the word 'dead' instead of an appropriate euphemism is difficult and frightening. And yet 'dead' is a much used word in our daily expressions: For example: 'dead lucky', 'dead-end', 'dead heat', 'dead weight', 'dead tired', etc. When 'dead' becomes a reality in our lives we avoid it and use 'passed away', 'gone to sleep', 'gone to rest', 'we lost him', 'he's gone', 'passed over', 'kicked the bucket', 'she's at peace', etc.

To say to a young child 'our baby's gone', 'we lost our baby', 'our baby passed away' instead of 'our baby is dead' increases the chances of creating anxiety and confusion in the young child's mind. Gone where? Lost? Let's go find him. Passed away? What does that mean? The child's responses may be complicated by what fantasy is attached to 'gone' and 'lost'.

But Dead? What is Dead?

Children need to explore and express 'dead' to reach an understanding of what this means in their lives. Depending on their ages and development they will do this in a variety of ways when they are given freedom to express their feelings, and explore their thoughts about 'dead'.

Marguerita Rudolph in *Should the children know* recounts some wonderful stories which demonstrate children's exploration and growing understanding of death in their immediate surroundings.

In the chapter 'Who deaded him?' she explores with pre-school age children the deaths of a frog and a berbil (mouselike desert rodent). From discovery of the dead frog, a three an a half year old child asks the question 'Who deaded him?' 'Why?' 'Will he bite?' and he gradually moves to touching the dead frog. He discovers the frog can't eat, doesn't respond to his touch, and can't jump or roll over.

After about half an hour, during which the teacher confirms again and again 'Yes, he's dead' the child takes the frog to the other children. 'See this frog, he's dead'. Some children are interested, others not. Someone suggests putting the frog in water to resuscitate it, to no avail. Eventually, Roger rushes to the housekeeper when she enters the room, and says to her excitedly: 'Miss Farrell! Look! This frog is dead; he didn't have any mud and he didn't have any water, so he dried up and *died.*'

Although the teacher hears her explanations accurately repeated she does not think the child really understands 'the complicated phenomenon of the cessation of life'. He will probably ask questions in the future when he confronts 'dead' again, but he has expressed and explored 'dead' on this occasion.

In relation to the death of a brother or sister, toddlers and very young children tend to want answers to questions such as:

1. 'How can he breathe in the box?'
2. 'Who will feed him now?'
3. 'Does he have anyone to play with?'
4. 'Where is he now?'

If these questions are answered honestly, the opportunity is taken to help the child towards expression and exploration of dead.

The first two questions 'How can he breathe?' 'Who will feed him now?' relate to needs of the body, and a child's 'self-ish' self-centred need to survive. These questions are simpler to answer than the two that follow. Most very young children will have seen a dead fly, or spider, or perhaps a bird. A dead fly or spider cannot move, does not breathe. A dead bird cannot swallow a worm. He is dead. He has no bodily needs. And so it is with a dead brother or sister.

As adults we know and understand the answers to the first two questions. Questions three and four are more difficult to answer because they introduce abstract concepts and religious beliefs. These questions are particularly difficult when parents have not worked out the answers for themselves. Often then the parents in their despair may seek for an answer that will comfort and protect both themselves and their children. If the parents' beliefs are tested before they are formed, confusion and uncertainties can result for children when the parents provide answers they may not necessarily believe in. Children pick up the inconsistencies, and bewilderment is the result.

To answer 'Where is he now?' with 'He is with God' or 'He is in Heaven' will probably result in more questions the parents will have difficulty in answering. To demonstrate the inconsistencies children pick up, it is easier to use a more concrete example. If parents deny themselves tears of sadness in the presence of their children, and at the same time exhort their children to feel and express sadness, the child senses a 'mis-match' in behaviour. The parent who weeps uncontrollably and then protests 'nothing is the matter' falls into the same 'mis-match' trap.

Concrete answers, although painful to deliver, usually make sense to the child because he has a concrete reality. Thus: 'Does he have anyone to play with?' could be answered this way: 'He can't play because his body doesn't move anymore'. To attempt to answer the question using abstract concepts could create difficulties as the answer rests largely on the adult's beliefs about an after-life.

It is important to remember the adult may find his/her own beliefs tested at this time. Many of us play lip-service at least to a belief of some kind that takes in the concept of an after-life. Regardless of belief, a parent whose baby has died struggles to accept the reality of death. 'Does he have anyone to play with?' focuses painfully on this reality, as well as testing the concept of an after-life. To answer 'I don't know' could be the best answer at this time unless the parent is certain of his/her beliefs.

On the other hand, parents who have firm faith or belief in an after-life will answer the question differently. If they say from their inner certainty:

'He has other children to play with—other children who have died',

or

'Grandma and Grandpa can play with him because they are dead too',

they reflect their certainty that the baby is dead; that dead is different to alive; that the brother or sister is with other dead people; that they are in another place; that you can only be in this place if you are dead; that when dead, the baby cannot come back home to play with his brother or sister.

In the following parent's account 'Where is she now?' is tackled directly:

'We just talked about it naturally. If I go to bed early and Jayne (three and a half years) is still up, she will come and plonk on the bed. "Hey Mum, do you want to talk?" "Sure, what about?" "About the dead Kelly. Not the alive Kelly. The dead Kelly." One time I tried to distract her by bringing up the good times, rather than the day she died, by reminding her of the fun times they had in the bath. She said "No—that's when she was alive, I want to talk about the now when she's dead. Where is she? She's under the water isn't she?" We couldn't work out what she was talking about at first. But you know the cremation thing where there is water for your flowers? Well, she thought she was under the water, and that's what she wanted to talk about. I think it was because she saw her at the service in her coffin, and the next time was at the cemetery when the plaque was fixed and we put flowers in the water. She wanted to know how she got under the water. I said she was in the coffin, and then buried in the ground, under the plaque, and the water is there to put flowers in. I didn't explain about cremation. I thought that might be a bit spooky.

'She used to run around the rose bushes, stepping from one plaque to another; hop, step and jump. Now she says "mustn't stand on that person" and jumps over them. That's Kelly's home now she reckons. Kelly hasn't got a bedroom now at El Greco Court. She lives at the cemetery. I think that's good. She's got a place. Even though we sold our house she's still got a place; still something that's hers. It was Jayne who pointed out to me that the cemetery was her home and we could visit her. It made me feel good too.

'She (Jayne) is quite funny when we visit the cemetery. I have to read out the names on the plaques that have flowers. We might come up to one that has the name George, and she'll ask ("Who gave him his flowers; his mummy, daddy, brother or sister?" We have to go around the whole scene—who's got flowers and their names. This one, and this one is who Kelly is with. I don't think she has any fear. Really, I have to watch her when she's out, because other people don't understand, and she's so blasé about the whole thing.

'When my girlfriend's dog died, she was extremely worried about telling Jayne, because Jayne used to play with it a lot. The dog was called Tara. My friend said, "I'll just tell her she went away". I said, "No—tell her what happened. I would prefer that". So we walked in and my friend said, "I've got something to tell you sweetie. Come and sit on my knee". My friend was getting herself all prepared for it. She said, "Tara is dead. She died." Jayne said, "Oh!", quietly. Then sounding quite excited, "That's great, really great. I'm glad she's died." My friend just looked at her. "At last", said Jayne, "Now Kelly has got someone she *knows* to play with".

'Now when the subject comes up, Tara is included with Poppa. "Don't forget Tara's up there playing with her too". I don't know where "up there" is because we've never said Heaven. She's got it all worked out. She has even said "I'll be glad when I grow up an' die, cos then I'll see Kelly again!" It's really *incredible*.'

Remembering that very young children have concrete realities, it could be wise to offer children answers that give only as much as they have asked for. To introduce spirit, soul and God may be more than they can comprehend.

To say 'He is in Heaven' may introduce another complexity. It is the writer's experience that very young children need to know where Heaven is: 'Is it at Luna Park?'; 'Is Heaven at Geelong?' 'Is Heaven at Nana's house?' These questions reflect the child's knowledge of these places that he has probably visited. He visited and came back from these places. Therefore a simple solution to the baby's disappearance is to go to Heaven and bring him back, or at the very least, go for a visit. Another problem with answering 'He is in Heaven' arises when Heaven is presented in glowing terms. 'It is a wonderful place', parents might say, 'only good people are in Heaven — no-one can hurt you there'. 'You can have everything you want in Heaven'. Dilemma: If Heaven is so great, how come everyone is crying? The child is sensing 'mis-match'.

Regardless of religious beliefs sadness at the separation from a loved one is a reality. If 'mis-match' is to be avoided this reality may need to be conveyed to the child. That is: 'Even though he is in Heaven, we miss him being with us. We are crying because *we* feel sad.'

Another simple reply to 'Where is he now?' that is often overlooked is 'He is in the cemetery'. This simple reply is sometimes avoided by the parents because it reinforces the reality that the baby is dead. The cemetery conjures up images the *parents* may wish to avoid. Here again children do not always flinch from concrete realities.

Parent's account:

I didn't take Travis out to the cemetery for a long time after Troy died. When I did take him it was about three months after Troy died and it was easier to explain what had happened. I not only took him to see Troy's grave, but we spent half an hour or so going around all of the family graves. I pointed out where my grandfather was buried, and grandma, and that sort of thing. He seemed to get the idea that cemeteries weren't places where you just threw people. That we had to do something with people when they died. I think his idea of death changed a bit from there. I know after I had taken him, he stopped talking about Troy being in Morwell. (Troy had attended a creche in Morwell.) Before that, every time we went through that town he asked 'When are we going to get Troy?' I think I finally realised that it was important to him that Troy was located somewhere. That there was a 'place' for him. It was important.

When Travis was about four years old, he was given a tennis racquet for Christmas. Of course, it was about 8 a.m., when I was racing around trying to get ready for work, that I discovered he had chopped the middle out of the racquet. 'You're father is going to murder you when he gets home', I said. 'Well, I did that so we could put it over Troy's grave'. 'What for?' I asked. 'So we can look down and see the conch (he meant coffin), and then we will be able to see what he looks like'. A little later he twigged Troy wouldn't be the same, because he had begun to think about decay; he started talking about bones and things. How on earth do you explain to kids that bones remain? I found it eerie. Even though I told myself I could manage, there were times when I found it difficult. From two and a half to the tennis racquet incident his questions had become more meaningful. He was trying to work out what death was.

Here is Kim's account: It demonstrates the simplicity which with this mother and child approached 'dead'.

(Sibling, two-and-a-half when her brother died from S.I.D.S.)

I took my daughter to the cemetery within a matter of days, and she came with me regularly every weekend. I think she accepted death very well. Although she talked about bones and skeletons, she just didn't seem to fear death. The horror part never came into it. She talks very openly about it. Somebody will say 'You're a lovely little girl, have you got any brothers or sisters?' 'Yes, but he is buried in the cemetery. We put flowers there.'

I used to find the cemetery very comforting, and very peaceful more than anything. I used to find that if my daughter was playing up, or very naughty,

I would get tense. I would visit the cemetery and feel the calm and peace come back to me. I found the same thing would happen to my daughter. She would calm down a lot more. My son was buried in Canberra, but we live in Melbourne now. She looks forward to going to Canberra to see her brother again. I keep her in constant touch. He's there. It doesn't matter if he is under the ground, he's still my son and he's still her brother. I think she accepted it very well.

Answering the question: 'Why did she die?'

When this question is asked on day one, or even day two or day three of the baby's death, the logical reply would be 'We don't know yet', but reason is difficult to hang onto in the immediate wake of the death. As related in Part One myriad questions whirl through the parent's head. Why is this happening to me? Why my baby? What have I done? Was she sick, and I didn't take her to the doctor? Why did she die?

When an apparently healthy baby is found unexpectedly dead in his or her cot, carry-basket, pram (or whatever) the situation demands a temporary diagnosis. Often the emergency responder acknowledges this circumstance by saying 'It could be cot death'. Normally this temporary explanation is followed by, 'A pathologist will determine the cause of death', or words to that effect. No matter what answer is given to a very young child, it would be true to say the child too will probably be anxious and confused about why the baby died.

When the cause of death is determined as S.I.D.S. the parents can be clearer in their explanations as to what didn't cause the baby's death. They can reassure themselves and others that the baby didn't smother or choke. They can stress that no one was to blame for the baby's death.

When children ask 'Why did she die?' they may be seeking reassurance that *they* were not responsible for the death. What didn't cause the death could be very important to the child. After all, even with the determination Sudden Infant Death Syndrome, it really boils down to the pathologist saying 'We don't know why your baby died. We don't know what causes deaths of this kind'. Nevertheless parents say over and over, 'but why?' 'Why did she die?' The question in medical terms is really unanswerable at this time, but parents will continue to say 'If only we knew what caused it?' In the light of this it is important for both parents and siblings to be able to say what didn't cause the death. For example, here is a record of a conversation between Keryn and Jayne.

Jayne: 'Mummy, I'm not going to bite Andrew'.
Keryn: 'What are you talking about Jayne?'
Jayne: 'I know why Kelly died. I bit her on the foot'.
Keryn then went on to give the background to this exchange:
'I thought, Oh God, that child has kept that inside her for so long. She was two-and-a-half when Kelly died, and three-and-a-half when we brought Andrew home. We had often joked about the biting, because one day when Kelly was screaming and I asked what had happened, Jayne replied, 'I bit her on the foot'. At the time I tried to keep my calm, jealousy and potential hassles being upper-most in my mind. I asked why she had bitten her. She replied, "I was hungry". Now I realise Jayne thought it had a lot to do with Kelly's death. She had bitten her about a week before Kelly died. When she said, "I'm not going to bite Andrew", I said: "You've bitten me before Jayne, and I haven't died; I've bitten you back and you haven't died. Do you want me to bite Andrew? I'll bet he won't die." We made a bit of a joke about it, but she needed that reassurance that Kelly didn't die from a bite on the foot.'

This account demonstrates the importance of exploring what didn't cause the baby's death. In Part One, parents explore these possibilities when they say, 'If only I hadn't played tennis *today*', '. . . worked so long when I was pregnant', ' . . . answered the 'phone *just* then', etc. Jayne explored 'if only' when she talked about biting Kelly on the foot. Parents eventually conclude that the 'if only's' didn't cause the baby's death, but not before they have been expressed and explored. Some children too may have this need.

When children in the two to five years (approximately) age group ask 'Why did she die?', there is another possibility to consider. When a new baby enters a family the sibling has ambivalent feelings of love and hate about the new baby. Sibling rivalry can be intense as the whole family adjusts to the new member. It is natural, normal and common for children in this age group to wish the baby away. Wish fulfillment and magical thinking is most prominent in this age group. When cot death occurs it may seem to the sibling that his wish has been granted. The power of his magical thinking can be frightening. Children need reassurance that their jealousy, or their wish that the baby would go away, did not cause its disappearance.

Parents too can harbour guilty feelings. Young babies are demanding, and when an exhausted mother wishes the baby would 'go away', just for a little while, just while she gets some sleep, she too may need reassurance that her ambivalent feelings are natural and normal. She may need reassurance that wishing the baby away for a short time did not cause the baby's death. Parents can regress to a state of wish fulfillment and magical thinking at this time. Parents who look for their dead baby in prams and pushers at the supermarket don't really expect to find him there, but they wish with all their might that their baby will magically return.

The sibling may also have the notion that the parents were responsible for the baby going away. This notion may turn to anxiety in the sibling, and can account for the distress of some siblings when separated from their parents, particularly the mother, in the aftermath of cot death. If the baby can go away suddenly, perhaps he, or his mother, can too.

Conversely, some siblings will protect their parents from the idea that they or their parents were guilty of making the baby go away, or that they or their parents harmed the baby in some way. Kim provides this example:

I noticed that my daughter was really protective towards me. I came to Melbourne with my son and left my daughter and husband in Canberra during the visit. My son died while I was in Melbourne. I was worried because my daughter saw me hop on a plane, and then all of a sudden I came back, but I didn't have him anymore. I was really afraid she was going to think Mummy took him away and threw him away—something like that. I sort of thought, God, what is she going to think? In fact, she took it really well.

'Why did she die?' might be expressing another question: 'Was it my fault?' or 'Was it anyone's fault?' or even 'Was it Mummy's fault?' Having reassured themselves (with some help from a parent) that it wasn't someone's fault, the child is able to freely express this whenever the need is felt. Sharnie, for instance, found it important to forewarn anyone who might think her Mummy had been careless with her sibling who had died.

So many people avoid you like the plague when you have lost a baby. All of a sudden your girlfriends with babies don't come and see you any more.

Sharnie would say to those that did visit and left their babies home, 'Oh, bring the baby around, my mother won't hurt it'.

I found that really comforting, the fact that she still believed in me.

I had one friend who came one day with her baby and said, 'I'm in a rush. Look after Kylie for me will you? I'll be back in an hour'.

I remember Sharnie standing at the door saying, 'It's alright, my Mummy will look after it. Mummy's not going to hurt it'.

It was really good. She was the best dose of medicine I'd got from anyone. She still trusted me, and so did my girlfriend.

The 'Other Mother'

Others who have written about the pain of grief agree that the depth of feeling and sorrow relates to the degree of attachment the bereaved person had with the deceased. In relation to cot death, there is a group of children who are particularly vulnerable. They are the 'other mothers', usually young girls between the ages of seven and twelve years. Sometimes a brother is the 'other mother', but more often it is a sister. Girls in this age group are not discouraged from participating in the mothering of their baby brother or sister. They are often involved in the bathing, feeding, dressing or caring of the infant in some way. They will respond to the baby's crying — soothing, patting, stroking. They will pick the baby up, and sometimes take the baby to their own bed for a cuddle, or in response to a parent's request to 'see if you can settle him down'. Generally speaking, young girls in particular enjoy this role of 'other mother'. It can be a pleasurable experience for both mother and daughter.

When the baby dies suddenly and unexpectedly, great care needs to be taken to ensure that the grief of this 'other mother' is recognised and allowed full expression. It is likely they will have feelings and responses in some ways similar to the mother's.

The child who has had this role often feels inhibited in the expression of her, or his, feelings as do many children in this age range. They may not feel entitled to full expression of their grief, guilt, despair, or their concerns about what caused the baby's death. They may be asked to take a more responsible role with other brothers and sisters while the parents deal with their grief and sorrow.

Parents may recognise the older child's attachment and involvement with the baby and decide to protect them from the awesome reality of the baby's death, and in so doing they deny themselves and their daughter (or son) the opportunity to explore and express both their love and sorrow. She/he too may have had moments of frustration with 'their baby'. They may have wished he would stop crying quickly so they could go out and play with friends.

There could have been days when they had wished he'd never been born, or that he would simply 'go away' when conflict arose between their own needs and the needs of 'their baby'. These 'other mothers' are subject also to the normal, natural feelings of ambivalence and sibling rivalry that are present in any family.

The grief reactions of these young girls and boys who may have enjoyed a 'surrogate parent' role are as many and varied as those of their adult counterparts. As they modeled their parenting on the style of their parent, they may model their grief in the same way.

It is particularly important for these children to be given every opportunity to express their feelings and concerns, while at the same time being given the freedom to respond very personally. They can be included in the funeral rites, directly or indirectly, according to the family's wishes.

Childhood Memories

Susan Patterson and daughters Emily and Celia, explore the path of childhood memories that lead back to the cot death of Thomas at five-and-a-half months, ten long years after the event.

'You didn't let us go to Thomas' funeral. Why not?' My daughter's accusation hurt. How could I explain that we were in such a state of shock at the time of Thomas' death that that sort of decision was taken out of our hands by well meaning kindly people who just didn't understand that five and three year olds needed to say goodbye to their brother, as did the adults?

Emily was thirteen when this outpouring of anger, resentment and frustration occured. As the elder of the two little girls whose brother had died suddenly at five-and-a-half months, she had worried me since. Celia the younger girl remembered very little. She says she doesn't remember Thomas at all, though I can't really believe that; perhaps there'll be a problem there too one day? But Emily always suffered, and now was the time to explain to her that Alan and I had always regretted that we'd sent them off to the beach with cousins whilst we buried Thomas in the lovely little graveyard at Lorne.

I reminded her how we'd encouraged them to play games of coffins and funerals when they were small, much to her grandfather's distress. I reminded her how we had taken them to every family funeral ever since!

'Don't you remember Aunty May's funeral when you and Celia clambered all over the grave and the priest encouraged you to look down to the other two old great aunts' coffins in the same grave?'

'Of course I do Mummy, but it wasn't the same'.

'Of course it wasn't darling, and really all I can say is that we're very sorry that you didn't go to Thomas' funeral. If we'd known then what we know now you'd have been there'. How inadequate.

At thirteen and fourteen Emily was beginning to get to the nitty-gritty of how she had felt for nine or ten years. We had always talked about Thomas; we'd never pretended that he'd never happened, and I'd hoped that we could have helped Emily overcome her grief. Another brother, and a little sister after him had helped, but obviously this long lasting resentment still had to be overcome.

A wonderful and understanding teacher of English at school, to whom I confided, helped Emily to express her feelings, and recently she wrote a poem which moved me to tears, and which seems to have helped her enormously. I pray that she can now accept the horror of those years as part of her development as a person and that she won't allow herself to be adversely affected.

The adaption on the part of a very young child to the death of a sibling can be a long-term process. To talk about it alleviates pain and anger, but a child has to be helped to recognise the source of the pain and anger, or resentment, or any other emotion, and to express it. In the older child a degree of sophistication in the ability to write may be necessary; the younger child can paint or draw his emotions.

I think this experience with Emily has shown me the healing process is a much longer one than I'd ever anticipated.'

Why so Young?

I'm out of sight under the pier
The waves are crashing and dying away
Life has ended so, so soon
Tears are flowing
Why so young?

Death is a virtue
When life is done. Not now.
A life is to be lived, not to be ended.
I don't understand
Why so young?

The tears had stopped and I wonder
It was God's will, so he must die.
But it should have been somebody else.
It wasn't
Why so young?

Easter isn't fun
Why aren't there any eggs?
People are crying, not rejoicing.
Where is he? I don't see him
Maybe he's asleep
Forever.

Emily Patterson (aged 14 years)
— on the death of her brother,
when she was five.

The Danger of Not Explaining a Death to a Child

Protecting a child from the facts of a sibling's death is not always in that child's best interest. Again we use a poem to illustrate this point far more poignantly than could be done through pages of prose.

This poem was written by Shirley Rutherford in her middle forties. She attended a seminar on death and was prompted to write this poem about a loss she experienced in her childhood.

She was two years old when her six year old brother died of rheumatic heart disease, but it wasn't until she was eight years old that she realised that he was dead. Although her parents said they had told her, it wasn't a topic the family talked about. She was under the impression that he'd gone to heaven, but fully expected his return, and was very upset that he hadn't returned.

When I Was a Child

When I was two you went away
    and left me.
I waited every day for you to come,
But you didn't and every day was empty.
I remember that you threw a block at me,
but they said you didn't, wouldn't, couldn't
Because you loved me.
So I dared not remember any more.
I've forgotten what you looked like —
a face fading as I remembered to forget,
But I remembered that you'd gone
while I forgot you.

Sometimes it was alright.
They remembered to buy me ice-creams
to eat while they talked about you
   and cried.
They told me not to be silly when I cried,
'What are you crying for now?'
So I forgot to cry.
I waited for you to come but you didn't.

They brought a baby home,
and I hated them because it wasn't you.
The baby didn't cry. It was just said it wasn't you.
I hated it too and wanted it to cry;
was glad when it did because it made them angry.
I didn't cry, I was good and clean
my hair in curls and bows,
a sash around my middle,
And quiet so they wouldn't notice me
except to say that dress makes you pretty.
They didn't see the pain inside, knotted
like a lump of cold hard steel inside
   my chest.

They talked about you often,
Faces carefully arranged to look normal,
Voices consciously steadied, solicitous,
False like the minister in church.
They said you wouldn't come back
and kept your paintings, and your photo
   on the piano
And deep inside I knew that they were right —
that you wouldn't come
and I couldn't bear it.

At night in bed I talked to you
begged God to get you back to me
God loves me I know, and I knew it then,
but he didn't find you for me.
So I cried inside, no tears, no sound,
until my throat ached and I couldn't bear
to breathe in case my chest burst.
And I hated God for letting you leave me;
and loved the picture at Sunday School
   of Jesus with the children
And I hated you for leaving me —
and tried to love you back to me,
but still you didn't come.

I learned to pretend —
to smile, to be glad, to be grateful, to be good,
Despising them for believing it, afraid
they might find out
I learned to hide inside me with you.
And they never knew that you were there
for you had gone away and were never
    coming back
They didn't know that I could feel,
only that I could act as if I could.

I found that I could make them laugh,
a sort of trick I didn't know I had.
But when I knew I used it all the time
and they saw me as a person,
not a thing that wasn't you.
The only time they could have found me out
    was when I sang.
But they thought I did it from sheer joy.
They didn't know the tears poured down inside,
salty on the wound left there by you
Not really true, for sometimes gladness
grew inside when something lovely sneaked
    behind my mask
and I sang in spite of you.

And then one day I *knew* that you were gone.
They said the word that told me you had left me —
and all my waiting would have to end.
Dead.
And it rang like a gong that wouldn't stop
vibrating
On and on —
Dead and dead and dead —
It rang and rang and I shrieked inside
and said 'Don't cry Mummy', gently.
All those years of waiting.
Morris has gone to Heaven.
Why?
Because he was sick.
Is Heaven far away?
No, not far, its lovely,
Morris is happy.

So I played my game of tricks and "good",
and made them pay for the empty years
    of waiting.
I didn't mean to do it,

except to make them glad that they had me.
I felt like an old old woman in a body
    only eight
Six years of vigil, all alone inside had
made me aged forever,
and that I had to hide
For children are 'so lucky'; they're 'protected'
from the pain of life and love.
'Not understanding' makes it easy
to bounce back, untouched by grief.

But I had lived alone and grieving,
Surrounded by the cushion of my pain
that protected them, not understanding,
and so lucky that they didn't have to share it,
that kept them from all blame.
When I was two you went away
and left me.
And my grief was real and sane.
I could have coped with 'dead'
at two or three or four,
But 'heaven' is a soft and gentle name
for dead.
At eight my grieving was renewed —
this time for Morris, died aged six.
I'd waited for you longer than you'd lived —
and felt so foolish for not knowing
dead and heaven are the same.

Shirley Rutherford's poem is important because it provides an alternative, albeit a very moving one, to the words written by the author on those aspects of the understanding children have of death, and of their need to explore and express their feelings about a brother or sister that has died. Both Shirley Rutherford's poem and that of Emily Patterson demonstrate the difficulties a growing child *may* have if they are 'protected' from the reality of which they were so much a part.

While inclusion of these poems is not meant to give *carte blanche* to parents and others to overwhelm a young child with more than they ask for, or indicate a need of, they show the capacity of children to absorb what is going on around them, how they think and how deeply their feelings run, and the richness of a child's imagination and fantasy, not to mention the anger, hurts and fears they are capable of harbouring.

CHAPTER THIRTEEN

The Community

In the first-hand accounts many parents have indicated what they need in both the short and long term. They know what constitutes effective support, and what they need from the community.

Counsellors and others who have been involved in crisis intervention following cot death report that parents, although in shock immediately after the death, are open to the laying of healthy foundations for the resolution of their grief. Empathic intervention is possible, even desirable at the time of crisis. The numbness that follows shortly after the death has not yet begun, and parents are extremely vulnerable and in need. An exception could be when sedation has been immediately administered. If this is the case, it may be best to provide a physical presence, while waiting until the numbing effect of the sedation has worn off. It may then be possible to begin the work of laying the foundations.

Contrary to popular belief it is often easier to make contact with parents immediately after the death, rather than waiting for a week or two to pass. It is commonly thought that parents will 'cope' better if contact is made when they have had a chance to settle down. This circumstance has not always proved to be the case. By the time they have settled down barriers between themselves and others have often been erected.

Immediate contact at the time of the crisis, on the other hand, creates a bond between the parents, their friends, neighbours and relatives that will allow ongoing grief to be expressed.

It is possible to support cot death parents in the first hours and days, but people are often afraid to confront such raw pain and distress. We are not taught the skills which would help us to deal with our own emotional responses to painful situations, and we are not encouraged to learn them nor do we take up the opportunity to learn. This can result in parents being denied effective support, as well as being thrust into isolation.

The community usually believes of a grieving person:

- time will make it better
- keeping busy will help, and
- getting back to 'normal' as quickly as possible is desirable

This can be interpreted by the parents to mean:

- take a holiday,
- have another baby soon, or
- return to work as soon as possible
- look and sound normal

They believe and hope these measures will help, and they may for a time, but they are insufficient in themselves for resolution of the grief and pain the death of the baby brings.

Because this view of grief and grieving is widely held, there is a strong probability that initially parents will adhere to this view, and perhaps suppress those voices inside that say:

- But I'm not feeling better as time goes by.
- I'm keeping busy at work, but when I come home I still have to face the pain and emptiness.
- I don't want another baby now. Sarah might think I have forgotten her already.

The difference between what the parents are actually feeling and the generally held view of a grieving person produces conflicts. These conflicts manifest themselves through parents struggling to maintain loyalty to the ways of their parents, friends, neighbours and relatives.

The friend or relative can sense this conflict when the words they say do not have the comforting effect that was intended. An act that is performed out of concern and kindness can produce an undesired reaction; for example, when a neighbour or relative decides to *do* something to help—perhaps empty the baby's room of every reminder of the baby's existence. Unless this is what is clearly desired by the parent, the effect could be very distressing.

Feelings of helplessness are common and often overwhelming. We feel we *must* help; after all, isn't that what friends are for in a time of trouble? As there is a widely held view of the grieving person, there is too a commonly held perception of 'comforter'. To comfort is usually interpreted as meaning: giving relief from pain or distress; to soothe; and to cheer. Giving relief is often translated by the comforter to mean 'take away' the pain and distress.

When a baby dies it is not possible for anyone to take away the pain. This emotional pain comes from deep within the Self and cannot be relieved with well meaning but empty cliches, nor with pain killers or sedatives. The parent's cry comes from their very heart and soul. In the face of such anguish, as friend, neighbour or relative, you offer to 'do something – anything'. The answer that is most difficult to accept then is 'there is nothing you can do' to take away the pain. This is the harsh truth, and the one that, as comforter, we least like to hear. To sit quietly with someone who is in this much pain, and to resist the urges to say or do, calls for inner resources we may not have at that moment.

There is another definition of the word 'comfort'. The meaning is: *whatever gives ease*, and it is this meaning of the word that best defines effective support. What gives ease to one person may not give ease to another. Therefore it is unwise to make assumptions about what kind of comfort or support will meet the needs of a friend, relative or neighbour whose baby has died. One person may need to shout and rail against God or the Fates, another may need to go to bed, be quiet and withdrawn in order to find some ease in the situation. Some will need the support of a large extended family, others might shun contact.

Parents may want to vent their feelings one day, and be silent the next. To physically hold close a reminder of the baby one day, for example a favourite toy, article of clothing or special shawl, may result in other reminders, such as photos of the baby, being packed out of sight the next day. In short, *effective support or comfort is letting the parent decide what gives ease at any time*.

Often what the comforter does not realise is that their quiet, physical, caring presence, in and of itself, can greatly diminish the bereaved parents' tremendous sense of isolation. A bereaved parent senses when a person is trying to help, and it is not unknown for a parent to invent some task for the supporter or comforter, and so allow the comforter to feel they are *doing* something to help. In these situations not only does the bereaved parent have to find ways of meeting his/her own need, they end up meeting the need of the supporter/comforter. This places an added burden on the grieving person at a time when they already have so many.

The supporter needs to remain sensitive to whatever does or does not give ease to the parent and must avoid making assumptions on the basis of their own needs. The parents needs are likely to change from day to day. For example: it may be agreed that a neighbour delivers the children to school for two or three days. When she/he arrives on day four the children may have already left. The well-meaning neighbour may not have yet satisfied his/her need to help, and, if this is so, may feel the support is rejected. However, that morning the parent may have needed to 'normalise' the family routine, found this too taxing, and the following morning may again be grateful to have the children taken to school by the neighbour. Such shifts in feeling can produce confusion and misunderstanding. Unless there is agreement that needs can be met on a daily basis, many such misunderstandings can occur, and rifts may develop in relationships that eventually become difficult to resolve.

The basic needs of a bereaved family:

1 *Acknowledgement* of their reality
>> disbelief
>> shock
>> emotional state

2 *Expression* of their reality
>> disbelief
>> anger, guilt and pain

3 *Recognition* that their individual responses are 'normal for now', remembering that 'now' lasts a long time

4 *Permission* to grieve in their own way and at their own pace

5 *An informed community*

How the community can meet those needs:

1 Acknowledgement:

When contact is first made, especially during the first few weeks, the statement 'it must be so hard to believe—I am so sorry' acknowledges the parent's reality, and allows your expression of sorrow at the death of the baby.

When death is sudden and unexpected it takes time for the reality as well as the fact of the death to be believed. Difficulty in believing what has happened is common for parents and community alike, and the statement, 'I can hardly believe Jane is dead. It was only yesterday/last week/last month . . .', lets the parent know that shock, as a result of her death, is a shared experience. It affirms for the parent that their overwhelming shock at finding their baby dead is a normal reaction.

Shock can be acknowledged no matter how the parents react. For example:

'I would cry and cry too',
or
'I don't know if I would be able to cry'.

The words 'I am sorry' are received by parents with either gratitude or disdain. One parent acknowledged her judgement of her friends, relatives, neighbours and health professionals by these words. She rejected those who did not utter the phrase. Others respond to 'I'm sorry' with 'What for? — It's not *your* baby'. Perhaps the variations lie in the sincerity expressed beneath the words as well as the degree of anger the parent is feeling at the time. If the words are only formally apologetic, a matter of form, then the grieving parent will sense this. Parents seek understanding of their distress, not merely sympathy.

Sympathy given can be felt as compassion, but it can also be felt as pity. Pity is often experienced as being looked down upon, and it can also have an edge of contempt as evidenced in this response to the news of a baby's death.

'Well I'm sorry for her. It's not something you would wish on anybody, but she needed taking down a peg or two'.

When that person says 'I'm sorry' it is unlikely to be said with compassion, or felt by the parent as such.

To respond to the baby's death in the following manner can cause more pain, not less, and leaves parents feeling angry.

'I'm sorry you lost your baby, but you can always have another one.'
'Be glad you still have John and Susan.'
'You are coping so well — keep it up.'

In these responses there is no acknowledgement of the baby who died, no acknowledgement of the pain, no acknowledgement of the disbelief and shock, and no acknowledgement of some parents' need to let someone else be strong, even for a little while.

Acknowledgement using euphemisms and cliches:

Everyone has difficulty acknowledging the death of a baby. When a baby is referred to as 'lost', 'sleeping peacefully' or 'passed away', it does little to help the parent face the reality of the baby's death. Yet the reality is what the parent is struggling to accept. The baby who is 'lost' cannot be found; the baby who is 'sleeping peacefully' will not wake; the baby who has 'passed away' now exists only in the minds and hearts of those mourning the death.

Parents feel a crushing sense of loss when their baby dies: we all experience such loss when we are separated from someone we care about deeply. The separation may come about through divorce, when a child grows up and leaves home, or when a best friend moves away. When we lose a child temporarily in the supermarket or at the park, she/he is found and returned to us. To substitute 'lost' for dead when a child dies makes little sense, for the child cannot be returned to us in a physical sense. On the other hand, the memory of the baby need never be lost, even though the baby is dead. When mourning is completed, which may take many years, the parent accepts the death of the baby, can allow their emotional grieving to come to an end, and reinvest their emotions in life. What remains is the memory of their experience with their baby – the memory of his or her life and death.

The words 'lost', 'passed away' and 'sleeping peacefully' are euphemisms for die or dead. Euphemisms are used to soften a blunt or direct expression which is disagreeable. The death of a baby is a tragic truth. Euphemisms assist parents and others to deny reality and provide a means to avoid the harsh reality. Parents are already experiencing the harsh reality. To disguise death in softer words is, in fact, a rejection of their experience.

Children particularly are confused by euphemisms. As has been shown in chapter twelve, their response to 'lost', is to seek and find, and the dangers in using 'sleeping peacefully' instead of 'our baby is dead' are extreme enough to have some young children refusing to go to bed, and resisting sleep out of fear of the consequences.

Sleep is a word all children know and understand. Even if children do not know what the word dead means, using the word dead will prevent them *becoming* confused about being asleep and being dead.

When used euphemistically, religious explanations or expressions can also be confusing and not necessarily comforting. For example:

'Our baby is with baby Jesus',
'God took the baby to heaven with him', and
'Our baby is in God's care',

are expressions that can bewilder and frighten young children. A young child may not see too many benefits in being with baby Jesus or God. At the very least it means being separated from his or her parents, and the thought of becoming a star in the sky, or another flower in God's garden may frighten instead of comfort. Great care must be taken if religious explanations are substituted for 'our baby has died'.

When a parent uses euphemisms:

'John passed away last week',
'We lost John on Sunday',
'John is sleeping peacefully. I'm glad he is with my mother/aunt/grandfather',

the friend, relative or neighbour could respond:

'Edith told me John died last week. Mary and I are so sorry.'
'Just yesterday; it must be so hard to believe he is dead.'
'The shock of John's death must have been great. I am glad you are comforted by the thought he is with your mother/aunt/grandfather.'

Acknowledging the death of a baby is painful for everyone, but the pain is not made less by avoiding the reality. *Being an effective supporter/comforter means assisting the parents, and supporting their attempts to accept the reality, as well as the fact of their baby's death.*

2   Expression

Parents need to express their distress, anger, guilt and pain. They need to talk about the life of their baby, and the hopes and dreams that have been shattered. In doing so they begin the hard work of putting back together the pieces of their shattered lives. This need is extreme during the first months, but parents are usually exhorted not to talk about their baby's life too often. Consequently, they are denied expression of their feelings as well as being denied the opportunities to assimilate their tragedy. Anger, guilt, pain and sadness are all components of grief.

Expression of grief facilitates mourning:

To allow only the expression of tears and to deny expressions of anger, shuts down, or forces out of sight, a major emotion in grief. To deny a parent an expression of longing for their baby does the same. For example:

When a parent says 'I miss him so much' and is answered with: 'Try not to think about it. Don't talk about it so much, you will only upset yourself',

the parent receives two messages. The first is: *hold the feeling inside*; the second is: *they don't understand*. In this situation, if we are going to be honest as supporters or comforters, we need to acknowledge that expression of the longing leaves us feeling helpless and uncomfortable, helpless because we know we can't ease their pain — we can't bring their baby back — and uncomfortable because we are left with feelings of failure and our own anxieties about life and death.

We feel we have failed to give comfort or support. There is also the fear of becoming upset ourselves. Why do we deny ourselves feelings of sorrow and distress at the baby's death? Surely it makes more sense to say: 'I miss him too, and I don't understand why it had to be your baby'.

When the parent cries or becomes angry and upset, the illusion we have of ourselves as comforter/supporter can be shattered. It is not always easy to believe that expression of feeling brings comfort to the bereaved person. We might say, 'I hope she's had a good cry', but secretly we don't want the parent to cry with us — let it be someone else.

What can give ease at this time is to allow expression of the longing. For example:

P. 'I miss him so much.'
R. 'It must be really hard not to be able to cuddle him anymore.'

A response of this kind facilitates a parent's expression of their grief, and indicates to the parent that we have some understanding of their sorrow, that we have allowed ourselves to imagine for a moment how *we* might feel in their situation.

Expressions of guilt:

Another aspect of grief that is often misunderstood by the community is the guilt that is felt by a bereaved person. In the case of cot death, guilty feelings are often extreme. When the death is deemed to have 'no known cause' parents need to examine their every thought and action prior to the death before they begin to believe the death was not their fault. It has been stressed in other sections of the book that parents impose the label of 'guilty' on themselves in varying degrees. *A comforter/supporter can give ease to the guilt by allowing its expression.*

To say:
'Don't feel guilty; it's not your fault' is not as helpful as
'Feeling guilty is a normal reaction when a baby dies from cot death, even though these deaths cannot be predicted or prevented'.

The first response denies the feeling as well as its expression. The second response allows the parent to explore and express their guilty feelings if they want to. If they don't take the conversation further, at least they are given the information that guilt is normal in these circumstances.

Guilt and theories:

It is not my intention to undervalue the commitment researchers have made and are making in their endeavours to discover the causes of cot death, but parents and the wider community need to realise that currently there are approximately one hundred theories about the causes of S.I.D.S. (cot death), and *none* as yet have been proved.

This situation is extremely frustrating for researchers and parents alike. When parents ask 'Why did my baby die?' most will need to examine, explore and express their thoughts and feelings about the many, many theories that abound.

Some theories are given prominence in the media with almost a 'flavour of the month' approach. For example: **Honey Causes Cot Death** screams a headline, or **Lambskins Dangerous—can cause cot death says researcher**. Both these headlines caused a great deal of confusion and heartache for parents when they appeared. They quickly fell from prominence. Adverse publicity was also given to immunization of babies, particularly against pertussis (whooping cough). Careful studies have been carried out into a possible link between pertussis vaccine and S.I.D.S. and no evidence has been found to suggest that there is a link.

One such large controlled study of D.T.P. and S.I.D.S. has been conducted under the sponsorship of the National Institutes of Health.

A large group of autopsy-verified S.I.D.S. cases and a set of age, race, birthweight, and area of resident-matched control infants were studied. Families were interviewed and medical records were reviewed to ascertain prior usage of D.T.P. It was found that 0.5 per cent of the cases, compared to 1.0 per cent of the controls, had received D.T.P. within the preceding twenty-four hours. Analysis for history of having received D.T.P. in the preceding two weeks also found no greater frequency among the cases compared to the controls. Thus, in this controlled study no association between S.I.D.S. and prior D.T.P. administration was found, and the investigators concluded that their data strongly support the view that D.T.P. immunization is not a factor in the etiology of S.I.D.S. (Loring Dales, M.D. Chief Immunization Unit, California State Department of Health Services)

Thoughtless promulgation of many theories causes extreme distress and confusion to parents and the community alike, as well as circulating misinformation. And irresponsible wording in media headlines suggests that the cause of S.I.D.S. has been found, a suggestion which is not only false but likely to make parents of cot death babies fraught with unnecessary guilt and remorse.

Expression of Anger:

Along with the normal feelings of guilt come feelings of anger and a need to find a cause for the baby's death. When a parent is told constantly 'it's not your fault', it requires only a small step to ask 'whose fault is it then?' No one really believes a baby dies from 'no cause', or in other words has experienced a 'natural' death. Dying a natural death may be a comforting thought for our old age, especially if it takes place quietly and while we are asleep. But the notion that an infant can die this way is so shocking that it is instantly rejected. This kind of death is accepted at the end of life, not at its beginning.

Anger is a natural outcome of this 'no cause' death, and so too is the need to blame someone. The parent has many choices when she or he decides to apportion blame. Self, spouse, in-laws, doctors and other health professionals, a surviving child, quality of present lifestyle, a past lifestyle, a previous sin, real or imagined, God, an unhappy family relationship, or the presence of a family pet. The list of possibilities is almost endless.

When, as comforter/supporter we are confronted by the force of the anger generated at this 'unjust' death, we quail, and the most common response is to arrest the flow of the outburst one way or another. We might say:

'Look, getting angry won't help',
or
'I'll come back when you're not so upset'.

Many of us will have difficulty in letting the parent continue with an angry outburst.

The situation is fraught with complexities when the anger is directed at us personally. For example:

(parent to doctor): 'But you checked him yesterday!'
the doctor may leave thinking: 'I must have missed something.'

Guilt, pain, anger and helplessness are all present for both parties in this exchange. The doctor could respond:

'I know his death doesn't make sense – we both know babies don't die from the common cold.'

The doctor needs to acknowledge both to himself and to the parent his own feelings of frustration and helplessness.

Rarely does the comforter/supporter stop to consider what the anger may be about. Anger may come from the shattering separation from the baby, – the totally unexpected dashing of dreams and hopes the parents had for the baby, or perhaps the years of toil to prepare a home that would give the child the best of everything in which to grow. The parents may feel as though their very reason for being has disappeared with the baby.

Their anger is justified, and yet we most often avoid allowing parents free expression of that anger. Parents need to be able to say 'It's just not fair!' *Being an effective supporter/comforter means allowing the parent expression of the anger they feel.*

3   Recognition:

Recognition of the fact that the parents' individual responses are 'normal *for now*' is fundamental to the comforter/supporter's role.

When a mother finds herself padding quietly towards her baby's room in the middle of the night, because she always gets up at this time to feed her baby, then remembers as she slowly wakes there *is* no baby to feed, she can surely be forgiven for thinking she is going crazy. When a mother has sent her other children off to school for the day, and she turns towards the laundry to wash the baby's nappies — as has been her custom — it is understandable that she may clutch the washing machine in fear as she realises there *are* no nappies to wash anymore.

At the supermarket a mother automatically reaches for baby-food or cereal, then realises at the check-out what she has done. Panic and fear can result. The mother *knows* her baby is dead, she remembers the nightmare quality of the funeral, or the empty bassinette at home. So why is she still doing these things?

'I must be crazy'
'I am going mad'
'I am so frightened — what is happening to me?'

These phrases are commonly heard by counsellors, home visitors and parent supporters at S.I.D.R.F. It should be noted that parent supporters and home visitors with the Foundation *are* bereaved parents whose baby died at least twelve months prior to commencement of their training for this voluntary work. If a parent supporter or the home visitor is the responder, the reply is often, 'Yes I did that too — and I remember how frightened I was'. Sometimes then there is silence, sometimes tears, sometimes a long exhalation of breath, sometimes words tumble out one upon the other; always there is relief.

The parent is not crazy; other parents and counsellors know these seemingly bizarre behaviours are 'normal for now'. So too are the lapses in concentration that resulted in forgotten appointments — even the ones the parent wanted to keep; finding themselves at the shopping centre and not knowing why they are there, or having to shop three times in one week because it is somehow impossible to bring home all the items on the list. A parent can sometimes tolerate friends and family's fearing for her sanity as she refuses to acknowledge sidelong glances, while she doggedly knits on to complete a jacket that will never be worn by the baby. The parent may not know why it is important, only that it is.

Parents may put every ounce of energy into a family celebration to convince themselves and others they are 'coping'. Their act can be so convincing that some guests wonder is she normal? How can she laugh? During the celebration parents may catch themselves laughing and think, 'How can *I* be laughing? My baby died only two months ago, I must be going crazy.'

Parents lash out at those they love—spouse, children, their own parents or their best friend, knowing it is not what they wanted to do. At a time when parents need those they love, they often find themselves unable to communicate their need. In their isolation they can become afraid. *Recognition of these reactions to the death of a baby as 'normal for now' is another way of being an effective supporter/comforter*. As such reactions arise they provide opportunities to give reassurance and understanding.

4 *Permission*:

It takes parents a long time to mourn the death of a baby; much longer than the three to six months customarily given by the community. Ernst de Frain and Taylor (1982) have stated it takes at least three years for parents to reach a comparable family organisation and level of happiness. Their research shows also that 'men and women often have different styles of communication and coping with grief'. They have identified dips and plateaux along this passage of time, with the first anniversary of the baby's death as perhaps their most significant marker. Many workers in the field have also observed these differences. While S.I.D.R.F.'s counsellors agree the anniversary is a very difficult time, there are other significant markers, with a notable one at between eight and fourteen weeks after the death, when parents may state 'I feel almost worse now than I did in the beginning'.

Regardless of where the plateaux and dips occur, the community could find it helpful to be aware that the journey through grief is long; that men and women may show their grief differently; and that resolution of grief rarely follows a simple uncomplicated path. It is not simply a matter of 'getting better' as each day follows another. It is a struggle through indescribable heartache, loneliness, confusion, rage and despair.

Giving parents permission to grieve in their own way and at their own pace is effective support. If as supporter/comforter we interfere with the parents individual journey we may unnecessarily complicate their grief. However, it is easy to collude with the bereaved person in their desire to sidestep, shorten, delay or deny part of their grief. For example:

In our desire to *do* something we may try to hurry the process along:

'You will feel better soon', *shorten the process*; 'Let me make the funeral arrangements', *sidestep the reality*; 'I have packed away all her clothes and toys for you', *deny the reality*; 'Go back to work as soon as possible . . . It will stop you thinking about it', *delay the process*.

In both the short and long term, *effective support means suggesting* **options** *when parents ask for your help*. If the question is a direct one:

Parent: 'What do I do now?' 'Do I ring the funeral director?'
the response could be:
             'What do *you* want to do?'
Parent: 'I don't know.'
Response: 'You don't have to decide right now.'
             or
             'Do you want me to ring the funeral director now, or
             would you rather do it yourself, — perhaps tomorrow.
             The phone call does not have to be made this minute'.

If the parent's question is an indirect one:
'I don't want to ring the Funeral Director [will you?]'
the response could be:
'It will be a hard call to make. I could make the call for you now and let them know what has happened, but you will need to talk to him/her at some stage to decide what kind of funeral you want, and when you want it'.

5 *An informed community:*

To become educated and informed about the impact and effects of cot death on families is another way of being an effective supporter/comforter. Knowing that each person will respond individually to the death, — that there is no 'right' or 'wrong' way to mourn; that parents need time to accept the reality as well as the fact of their baby's death, is important information to have if you wish to give effective and comforting support.

Throughout the world there are organisations who are able to inform you and support you while you support a friend through their grief. Brigid Hirschfeld, a skilled and experienced grief counsellor and educator offered these words:

Grief is a natural process that is painful, necessary and common to all of us. The real skill in caring for poeple in grief lies in allowing that natural process to take place, and not to speed it up, interfere with it, or change its direction. Sharing grief with another person can facilitate and can ease the process.

To conclude this chapter on effective community support it is helpful to remember:

In the early months it is easier to allow tears and sadness, but as the months drag on it can become more difficult to understand that today your friend appears to be in as much pain as in the beginning. Being an effective supporter requires some understanding that this day is causing your friend heartache.

PART IV

THE FUTURE

Only that day dawns to which we are awake

Henry Thoreau

CHAPTER FOURTEEN

The Next Child : A Dilemma

Pregnancy is normally a happy and exciting time for parents. This is not necessarily so for parents who have experienced cot death. The community often is unaware of the complexities of pregnancy following cot death, and misunderstandings are common. This is hardly surprising as the parents themselves are grappling with many issues, often of a conflicting nature. Parents state categorically 'I want another baby' one day, and the next find themselves saying 'I will never have another baby—I can't take the chance of cot death happening again'. Somewhere between these extremes parents deal with the complexities, and usually decide to go ahead with the next pregnancy. *Whether* to have another child and *when* to have another baby are decisions they ultimately must decide for themselves.

A parent presents an overview of the complexities and misunderstandings in this account:

Doris: 'It begins from the time you announce you're pregnant. Everyone says: "How wonderful, you must be so excited; baby number two" when actually it's baby number three. "Won't it be wonderful to have a sister for Johnny?" But Johnny has already had a sister. Right from the first you are misunderstood.

'People wonder why you're not rushing out to buy baby clothes, why the nursery hasn't been reorganised, why you're not terribly excited, why you're not going to ante-natal classes, why ante-natal classes upset you.

'Everything upsets you. Nobody ever owns up and says "It's not much fun this time around"; or "Of course you haven't bought seven different growsuits in seven different colours because last time you didn't get to use them all".

'. . . it annoyed me. I was supposed to be happy; I was supposed to be excited; I was supposed to be shopping and I wasn't. Nobody seemed to understand why it's so hard to get that joy — that mothering glow about you. I think that's where the misunderstanding starts and [it] continues in hospital; continuing when you bring the baby home.

'This baby isn't the miracle cure . . . . People think you're wonderful and happy again. I know people said to me, "You have another wonderful daughter — aren't you lucky?" So that solved the problem. [They] replaced one with the other, so everything's fine at their house now. It just goes from one misunderstanding to another.

'It ends up with you having to say, "But this is the way things really are — I perservered with the pregnancy; it was awful. Put up with the birth and thank God it wasn't a stillbirth — that became another preoccupation. Not only could another S.I.D.S. occur, but maybe a stillbirth could occur, and all the other things that can go wrong".'

In attempting to write this section of the book several false starts were made. The interviews had been recorded, synopses and outline drawn, and it seemed all that was required was the actual writing up of the material. It wasn't as simple as that. The next child . . . (in chapter form) has been difficult to produce. No matter where the beginning was made, complex issues arose. As it was for the writer, so it is for the parents.

Each time the statement is made: 'I want to have another baby', the conflicting thoughts '*Can* I have another baby?', '*Can* I take the chance of it happening again?' arises for many parents. In this enormously complex issue the dead baby can seem ever present.

Loyalties are difficult to resolve. Each time a new baby is thought about, it is invariably accompanied by the thought 'What would the other baby feel?' Would she feel forgotten, cast aside or rejected? The thoughts and feelings of other people become involved in the decision making. If they suggested having another baby, did that mean they too had already forgotten her? The longing to have the dead baby recognised and remembered is an important issue for parents. The longing for a new family, the proof that survival is possible, that life could be 'good' again is finely balanced against the loyalty, love and longing for the baby that has died. Fears, uncertainties and conflicts make decision-making almost impossible.

The urge to push the grieving for the dead baby along as swiftly as possible seems to make good sense. To 'get on' with life and living is difficult to resist. It seems to make sense to want to be free of the pain as quickly as possible. Often relatives, friends and helping professionals urge parents to look to the future with all speed. After all, nothing is going to bring the baby back. Parents know this. And yet — ?

Most parents continue to search for their baby for some time after its death. This timing is extremely variable. Walking into the baby's room to see if it has magically returned; searching the faces of babies in pushers and prams; fantasising a return to the hospital to collect the baby — all are commonplace. It takes time to accept the reality as well as the fact that the baby is dead and won't be coming back.

Some parents find themselves trying to make the decision to have another baby before they have accepted the reality of their baby's death, and while they are still in a state of conflict, and are still struggling with loyalty issues. Many parents are uncertain of how they do feel, and most have a need to explore and express their fears and nervousness. Their conflicting feelings are often difficult for others to understand. Misunderstanding between parents, health professionals and the community are common.

Sometimes attempts are made, one way or another, to encourage parents to have another baby before they are certain of their feelings. This attempt is as potentially disastrous as to tell them how to grieve for their dead baby. As has been shown, it is unlikely two parents will grieve in the same way and at the same pace. Also, experience has shown that partners may have different ideas about 'the right time' to have the next baby.

Parents need to feel supported while they are trying to make the decision when and whether to have another baby. Listening to parents can provide a supportive atmosphere in which they may feel free to express and explore. The answers to 'When?' and 'Can I?' and 'Will I?' have to come from within themselves.

Restoring Parenting Roles

The sudden and unexpected death of a baby brings with it the sudden and unexpected loss of the parenting role. Thinking about becoming pregnant again throws the lost role into focus and brings feelings of uncertainty about the new one.

We need to examine the role loss to be able to understand what is involved for parents as they contemplate their future and 'the next child'. Parents/couples react to this loss with varying intensity, and husbands and wives usually react differently.

The loss can be very intense when the first baby dies from cot-

death. Parents have had little time to build confidence in their parenting role when it is suddenly ended. Often the wife has worked almost to the end of the pregnancy, and spent the last few weeks making final arrangements for the baby's birth. The husband also has probably attended ante-natal classes and has high expectations of his parenting role—both during the birth and for the ensuing years.

Fantasies, dreams and hopes for the family they would have been, would often have been shared with friends and relatives. The lost role can be reinforced in the company of these people.

Parents report other issues surrounding first born cot-deaths:

— They may have saved for several years to buy their house and so have their baby in the best circumstances they can afford.

— When a first born baby dies from cot death parents can find themselves asking — 'Why did we work so hard?' 'Why did I give up my job?' 'Perhaps I'm not meant to be a parent?' Feelings of failure are high.

— The question of what to do with all this spare time (the loss of the parenting role) is a difficult one for parents to resolve.

— Many parents attempt to redress the imbalance as quickly as possible:

Two options quickly become apparent:

1. Go back to work.
2. Restore the parenting role as quickly as possible.

In relation to the first option, parents usually report: 'I'm just filling in time—this job, another job, it's all meaningless'. The role *loss* is *keenly* felt.

Going back to work needs to be looked at from two perspectives.

1 The job that existed *before* the baby's birth.

2 The job that existed *after* the baby's birth.

For the mother involved there is usually no contest. The work of mothering is the job she wants to return to.

For the father, the issue is a little more complex. He had two jobs—one as provider for the family, the other as a parent. His role as provider needs to be maintained; restoring his parenting role is not so easy. The point here is that with a first born cot death, the father already has a job to return to and a role that is sanctioned by friends, family and the community. The mother seems to lose all.

I was a mother, what am I now?
Before that, I had a job – I don't have that now either.

When we talk about 'the next child' for families of first born babies who die from cot death we need to remember this role loss and its intensity.

When the second, third or fourth baby dies, while the preceeding issues are usually present, they may not be quite as intense. When these parents prepare themselves for the next child some different issues arise:

1 *What did I do wrong last time?*

Parents begin to compare and examine their pregnancies and parenting for the surviving children, the baby that died, and the child to come. They look for similarities and differences and some choose to make the pattern as different as possible. This can include:

(a) changing the doctor, physiotherapist and hospital

(b) moving to a new house or location

(c) become pregnant at a different time of year (with seasonal incidence and 2-5 months peak age this makes good sense for some)

(d) change dietary patterns – although if diet was perceived to be about the same for baby number one and two, with the third as cot death it is not likely to be as important.

2 *Will this baby die too Mummy?* is a painful question for parents and a puzzling one for siblings.

Most parents deal with this question with common sense, provided they are able to recognise their own fears and own up to them. During a discussion with her young daughter this parent said:

'She is really excited about the baby. She's older this time (two-and-a-half years) She's asked me a couple of times if it's going to die like Kelly did, and I felt very insecure then, because I couldn't promise her it wouldn't.

I said 'I hope not – what do you think it will be, a boy or a girl'. I didn't want to talk about it with her. I think she was satisfied being the age she was. *I'm* not satisfied with the answer. I want to promise her it won't happen, and promise everyone else around, me included, that it won't happen.

This parent did in fact deal with the question. 'I hope not' is as truthful an answer from all angles, anyone can give.

The Early Pregnancy

Becoming pregnant again soon after a cot death has certain inherent difficulties for parents who are still in the early stages of their journey through grief.

The replacement baby

As a member of the Counselling Unit and as a cot death parent one of the questions most frequently asked of me was 'Did you have another baby?' The importance of this question is not only that it is asked, but that it is very often asked on day one of the baby's death, or when first face-to-face contact is made with the parents. The question is not '*when* did you have another baby?' but '*did you*'.

The parents' question is easily misinterpreted, and it is all too easy for the responder to launch into the future, and so miss hearing what the parents are actually saying.

The parents are really asking:

'Will I ever get over this?'
'Can I survive?'
'Will life ever be normal again?'
'Does the pain ever go?' etc.

Present too is the anxiety surrounding the decision to have another baby. There can be much agonising over this decision. The question of whether to and when to is a complex one. For example:

'I think the first time we actually discussed it [having another baby] was the day of her death. I wanted another baby straight away — immediately — more or less just to replace Kelly. We didn't discuss it much after that . . . until my husband was almost pressuring me. He wanted another baby. [By then] It was around the three month stage when I was more over the shock of losing her, and I was starting to grieve for her. Then I didn't want another baby at all.'

'When I did get pregnant (five months after the death) it was an accident. I think subconsciously I probably did want another baby because we didn't take any precautions, but I was being very careful. I felt I couldn't cope with another baby at all. If it hadn't happened how it did we would never have made a decision to have another baby. *I* wouldn't have anyway. My husband always did want another one.'

It sounds confusing—and it is.

Some of the confusion can arise from messages received from the community. Parents are often flooded with well-meaning advice to restore the parenting role quickly.

'Have another one soon.'

'You can't leave James without a brother/sister.'

'It will be good for you.'

'There's only one way to get over it—have another baby.'

Parents are often given this advice when they are missing their dead baby so badly that the advice given is very attractive to them.

Perhaps another baby will take away the pain; take away the empty feeling; ease the ache in arms, legs or chest; stop the tears that come when they are least expected; restore the relationship with partner that was so good a few months ago; maybe the children won't be as demanding as they seem; maybe forgetfulness is possible . . . maybe . . . maybe . . .

If parents heed the external messages given by the community, a replacement baby may be the outcome. Consciously or unconsciously community pressures can influence the parents decision about when and why they should become pregnant.

Inhibition of mourning by pregnancy

Early pregnancy following cot death can be counter productive for grieving parents. Emanuel Lewis in his article 'Inhibition of mourning by pregnancy' in the *British Medical Journal*, (1979, 2.) states:

A pregnant woman becomes increasingly preoccupied with thoughts and feelings about the baby. Eventually, around the puerperium, there may be little mental space left for anyone else. Winnicot identified this intense concern as the basis for maternal bonding, and called it 'primary maternal preoccupation'. *Mourning entails a comparable intense concern with the dead in order eventually to become free from the loss.*

A bereaved pregnant woman has conflicting and paradoxical needs to think and feel intensely both about the new life and the dead. She opts for her live baby and mourning is interrupted, it is often too difficult while she nurtures her new baby, and is often impossible to resume later. Unresolved mourning may be reactivated in pathological forms by later events. With incomplete mourning there may be a persistent identification with the personality and diseased body of the dead resulting, for instance, in prolonged depression, hypochondriasis, or somatic conversion symptoms. Strong feelings about the loss may be suppressed, leading to a sense of being emotionally cut off; and this may impair the tie to the new baby.

Anxiety

Kerry Bluglass in *The Practitioner*, (May 1980, Vol. 224) has documented some effects on parents when a 'replacement' child was conceived 'almost immediately' following a cot death. Severe anxiety and over protection of a replacement child in one case, and paternal neurosis, anxiety after replacement, in another. Her findings are consistent with some experiences related to the Counsellors at the Foundation when the next baby is born close to the first anniversary of the cot death baby, as the following case study demonstrates.

This case study was also used in Part I. It is used again here to demonstrate the importance of the level of awareness needed in crisis intervention.

The Foundation became involved with this family when the maternal grandmother rang us, asking for help with her daughter who was unable to be left alone with the new baby due to her severe anxiety and panic attacks. Either the grandmother or the husband had to be with the mother at all times. The husband's employer was finding it difficult to be sympathetic as the husband was absent from work frequently.

The parents had their next child twelve months after the cot death of their first baby. The father was twenty years old and the mother nineteen. When the Home Visitor arrived at the home, the mother had just finished bathing the baby. She offered to hold the baby while the mother removed the bath and tidied up, etc. The mother handed over the baby and then began to shake all over.

The mother's story revealed the reason: At her scream 'Steven isn't breathing' her husband 'wrenched' him from her and tried to resuscitate. He continued until the ambulance arrived and the Ambulance Officers then took over. She said 'I just stood there watching it all — I couldn't move and it was like I wasn't there'. She didn't see or touch her son again. She said: 'By the time I came to, it was all over and Steven was gone.' Since the birth of the next baby she reported 'When anyone tries to take him, I see Steven and it's all happening again.'

It seemed clear to the Counselling Unit that the death of Steven had still to be dealt with. Retracing the first hours and weeks following the baby's death was essential to this parent as she had no clear recollection of what had happened, and no time to deal with grief before she became pregnant again. Support for this couple also meant recognition of their fears and anxieties — 'Yes it could happen again'.

Within one week after contact with the Foundation the husband was attending work for half days; within two weeks, he was back at work full time; panic attacks still happening, but decreasing in frequency and severity; within seven weeks maternal grandma was interstate on holiday; no panic attacks for three weeks. There was a surge of anxiety again when the next baby reached four months of age — the age at which Steven had died. The anxiety gradually diminished, and the next child has had his first birthday. The family is now stable.

Loyalty

As mentioned earlier, loyalty is one of the complex issues that arise for parents when they approach the next pregnancy. Feelings of loyalty to the dead baby as well as loyalty to a community that has certain expectations, i.e. that a new baby, whenever it comes, heralds the end of grief, can throw the parents into conflict.

Parents who become pregnant early in their grieving report:

'I have a lot of mixed feelings. There are days when I don't want it (the unborn baby) because I feel guilty to Kelly (cot death baby); because no matter how I look at it I feel I'm replacing her. And then I feel guilty to the unborn baby because *she's* got so much to live up to. Obviously we want a girl. I feel guilty to this baby because it is in Kelly's image and I don't want it to be. I want it to have its own identity.'

This same parent commented on the community's expectations when she said:

'I think people's reactions count too. They don't say it, but you hear it. Because I'm having another baby everythings going to be alright again . . . suddenly when this baby is born the sky is going to be blue and Kelly is going to be forgotten about. I don't want that . . . .'

What parents are really saying is:

1 'What will my dead baby think if I have another child?'

2 'Will he think I have forgotten him already?'

3 'Have I grieved enough for my baby?'

Until parents have resolved these issues one way or another for themselves, and allowed the dead baby a realistic place in the family structure, conflicts during pregnancy can occur.

Reincarnation

Emanuel Lewis (see above) says: 'A bereavement during pregnancy is difficult to mourn: a pregnant woman is so increasingly preoccupied with the new life that mourning is interrupted and often impossible to resume later. This may lead to idealisation of the child as a reincarnation of the dead person, or child abuse. A bereaved woman should be helped to mourn at the time of death and to keep alive the expectation of future mourning once her baby is thriving.'

If pregnancy occurs during bereavement, it is possible for some parents to fantasise a return of the dead baby with the next birth. Certainly at S.I.D.R.F. we have talked to parents who cling to the dead baby in this way. Not only can this bring problems in the parent/child relationship, but also for any siblings. Young children can become very confused between Simon who died, and Simone who has been born, or Robin spelt with an 'I' instead of a 'Y'. Another possibility for a fantasy reincarnation occurs when a baby dies while the mother is pregnant.

Cot death During Pregnancy

When Vivian died at sixteen months, Eve realised that as she was pregnant, and had a baby Sarah four months old, she could 'indulge' her fantasy that Vivian had not died. She could take herself back twelve months – she had been pregnant then and had another baby of four months. Psychologically it was 'easier' not to grieve, just pretend that none of this had happened.

The scenario for this S.I.D.S. family differed from the average S.I.D.S. family in three major ways:

(a) Vivian who died was 16/12 months old

(b) A younger daughter Sarah 5/12 months old

(c) Eve was already two months pregnant.

Because of these differences, a number of reactions and responses by the parents were observed:

(1) Husband Robert regularly presented himself either at the local G.P's or the hospital. A diagnosis of 'hypochondriosis, possibly secondary to depression' had been made.

(2) Eve had developed 'quasi delusional ideas about Vivian inhabiting Sarah's body'.

(3) Eve had been taking Valium and Percodan for headaches and depression since the birth of her 'next child' Richard.

(4) Eve had the idea that at Vivian's anniversary (death), the younger two children would be the same age as the younger two that existed twelve months ago, therefore the same thing would happen again.

(5) Eve refused to look after Richard (who was admitted to hospital) and Sarah (who stayed with relatives until after the anniversary date).

Medical and psychiatric intervention were used to ensure that Eve and Robert felt they were being listened to. Even though there was a question as to whether Eve's behaviour exhibited pathological grieving signs, collaboration between health professionals gave her the support she needed. Since the anniversary date Eve and Robert have reached some resolution of their grief — enough to allow them to plan ahead with the hope of future happiness.

Delayed Pregnancies

Emanuel Lewis has given the case for inhibition of mourning by pregnancy. I would like to explore some issues now where a case could be made for mourning delaying or preventing pregnancies. There is a mass of anecdotal evidence to indicate that pregnancy following the sudden and unexpected death of an infant is sometimes difficult to achieve.

Timing:

Parents who have had no difficulties becoming pregnant prior to a cot death can react with dismay, anger or confusion if the next child does not follow immediately upon the parents' decision to become pregnant. Often parents will build into their expectations a time-span that relates to prior pregnancies. 'I always get pregnant straight away' or 'It takes me three months to get pregnant', or they might devise a new time-table: 'I will give myself six months to grieve, and then get pregnant'. It can be harder still for the parents who decide they have worked diligently towards a resolution of their grief, perhaps for a year or more. Parents who have 'done it right' expect another baby for all their labour.

Memories or mourning?

It is difficult sometimes for parents to know when mourning is complete. It is easy to confuse memories with mourning. It is not easy, nor always advisable, to suggest to parents who are anxious to become pregnant that perhaps their body, or mind, is throwing up delaying tactics while their individual mourning process is still in progress. Nonetheless, many parents are anguished by their apparent inability to conceive during the first year of mourning, and seek answers to why this is so.

It could be said also that for some parents the next child is connected to the grief process. One parent expressed this very clearly when she said:

The new baby is part of the grief until it passes the age at which the previous one died — then it emerges in its own right.

(This parent was pregnant five months after the death of her daughter). This statement contains other elements also. Parents pass a milestone when the next child passes the age at which the previous one died. There is a surge of anxiety at this time which usually dissipates rapidly. Parents will usually be anxious in the following months, but almost all report that it is at a much lower and more manageable level. That a second cot death is unlikely begins to have real meaning for the parents.

Loyalty to baby, husband or community

If a pregnancy is contemplated before such issues as loyalty to the dead baby are dealt with, parents may push themselves too quickly towards pregnancy. Parents then can find themselves in conflict with inner and outer messages.

Outer messages are those that are imposed by others, including a well-meaning community, friends and relatives. After allowing several months for grieving, people begin to say its time to have another baby. The husband too may apply subtle pressures to his wife. Cot death mothers often reveal this influence in such statements as:

'I want to be a good wife – give my husband another child.'

or

'My friends have babies. I can't join with them unless I have one too.'

or

'I want a reason to live.'

If her inner voices, which she may be trying to quieten or damp down, are saying:

'But I don't want another baby yet – I am not ready – am too frightened',

or

'But I am still hurting inside',

conflict can result. If the age of the mother is a factor, the matter can become even more pressing and more difficult to resolve.

It may seem far-fetched to offer this explanation as a reason for a delayed pregnancy following sudden infant death, but some parents do become confused or frightened when pregnancy is delayed following the death of a baby. Anxiety has been found to act as a barrier to pregnancy.

Medical reasons for delaying a pregnancy

Today there are few medical reasons a doctor could give to delay a new pregnancy. As a consequence the advice to delay becoming pregnant on medical grounds will rarely be given.

Of some relevance, however, would be the concept of an appropriate time to embark on a pregnancy from an emotional, psychological or economic viewpoint. These are considerations which apply to any pregnancy. Hence it is unlikely that a medical viewpoint will be at variance with the couple's own decision as to the appropriate time to begin the next pregnancy.

CHAPTER FIFTEEN

Facing The Reality

Making the decision to have another baby allows parents to confirm the belief that *this* family, just as any other, has a future; even though it can seem both fragile and very precious at this time. Parents have come to understand that life goes on when a baby suddenly dies, and they need to affirm and confirm the belief they have in themselves, their family and the future.

Having decided to have another child, the cot death parent invariably encounters difficulties, many of them unexpected, both during the pregnancy and during the rearing of the child. As long as health professionals and the community at large realise this, they can help to alleviate some of the stresses, anxieties and difficulties that now face the family.

When others reinforce the notion that the family can survive the natural fears and uncertainties inherent in having another baby, they give support to the family in a positive manner. However, recognition of the stresses, not denial of them, is required.

Ante-natal Classes

When the decision has been made to have another baby and pregnancy follows, complexities can surface that were not present during previous pregnancies

This chapter first addresses the role of ante-natal physiotherapists with couples who have previously had an infant death. Couples are encouraged to participate in classes which are designed to educate and inform them about pregnancy, birth and ante-natal care.

Rarely are parents informed that not all pregnancies succeed through to birth, nor do all babies survive to fulfill their long-term expectations. It is a fact of life that unsuccessful reproduction is more common than we would like to think. The range of experiences covers infertility, miscarriage, stillbirth neo-natal death and sudden infant death syndrome and deaths from other (medically identified) causes.

There is a myth perpetuated in our society that all babies will survive. Medicine, science and technology have combined to lead couples to the assumption that nothing can go wrong, and if it does, that it can be put right. This line of thinking does nothing to prepare couples for either the disappointment or overwhelming grief that follows the range of experiences outlined above.

From the Australian Year Book (1985), figures for 1983 show that 1:100 babies born alive will die before 1 year of age. Of foetuses who reach 500 grams weight, 1:150 won't be born alive. If these two figures are combined, then of foetuses that reach 500 grams, 1:60 will die before their first birthday. (These figures relate to deaths from any cause.)

When parents present in an ante-natal class with any of the above experiences, they need acknowledgement of their individual situation, not denial of their fears and anxieties.

Time and again, parents have indicated to the Foundation that they should have been warned that something might go wrong. They emphasise that they only needed acknowledgement of what their own commonsense already dictated. Every mother knows of someone who has had a stillbirth, cot death, congenital abnormality, miscarriage or neo-natal death, or who simply didn't become pregnant when she wanted to. Nevertheless they are exhorted not to consider it, and never talk about it. People seem to conspire especially not to mention it to someone who is pregnant.

Parents need support during ante-natal classes to cope with the facts of life and death. It is important to families that a failed pregnancy or infant death be given recognition during the next pregnancy so that fears and uncertainties can be dealt with when they surface.

A response like 'Don't be silly, why should anything go wrong?' will do nothing to allay a parent's fears, while a comment that includes acknowledgement and recognition, such as 'It is natural for you to remember what happened last time and to hope that everything will be alright this time', will let the parents know that a heightened level of anxiety is normal.

The reaction that swings in the other direction—apparent detachment—is normal too. Some parents use this mechanism to keep the fears and uncertainties at a manageable level. However, extreme responses at either end of the spectrum can signify deeper difficulties.

It is not suggested that undue emphasis be placed on the unfortunate things that can occur, but simply that they be acknowledged during the preparation for birth. Inclusion in general conversation of such phrases as 'Wouldn't it be awful if . . .' would bring fantasies out of the closet. It is far better that such happenings as cot death, be acknowledged as a reality of life and recognition given to the fact that not all pregnancies can meet the expectations of parents, no matter how advanced the technological society in which we live.

Volume 3, No. 1, April 1984 of *The Journal Obstetrics and Gynecology Group of the Australian Physiotherapy Association* addressed the problem of presenting grief in ante-natal classes. Here Julia Sundin, M.A.P.A. stated:

Unexpected outcomes and the resulting feelings of grief and loss, during the childbearing year is an important, though somewhat minor component of any comprehensive childbirth preparation program. Information regarding the effects on the family and the role of the support persons, can lay the foundations for life skills, whether the couple be the ones experiencing the loss or supporting the grieving family. Are we as educators aiming a little high considering the time allotment given the topic in the syllabus? At best then, we can prepare each couple a little for the feelings they might experience if faced with a disappointment, and increase their awareness of the options and choices during the immediate and critical period. The most important objective is that couples *do* confront it, and *do* discuss it. One certain advantage, is that it gives the group permission to show sympathy and support if one of their fellow class members has a shock or tragedy during the pregnancy, or as a result of the birth. They will phone, write and meet, at least in the short term, with this compassionate bond sometimes developing into a much longer source of understanding and rapport.

The Birth

When parents arrive at the hospital for the birth of 'the next child' there are some points for those in attendance to remember.

A nurses-aid told me of her discomfort when she witnessed the admittance of a patient to the hospital. Her story reflects a common experience for both patient and staff. No doubt the procedure for gathering a patient's history varies from hospital to hospital, as would the individual's response. It seems that even the most simple questions can throw parent and nurse into confusion. For example:

Nurse:	'How many children do you have?'
Patient:	'None.'
Nurse:	'This is your first then.'
Patient:	'No – my first baby died from cot death.'

At this point the nurse looked flustered and completed her note-taking with no further reference to the death of the previous baby.

The nurses-aid reported that this exchange took place in a curtained cubicle where there was little real privacy. She commented that this situation created difficulties for other patients who overheard the conversation, and that no one dared, or knew, how to broach the subject.

As is stated in the section on ante-natal classes, it is not easy to introduce the subject of death to a couple who are happily anticipating the birth of a baby. However, the situation described above demands a realistic response from those present if any degree of comfort is to be achieved for all concerned. The parent whose previous child died wants to approach the imminent birth with as much optimism as the situation allows, and at the same time have acknowledged that this birth is a 'special' one for her. Cot death parents have explained that they often feel extremely uncomfortable in this situation. They do not want to spread fear and uncertainty through a maternity ward, but at the same time need to acknowledge the birth and life of a previous child.

Parents report they have two options:

(a) to become evasive in their replies
(b) to simply state the truth

With regard to becoming evasive, parents report feeling uncomfortable at the time, and that their discomfort can escalate. If parents say they have experienced cot death, they are aware they may upset other mothers in the ward. When this issue arises in the maternity ward, the outcome of the exchange between the mothers may depend on the individual's ability to absorb and deal with the information given. Here are two examples:

A   *Mother No. 1:* 'Do you have any other children?'
          No. 2: 'I had a son two years ago, but he died from cot death. This is my second birth.'
          No. 1: 'Oh.'

B   *Mother No. 1:* 'Do you have any other children?'

          No. 2: 'I had a son two years ago, but he died from cot death. This is my second birth.'

          No. 1: 'That must have been an awful experience for you.'

          No. 2: 'It was. I feel a bit nervous/scared/frightened now — but I hope everything will go well for us.'

Example B leaves the way open for further discussion if both parties wish, or it can simply rest there. There is also the possibility here that mother No. 1 can ask questions about cot death; questions she may have been unable or afraid to confront previously. Cot death parents are generally very well informed about the syndrome, and can do much to dispel myths and inaccuracies that still exist in the community. One could be almost certain that information given by the mother who had experienced cot death would be presented in the most optimistic way possible.

There is a third possibility:

If a hospital staff member becomes aware that a mother on her ward has had a cot death, and if that staff member is reasonably comfortable with the knowledge she already has about cot death, she can assist in alleviating the discomfort generated by this 'unwelcome' news.

1   She can acknowledge the situation using the example quoted in *Example B* above.

2   She can be aware that there will be a ripple of uncertainty throughout the ward.

3   If she is informed about the syndrome she can dispel the myths and reinforce the facts, i.e. that for every 500 babies born alive 499 will *not* die from S.I.D.S.

4   She can decrease the sense of isolation the cot death mother may be feeling, and so allow her to join with the other mothers in anticipating the birth of her next child.

As the birth becomes imminent, nature seems to assert herself strongly as energies are directed to bringing a new life into the world. Parents rarely make any negative comments about the actual birth of the next child. They usually recount feelings of overwhelming joy with the birth of the next baby. Even parents who longed for a baby of a particular sex report 'It just doesn't matter – he's alive – that's all that counts.'

Some parents may need a little time following the birth to work out just how they do feel about their new baby. The pain of the previous loss may be an initial barrier to total, joyful acceptance. Some parents will worry during pregnancy about the depth of their love for the unborn baby when weighed against the known and tested love for the child that died.

There is one birth experience I would like to recount here. It is not a common experience – at least to the knowledge of the Foundation's counsellors, and one could only speculate as to why it happened this way. It is offered therefore without comment.

Background: The parents had given birth to three children. The third child died from cot death at eleven weeks. The family had been part of the Foundation's support network with infrequent contact. Subsequently the mother came into labour with the next child.

Birth: On the morning of the birth the Foundation received a phone call from a distracted doctor who explained the mother was in labour and was ready to deliver. The mother however was reluctant to complete the birthing process. At this point she began questioning the doctor about the availability of a home monitor for the baby about to be born. The question of monitoring the baby had not been raised before apparently. The Foundation assured the doctor that a monitor could be made available to the parents when the baby was due to go home – and that the home visitor would come to the hospital the following day to discuss the issues. The Foundation asked the doctor to let them know when the birth was completed. Ten minutes later he was back on the phone with the news that a healthy baby boy had been delivered. There was relieved laughter and rejoicing all round.

Follow-up: The home visitor made the promised visit the next day. The mother was ecstatic and proudly presented her new son. When the serious discussion of the monitor was introduced, the mother reported, 'Oh – I don't want one, my husband does.' The pro's and con's were considered over the next few days and the parents finally decided to take their son home with a monitor. One month later it was returned to the Queen Victoria monitoring program with the comment 'We've had enough thanks'.

As a final point to this section it is probably important for those in attendance to know that this birth is indeed a 'special' one for parents, and at this emotional moment tears may flow and continue to flow but these tears are a mixture of relief, remembered pain, and *intense joy*.

Monitors

Mention of monitors and S.I.D.S. in the one breath will be sure to bring confused and heated responses from researchers, cot death parents and health professionals. The major difficulty surrounding monitors is the claim that they *might* prevent Sudden Infant Death Syndrome.

At the time of writing, monitors have not proved their success as a preventive health measure in relation to S.I.D.S. Babies have died on monitors, even on sophisticated monitors which electrically record respiration and heart activity.

That monitors are useful, perhaps even life-saving for an apnoeic child is not questioned. When apnoea and Sudden Infant Death Syndrome are confused, or when it is claimed that monitors might prevent a S.I.D.S. death, controversy arises. It is not my intention to enter this debate.

While researchers into the usefulness of monitors attempt to resolve this contentious issue, parents, paediatricians and others who find themselves in the role of supporter or advice given will have to weigh up the advantages and disadvantages and make a decision that best suits each individual family's needs.

To assist with clarification of the term 'apnoea', the following comments are offered by Sue Cranage, Department of Paediatrics, Queen Victoria Medical Centre, Monash University, Victoria. Sue has had extensive experience in the monitoring of infants, and close contact with their parents at the above centre.

It is felt that only 5 per cent of S.I.D.S. victims may be accounted for by unexplained, prolonged breathing pauses (apnoea) from which the baby did not spontaneously recover.

It must be remembered that breathing pauses of up to fifteen seconds are normal in infants up to three months of age, and are a normal pattern of their development. An apnoea is usually considered to be a prolonged breathing pause of more than ten seconds. Apnoea is considered abnormal if the breathing pause is twenty seconds or longer, associated with a colour change, that is the infant is blue in the face and needs stimulation to reestablish breathing.

When babies sleep they have two states of sleep: active sleep, and quiet sleep. *Active sleep* is when the infant has a lot of facial and body activity, eye movements, irregular breathing pattern, with many short pauses in breathing. *Quiet sleep* is when the infant is in a very deep sleep, and the child's face will appear very still and pale; the breathing is now very regular, and can be very shallow with the occasional breathing pause.

The sleep states of young infants cycle through active and quiet sleep. Their active sleep last for between forty and sixty minutes, and their quiet sleep for between twenty and thirty minutes. In other words, the cycle is active . . . quiet . . . active . . . quiet . . . active . . . until the baby wakes.

If in doubt about whether the baby is breathing or not, gently pull back the covers and either observe the baby's tummy, or gently place your hand on the tummy and feel the breathing movements; remembering the breathing may be very shallow. Never pull a baby out of its cot and begin to shake it violently without checking that the baby has actually stopped breathing; unless of course there is a definite reason for immediate action, such as when an infant is found blue. Always remember to support the baby's head and neck if you feel the need to shake the baby.

While monitoring of a subsequent baby (following upon a cot death) is an option taken up by a few parents, most will manage the heightened anxiety that is a natural consequence in these circumstances, using other ways.

Many cot death parents, as well as anxious non-S.I.D.S. parents, ring the Foundation with the request 'Can I have one of those monitors please?' or 'I am pregnant and scared my baby will die from cot death'. Experience has shown that despite this direct request, most parents either do not really know if they want a monitor, or know they *don't*, but need to acknowledge their fears and anxieties, and have them recognised. To help parents towards a solution which meets their individual needs, the following procedure could be adopted:

1 Encourage parents to talk about their fears. This requires listening skills.

2 Provide accurate information about monitors – the advantages and disadvantages.

3 Point out that babies have died while on sophisticated monitors.

4 Emphasise that 499:500 babies won't die from cot death. If cot death has been experienced parents will ask, 'Is it likely to happen

again?' To reply: 'There are probably between 490 and 497:500 chances that it won't happen again' could be generally accepted. These figures vary depending upon the expert opinion sought so it becomes impossible to state a firm figure. For those who seek more detail on this, the book *Sudden Infant Death: Patterns, Puzzles & Problems* by Golding, Limerick and MacFarlane, published by Open Books in 1985, deals with this on pages 87-89, 106 and 107.

The Community Education and Counselling Units of the S.I.D.R.F. receive many calls from parents, who are trying to decide whether or not to monitor their baby. To help parents come to an informed decision they:

1 During the first phone call, ascertain parent's reasons for wanting a monitor. The most common reasons given are:

   (a) My last baby died from cot death.

   (b) I hear so much about it.

   (c) I want to give my baby every chance to live.

   (d) I know there's something I can do to prevent it – there's a machine or something I think.

When parents offer these reasons, an attempt is made to try and find out what lies behind the particular inquiry. Here are some examples in relation to the above points:

   (a) I'm scared it will happen again.

   (b) They don't know what causes it.

   (c) I don't want it to happen to me – I want a guarantee.

   (d) I will be a good mother.

Using (a) to demonstrate, an acknowledgement could be made that to be frightened is natural. As one parent expressed it: 'Nothing and no one could have convinced me there was no need to worry. Moments of panic and fear are the lot of a parent who has decided to have another baby after a cot death.'

It is difficult for parents to deal with their fears if they are told by well-meaning friends, relatives and health professionals:

'Don't think about it.'

'Of course it won't happen again.'

'You'll do harm to yourself and the baby if you think like that: pregnant women should be happy.'

2 After the first contact is made, parents can be sent literature about monitors. S.I.D.R.F. has found the Canadian Foundation for the Study of Infant Deaths' article, 'The Monitoring of an Infant in the Home—A Commentary by the Scientific Advisory Committee, 1981' most useful. Also useful is an excellent article by Mary Rothschild, 'The Mystery called SIDS' in the (1983) Seattle Post Intelligencer. S.I.D.R.F. may be contacted in order to obtain copies of these and other articles which discuss the issues surrounding the next child. See also bibliographical section of this book.

3 After a couple of weeks, contact can be made again, and any questions that have arisen can be answered.

4 Parents can be encouraged to make an informed decision about monitoring. If parents decide to monitor, they should be encouraged to:

(a) enlist the support of their general practitioner or paediatrician;

(b) check service agents for the monitor. (Make sure they are accessible);

(c) have readily available the name and telephone number of a parent who has used a monitor, or ready access to a professional who can give advice and support *at any time*, should the monitor be recording frequent false alarms, or for those occasions when a parent simply needs to talk about the experience of monitoring a baby.

5 If parents decide not to use a monitor, they can be offered the support of another parent who has survived the fears, uncertainties and anxieties of having the next child. Parent matching at this time can produce positive advantages, that is, proof that the next child can survive, and also its parents. (At the S.I.D.R.F. in Melbourne parents also have ready access to the Counselling Unit who are able to offer support and understanding.)

6 Another support for parents can be the forming of a group for parents who are pregnant or have had the next child. In the past

this group has met at S.I.D.R.F. with two members of the Counselling Unit acting as facilitators.

Hospital and Bringing the Baby Home:

Parents indicate that one of the major difficulties in hospital is the lack of recognition that they have had a cot death, and the lack of acknowledgement that it is normal to feel anxious about the new baby's sleeping patterns, birth weight, weight gain, or even the need to have the baby constantly by their side. When the time comes to leave hospital, anxiety can be intense.

A parent who is also a nurse educator describes this lack of recognition and acknowledgement:

The day I left hospital with Alister was the first time someone broached the subject of S.I.D.S. with me. I was terrified and on my own now. No one had acknowledged that I would be feeling vulnerable. No one said 'Do you feel you will be able to cope when you go home?' or 'Have you got enough information?' There was no acknowledgement that you would worry . . . . Unless you say something, they don't mention it. Perhaps my expectation is unrealistic that they will mention it. I think it would be appropriate for them to say: 'I imagine you are very worried, and I feel for you.'

Parents are vulnerable when the next child is born, and may report feeling relatively safe in hospital; the responsibility for the baby is shared. Sentiments such as this are common: '. . . I felt like saying . . . well, here you are . . . . I don't want to bring them home until they are past the age when they are at risk . . . I will sacrifice them for that time if you can prevent it happening.' This statement refers to two subsequent births).

Birth weight can be a concern. Alister's mother (see above) explains:

He was just below birth weight. I was in a bind. I wanted to take him home, but had this nebulous idea that while he was in hospital they would be able to look after him if anything happened. Sister said 'we never send babies home below birth weight,' and I knew they had packed Troy (her cot death baby) off home below birth weight, and of course I just fell to pieces. I wanted to go, and I wanted to stay. Sister was oblivious to the fact that I was nervous about going home with this new baby. They didn't realise how I might be feeling.

Another parent stated:

I was so sensitive anyway . . . . The morning I was to go home a sister said 'You realise this child has lost 9 ounces'. I just packed-up; the waterworks started and could not be turned off. I decided I just didn't want to go home. The gynecologist was brought in. He was great and said it didn't matter, she was getting good feeds, etc. Perhaps it was for the best — it brought it all to the surface.

Author's own case:

The morning to leave dawned, and I was excited and nervous. I was determined to breast-feed Katie as I was still guilty and worried that bottle feeding Clare had somehow contributed to her cot death. The hospital staff and Nursing Mother's Association had been extremely supportive. I stayed ten days in hospital, again to be as rested as possible, and to give Katie and I the 'best chance' of survival. Really, I wasn't in a hurry to leave; I felt safe there. I could hardly pretend that the flow of milk was more than we needed, but there seemed to be enough. Some weeks later I met Matron in the street of the small country town where we lived. In response to her question 'How is the feeding going?' I proudly reported that Katie was putting on 6 to 9 ounces a week. Matron was astonished, and said she didn't have the heart to tell me when I left the hospital that she gave me little or no chance to breast feed. Because they knew my reasons for wanting to breast feed, and how important it was to me, they decided to keep those feelings to themselves, and give me what support they could.'

The comments above reflect how parents may be feeling. Parents will readily acknowledge their fears and uncertainties if given the opportunity. To do so in a supportive environment can lessen the anxiety.

Parents are resilient. They find many ways of managing their anxiety:

We've done it once. We have Katie and she is alright. We've done it once and we'll do it again. I think I always looked ahead. Things were going to be all right. We had proof that friends had had subsequent children after cot death or some other sort of death. They had done it and I was going to do it. I was stubborn; it didn't stop me being afraid, really afraid, but something at the back of my mind just said it was going to be all right.

Some parents are able to acknowledge their fears to some degree and they find this helpful.

Gail said:
I was a wreck when we first came home. She (baby) was terrible – she would sleep 8 to 9 hours a day. My other kids woke at proper times, and this one I wanted awake all the time. At first I would not wake her; I could not go in there. I wanted to go in, but I was trying to be sensible, saying to myself that of course she was alright. I was just a mess until I rang the Foundation.

They said: 'Try not to be sensible: do what you want to do. At first that may mean checking her 50 times in 5 minutes.' So I just did what I wanted to do, and if I couldn't go in I didn't, and if I felt I wanted to, I did before I had second thoughts. It was a big turning point for me.

Although the perplexing issue of whether to monitor or not is covered earlier in the chapter, many parents consider the possibility of using a monitor as a means of lessening anxiety when the baby comes home from hospital. The following comments demonstate the process by which some parents come to their decision:

Doris had this to say:
My doctor had discussed monitors with me. I think he thought it was a good idea to use one, but I felt it was a safeguard for him. My husband didn't want one and I felt a monitor would be a permanent reminder for the new baby that Claire had died (of cot death). I felt it would be difficult for babysitters; that they would feel uncomfortable. My mother did a fair amount of babysitting and I knew she wouldn't cope with a monitor. If we were late home she always put the bassinette beside her bed, and monitored the baby that way. There were other issues too. I thought about being out at the letterbox talking to the postie while the monitor was buzzing inside; then going in and blaming myself for falling down on the job.

There were times when I thought a monitor might have helped. For example when Pete and I finally had a 'blow-up' about who should be the one to check if she was alright. Pete said he just couldn't go into the room for that reason (what if she wasn't all right?) That was when we thought we should have got a monitor. Also when there were surges of anxiety for no apparent reason.

We decided against a monitor because it is a physical reminder that something had gone wrong (before). I thought it would take away the pleasure of just looking at the baby and thinking 'isn't she gorgeous'. Straight away the monitor would be there and it would deprive us of some of the happiness.

For some parents, using a monitor when they bring the next baby home can lessen anxiety, as evidenced in the case of Olive and Graham.

Our first son, Michael, had died at sixteen weeks from cot death. Five months later a twin pregnancy was confirmed. After an apparently normal pregnancy the first born twin was stillborn. The surviving twin Robert, weighing 5 lb 14 ozs., was monitored while still in hospital, and after discussion with both our paediatrician and the Foundation, we decided we wanted to use a monitor at home.

When we first brought ten day old Robert home from hospital, we had a mattress monitor on loan from the Queen Victoria Medical Centre. In hospital, the monitor had worked perfectly but those first few nights at home were so bad that we were both ready to let Robert take his chances and go without the machine. We did persevere however, because we had been warned by the hospital that early days are the worst. There were difficulties with the mattress monitor and after three weeks we bought our own Tenby alarm and found this much better in the long term, but there were problems initially. In nine months we have had many broken nights' sleep, and at nine and a half months we decided to take Robert off the monitor. Robert had become very active, moving around a lot in his cot at night. One night the alarm went, and when we went to check we discovered Robert with the monitor cord wrapped around his tummy. Then and there, our problem of deciding when to take him off the monitor was solved.

The problem then was how to achieve a sense of security. Graham and I felt insecure and strange at first, with the result that we had a couple of sleepless nights immediately afterwards. We soon settled down though to enjoy uninterrupted peaceful nights. Robert has been sleeping much better without the alarms going off, and without being disturbed to reposition the monitor. Now he can wriggle to his heart's content.

I'm glad he's off the monitor now, but I don't think we could have coped without it. Its presence was very reassuring to us for those months we used it.

Perhaps this parent speaks for many:

After I had read everything available, [on monitors and monitoring] *if* I could have been convinced, *if* there was the slightest hope that a monitor could prevent cot death, [then] my children would not have gone without one.

As education about the effects of cot death on families reaches all levels of the community, misunderstandings between hospital staff and parents will decrease. Parents do have a higher than normal level of anxiety when they give birth to the next child and approach the time to go home. Recognition that they have sound reasons for fears and uncertainties can lessen the anxiety.

The hospital environment can provide a sanctuary for the mother who has given birth when a cot death has been the preceding experience. A hospital staff, well and accurately informed about the effects of cot death on parents and families, can restore some parental confidence by simple recognition of anxieties, and quiet reassurance that their feelings are 'normal for now'.

The Next Child and Illnesses:

Anxieties about the next child and other children in the family are reported by parents when they have had a baby or child die suddenly and unexpectedly. Parents struggle with this anxiety. They can feel rather foolish when the illness of the child is not severe and they know that normally they would not be consulting a doctor for something as trifling as a cough or cold, or a slight rise in temperature. Parents *know* they could not have prevented the death of their child that died from cot death. They *know* the child with a cough or cold is only mildly ill, but reason and commonsense may disappear when the next child or other children develop symptoms of normal childhood illnesses. A parent's anxiety may become extreme if the child needs to be hospitalised for any reason.

The two stories that follow demonstrate that parents need to be heard and understood when their child becomes ill.

The sick child at home (author's own experience)

Glen must have been about fourteen years old when he came down with some virus. He was tired and lethargic, with high temperature, and after a couple of days I really started to worry. It was late afternoon when I realised a weekend was coming up, and if I was going to get a doctor at all it should be now. Glen complained of headaches, and when he tried to stand he was dizzy and his legs wobbly. I rang the doctor I had used a couple of time before, and got the locum service. I explained the problem and said I wasn't too sure who actually needed the doctor, my son or myself. I told them I had had a daughter die from cot death, and was very anxious and frightened, that probably Glen was okay, but I needed some reassurance.

The locum turned up about an hour later. Right from the start he was terrific. I was feeling foolish about my anxiety and said so. We went into Glen's room, and before the young doctor did anything he sat on the bed and chatted to him. The doctor had attended the same school that Glen was at, and they talked about it and Glen's hobbies and interests.

My anxiety was dropping by the minute, and I thought this is going to be okay. This guy somehow seems to understand what's happening here. He then examined Glen thoroughly, said he thought he had some 'bug', would need rest, something for his headaches, and that I could ring again if the situation changed, or I needed to talk about it. I was so impressed with the doctor's manner that I asked could we have his name, and was he in practice anywhere? The answer to that was 'no'; he was just doing the locums, and at this stage of his career that was what he wanted to do.

The doctor said my anxiety was understandable, that cot death was frightening, and that he didn't mind in the least talking to me about it. I found myself explaining that it was the 'little bit sick' that always brought me undone. I could handle the cuts that needed stitching, or a broken limb that needed setting, but that a vague virus or illness-in-the-making reduced me to a state of panic and, oddly enough, so did a lump on the head. I told him that the only sign with Clare the night she died was a 'sniffle'; she had never been ill before, to all intents and purposes was strong, healthy and happy and yet she died.

I remember that doctor with affection and gratitude for his doctoring skills, because he treated the *whole* situation. I'm sure my children catch my anxiety when they are a little bit sick and that can't be good for them. That doctor reduced my anxiety and allowed me to regain some dignity in my own eyes, and I like to think – in his.

A couple of extra points:

Clare had been dead for nine years when this happened. My anxiety rockets out of proportion in these situations. I know this, but no amount of rationalisation will alter it.

My marriage ended three years after Clare died. Being alone exacerbates the problem. Also, I was alone in the house (except for the other children) when she died, and that weight of responsibility bears heavily upon me still when the children become ill. Because I am now a single parent, dealing with my anxiety in these situations is still a problem for me. Even if I ring a friend, the suggestion is usually to ring a doctor if I am worried. I guess that makes sense whichever way you look at it.

The sick child in hospital:

I remember taking Michael to the Casualty Department at the Royal Children's Hospital in the middle of the night. I said he was dying. I could see it. Michael looked very much like his brother Glenn did when I found him. Glenn was quite purple and clammy, and that was what really freaked me out. I could see Michael starting to look like Glenn — that sort of death look. The interns were not terribly interested, and sent us home again. I heard one say to the other, 'she'll be back before 10 a.m. tomorrow' and if it hadn't been 4 a.m., and if I hadn't been so tired (I'd been awake for 36 hours) I would have gone back and demanded they admit him. I think I felt like saying — look I've already had one kid die — I don't want another one to die. It went through my mind that if I said that they are just going to say she's just a hysterical mother who really hasn't resolved the death of her child, and I didn't want to get that confused with the living kid.

At about 7 a.m. I rang my own doctor, and said Michael was really ill and he's just got to get attention immediately. So I was back over at the Children's at 9 a.m., waiting to see the renal specialist. I knew my own doctor very well, and he had rung ahead. The specialist took one look at Michael and they rushed him straight upstairs and put him on an intravenous drip. They said this kid is really sick and should have been admitted last night, and I said well I tried. He was on a drip for three days . . . .

I had a major fight with the sister-in-charge which didn't help. I slept in the hospital and stayed with Michael until he came off the drip . . . . There was a feeling that they knew I had had a child die, but they didn't talk about it. I don't remember mentioning it. I felt it was really going to get in the way of what was happening with Michael.

I didn't want them to feel influenced by the fact that I might be confusing the severity of Michael's illness with my anxieties because I already had a child die. I think I felt that as a handicap. [It was] as though they would cut everything I said in half, because I was over-emotional because I had already lost a child.

The very junior staff were the best. They were the ones that had the caring attitudes. There was one nurse in particular; very junior on placement doing her children's training. She tried really hard to be very nice to me in a surreptitious way so the senior charge sister didn't see. She would say little things to me out of the side of her mouth as she went by, giving me little touches. She was really fantastic because I had no physical contact with anyone for about two days — just sitting there and worrying about Michael. I remember she really cared and it was quite obvious she cared about me as a human being. And yet the actual standard of caring for the kids was superb — I couldn't knock that in any way at all, but there was no emotional support.

That nurse was terrified the charge sister would castigate her, and that she would get black marks on her report. She said that to me. She would say: 'Sister's out having lunch, why don't you sit on his bed and hold his hand for a little while. It must be more comfortable than sitting on the chair and leaning over. She was so gentle and nice. I'm sure it didn't affect her nursing at all. All those problems with the charge sister — I guess that was just the luck of the draw, but she [sister-in-charge] made me feel guilty for being there.

I would have liked some communication. People talking to each other. I'm sure Glenn's death would have come up in normal, around-the-bed conversation. It wasn't so much that Glenn had died from cot death, rather I needed to have it acknowledged that I had had a child die. I think that was what was important. It's rather like when you're having another baby and everyone says 'isn't that wonderful' when really you're frightened, and nobody says anything to you about that. You feel so relieved when someone says 'I bet you have mixed feelings about being pregnant again. If (only) someone had said, 'I guess you're feeling pretty sensitive or anxious about Michael being sick because you have had a cot death. You know, it only needs some type of acknowledgement of your anxiety to make you feel okay. It is similar to the anxiety of having another baby. It is recognition of that anxiety.

In conclusion to this chapter there is a need to emphasise the positive aspects of having 'the next child'. Although the baby born following cot death is surrounded by the anxieties and uncertainties mentioned, this new family experiences many joys and much happiness. The excitement of a new baby is a factor for this family as it is for any other.

Because parents have experienced the reality of death, they understand also the fragility and beauty of life. They can share with others, as well as with their baby, their new found understanding of the joy of life.

Parents have reported they often spend more time, and have more patience with this child; that every day is a gift of life to celebrate, moment by moment. This baby is indeed precious to its parents, siblings, grandparents and extended family, for this growing child represents, with all its mixed blessings — the future.

The purpose of Part IV of this book is to look at the future on behalf of those who have had a cot death. So far the focus has been on the next pregnancy and having the next child. 'The future', however, is much more than this event. Couples who do have another baby have attested to the fact that the birth alone does not solve all their problems or banish their uncertainties about the future.

Some parents who have had a cot death find themselves having to adjust to the reality that they can't have another baby. What is the future for them?

Usually there is a medical reason as the basis for not being able to have another child, for example when the mother has had a hysterectomy, or the father a vasectomy that is not reversible. Adoption of an infant may be a possible solution; certainly if the cot death baby was adopted it is a realistic possibility. However, adoption of an infant, post cot death, is comparatively rare for families who have previously given birth to their children.

Sometimes there are other reasons. Couples whose child-bearing days were coming to an end at the time of the infant's death may have to face the fact that there will not be another child. Those who adopted a family and subsequently find this avenue closed, as well as single parents and divorcees, need to find ways of reestablishing their lives and discovering a future that is rich and meaningful.

A mother who had given birth to five children, and whose fifth child died from cot death, asked me to include a segment on what happens to people who can't have another baby — and offered her own story as a case study:

Following the birth of their fifth baby, the parents decided the husband should have a vasectomy. The mother stressed that it was a mutual decision and they did not rush into making it. It was suggested they have some sperm frozen prior to the vasectomy. The mother reported they later regretted not taking up this suggestion; religious issues were influential factors for this family.

When their baby died the mother felt she was being punished for their decision to prevent a future pregnancy. 'It was a stick to beat myself with', she said. Again because of their religious persuasions they felt unable to share with their extended families the knowledge of their earlier decision to have a vasectomy, so when their baby died from cot death they were thrown into a double-bind by their guilty secret.

'Never mind, you can have another baby' and 'Soon you will be pregnant again' were typical responses that added to their guilt and sadness. The parents then decided to take some action. The father consulted a doctor and underwent a reversal operation many many miles away from their home town in the hope they could keep their secret. There followed months of living in hope. During this period the conflicting thoughts and emotions that beset most parents were felt by this couple: 'I want another baby' one day, and 'I never want another baby' the next. They alternately looked forward to the idea, and then tried to convince themselves they were resigned to their loss. Eventually they had to accept the doctor's verdict that the reversal had been unsuccessful.

Then came the disappointment and anger. Disappointment that all their efforts were in vain, and anger at themselves that they had chosen vasectomy in the first place. The mother's menstrual cycle was also a constant reminder of both hope and disappointment. She attempted to force herself to make the adjustment to 'no more babies' and reported that she then went into a year of very severe depression. She became involved in community work to keep busy, and took some pleasure and comfort from the fact that 'the other kids needed me'.

The turning point came eventually. Three years after the cot death this mother told me:

'I decided if I was going to survive, I had to take stock. I told myself:

> I can't have a child!
> I don't want to live in a world of unrealistic possibilities!
> It's easier to live the reality that I can't have another child!

I felt I didn't have much choice — and made the adjustment. I had some help. The Early Childhood Development Program sent someone each week, then fortnightly. This person helped me a lot — the kids too. When I see parents with another baby I am still reminded, but it's getting better. Last night I was talking to two pregnant women who were looking forward to having their babies. I was able to say "that's nice". It doesn't rip me apart any more.

'I know I can't have another baby – I know I wish it was different.'

The parent whose story this is subsequently made enormous progress and growth in her personal life. She is a woman of boundless energy who developed the capacity to use her energy in new fields of endeavour, and has gone on to enrich the lives of many others. In so doing she acquired new skills, discovered new horizons, and in various ways added depth and meaning to her own life and that of her family. When I spoke to her last at a seminar for health professionals and cot death parents, her growth was evident, her happiness contagious, and her hard-won inner strength obvious to all.

This story contains many elements that pertain to 'the future' of parents and families following a cot death. Whether or not another child is born, parents find themselves making adjustments to their lives.

Some of these adjustments can be extreme; couples may separate and some divorce. Friendships falter and new ones are formed. The bonds that held extended families togther may be broken prior to a deeper understanding of needs and wants being recognised, understood and accepted by a family. Any relationship may be subjected to this analysis.

Parents can find themselves asking 'What future?' or 'How can there be a future without my baby?' In the early days of mourning each dawn represents only 'one more day to endure'. It takes time and hard work to heal the hurt, and much painful searching for a future that makes any sense.

Later still comes the realisation that this potentially crushing experience holds within it the seeds of future growth; that it is possible to nurture not only *a* life, but life and living itself. This intimate understanding of death and life comes at a high price, and those who have this knowledge have paid dearly.

Within us all there is a tremendous source of resilience – the ability to spring back and live life to its maximum within the context of one's circumstances and conditions. Parents who eventually resolve the death of their baby one way or another, accept what cannot be changed – the past.

In the past is 'if only . . . everything could be as it was before'.

While mourning their baby's death parents examine the past very carefully. They evaluate what was meaningful in their lives, what values, habits and lifestyle they want to bring forward to the future. For some, 'letting go' may amount to a large portion of life as they lived and knew it, for others the price they pay for the knowledge gained through this most unwelcome event may not be as high.

Those who bring their mourning to an end make decisions for themselves, and begin to take control of their lives. For some this may be the first time they have done either of these things, for others it may mean determining to take control of some particular aspect of their future.

Although honestly examining one's life is a painful experience, and is at times difficult to endure, it can in the end be rewarding. Parents who find holistic resolution of their baby's death know this. Living a present without a cherished baby is a difficult adjustment to make, but parents do. They not only make the adjustment, but many agree they live a life more personally fulfilling as the years unfold. Many parents' lives have changed radically as a result of having had a child die. When the very foundations on which you have built your life come tumbling down, and the abyss is before and beneath your feet, it takes tremendous courage to build a bridge to new ground; to lay new foundations for a life that in the future can take a direction never thought of before.

To step back, not forward at the edge of the abyss is understandable, but those who find a way to go forward acquire new insights, a different view of the world in which they live, and a richness in their daily lives that others may puzzle over.

Families who experience cot death are never the same again – this is a truth. There is sadness at the ending of a life, and new beginnings bring their own anxieties, for the future is unknown and untried; certainty is an elusive ghost, uncertainty the resident spectre. There is tension in this uncertainty, but in that tension lies the potential for creativity.

As long as the inner voice is allowed to be heard, 'come on', 'keep heart', 'this you *can* survive', and the nearly extinguished light deep inside is gently fanned, there *can* be new birth or rebirth, creation or re-creation, and in the end, any future is possible.

> For a man must some day lose
> one who was closer than this;
> a brother from the same womb,
> or a son. And yet he weeps
> for him, and sorrows for him,
> and then it is over, for the
> Destinies put in mortal men
> the heart of endurance.

Homer, *Iliad*

APPENDIX

Guidelines for Responders

The following guidelines have been formulated to assist those persons who may have to respond to a cot death. Since the needs of ambulance officers will differ from those of the funeral celebrant or the community support person, separate sets of guidelines have been prepared and are listed here in alphabetical order rather than their order of appearance in the overall scenario of a cot death. Further guidance can always be obtained from S.I.D.S. organisations. These exist in every Australian State and Territory as well as internationally. In Victoria S.I.D.R.F. is located at 2 Barkly Avenue, Malvern. Their telephone is listed at the time of publication as (03) 509 7722. A call to this number will provide the address and latest telephone number of S.I.D.S. organisations in other locations. Guidelines for responders are presented here in the following order:

A Ambulance Officers

B Childbirth Educators

C Clergy and Civil Celebrants

D Community Support Persons

E Doctors

F Emergency Staff at Hospitals

G Funeral Directors

H Infant Welfare Sisters

I Police Officers

A Guidelines for Ambulance Officers

Formulated in consultation with the Ambulance Service-Melbourne and the Sudden Infant Death Research Foundation

- Attempt resuscitation – parents need to feel that everything possible was done for their child. They may feel helpless because they did not resuscitate effectively.

- Explain that it could be S.I.D.S. (cot death) but that it will be confirmed after an autopsy is completed.

- Reassure them that if it is cot death there is nothing known that they or anyone else could have done to prevent it.

- Allow parents to express their shock and disbelief; allow them to be distressed. Respect other cultural mourning customs. No matter how bizarre or off-hand they may seem to you, families need to undertake certain rituals.

- Provide *options*: ask the parents would they like to hold the child before you take him/her away; offer to show them the child in the ambulance; also suggest that they can see the baby at the funeral parlour; etc.

- Ask if they'd like you to 'phone anyone for them so that they can have some support e.g. Sudden Infant Death Research Foundation counsellor, local doctor, relatives, work.

- Tell the parents where you are taking the baby, and what the procedures will be, i.e. that the baby will go via the Coroner's Court, to the Royal Children's Hospital for autopsy and that the police will visit, as they must visit *all* sudden deaths no matter what age.

- Explain, if the baby had blood, vomit, facial or body discolouration that these can occur after or during the dying process and are not the cause of death of their child.

- Use the baby's name if you feel comfortable doing so.

- Do not take personally any anger expressed. Anger can be a healthy expression of their despair, dismay, loss of control over their lives, etc.

- Try not to hurry the baby away from the house – particularly if the husband is not home. If you can, try and wait for him to arrive home.

- Other children need not be removed from the home or shielded from what has happened. They can cope with death, but have trouble handling further disruption and false explanations.

- Always leave a copy of the booklet *'Facts about Sudden Infant Death Syndrome'* (obtainable from the Foundation).

- It can help to talk to someone else who understands what it's like for you too. The S.I.D.R.F. is as available to you as it is to the parents.

B Guidelines for Childbirth Educators—Presenting Grief

Reprinted with kind permission from Julia Sundin, M.A.P.A., and the Journal of the National Obstetrics and Gynaecology Group of the Australian Physiotherapy Association

Each educator has her own method of introducing 'grief' and 'unexpected outcomes', in the way he or she is most comfortable. It is in the nature of the presentation and discussion, that couples will build trust in the educator as a potential resource person if needed.

Discussion on Grief and Unexpected Outcomes can be triggered by:

- Class handouts e.g. Elizabeth Kubler-Ross leaflet and a tragic birth experience report—at an appropriate time in the course.

- A couple returning to class to relate details of their birth experience. Stating things that caused them disappointment, anger or shock.

- A forum or discussion at a film night. It's not uncommon for the guest speaker to have to respond to questions such as, 'What if the baby dies?'

- A tour of the hospital labour ward or birth centre and intensive care nursery.

- Fears and anxieties voiced by couples, often reported to the educator by phone, before the course begins, or occuring spontaneously at any stage throughout the course.

- Planned input by and discussion with the educator during the course.

Some things to consider

- Presenting grief and loss or unexpected outcomes as an isolated topic on an isolated night, could cause a shock reaction, with couples switching off, crying, or even becoming angry, seeing only the negative aspects.

• When discussing grief in relation to the baby, give the class enough notice, in advance, stressing its importance and value, so that they may prepare themselves emotionally and intellectually. Set it up early: 'Spare some time over the next few weeks to think about how you might *feel* if things don't go exactly as planned, either with the birth, or the baby.

• Grief and loss can be comfortably *introduced* as early as the first class, in relation to circumstances the couples are themselves experiencing, and, more importantly, can relate to (rather than a sick or malformed child) such things as 'I'm really upset (angry!) because my doctor has just told me he'll be overseas for the birth' or, 'I finish work next week, and although I'm excited about the baby, I'm depressed about the independence I'll be losing', or 'Our doctor has told us I might have to have a ceasarean – every time I think about it, I burst into tears'. Three wonderful triggers for loss, shock, disappointment and the resultant feelings.

• Be realistic, but stress the positives. 'If your baby dies, it is not only possible to bond with your baby after death, but it can also be a wonderful experience', or 'A very special kind of bonding can occur even though the baby is inside a humidicrib', or 'Breastfeeding or expressing milk for your baby, evokes unique feelings of pride in enhancing the quality of life of your baby, whether he is to live only days or just hours'.

• As an educator, it's important to be yourself and not hide behind any elaborate facade, no matter how professional you aim to be. Acknowledge with sincerity and respect, any watery eyes, yours might be watering too.

• As a post natal resource person, be there to help, but not to take the place of couples' self-help coping mechanisms.

• Talking in abstracts, such as statistics, is usually *not* helpful and can even cause anger and conflict.

We all have some degree of uneasiness about this component of the course. If you as an educator have trouble with this component of the course, talk to other educators about methods of introduction, and try to organise (or attend) a workshop where you can share and discuss ideas, as well as examining your own feelings about the subject, and refresh the communication skills, so helpful when needed as a support person.

C Guidelines for Clergy and Civil Celebrants

• Acknowledging the difficulty you might be experiencing in accepting the death of a baby confirms the parent's reality that the death of their baby makes no sense to them.

• Gauging whether the family is seeking spiritual guidance before you offer it gives parents the freedom to express and explore their feelings about God.

• Parents may need to express their anger at God, or you His representative.

• Reinforce whenever possible that the death is not a punishment for sins, real or imagined. This will sometimes mean you may have to bring up the subject. For example: 'Some parents will blame themselves believing God is punishing them for something they did or didn't do. This is a natural reaction when the medical explanation of the death does not make sense'.

• To feel guilty is natural. Parents, after all, do have responsibility for the caring and well-being of their baby, and may need assurance that the death was not their fault.

• Some parents will avoid you. This may not be a personal affront; rather parents may need time to work out a new philosophy in which faith can still play a part.

• The use of cliches or platitudes can force anger underground. For example: 'It's God's will', 'Have faith', 'Time heals'.

• Talking with the parents about the eulogy you will deliver allows you to draw on experiences in the family's life. Family outings, picnics, celebrations, the baby's developing relationship with siblings, or even a family pet. Friends and family, especially grandparents who may have looked after the baby can have something special to contribute.

• Some members of the congregation may feel guilty for being alive. This is especially difficult for the old and infirm who may believe their life is over.

• Use of the baby's proper name is important. Check with parents if they want a pet name used, full name, or an abbreviation. Nothing hurts parents more than the incorrect use of their baby's name. It somehow diminishes the baby's worth if the name is not pronounced or acknowledged correctly.

• To become familiar with resources in your community is beneficial both for the parents and yourself.

• Providing as many options as possible for parents is helpful. Let them decide what kind of funeral they want and where they would like it performed. If the baby is very young, it may not have an identification in the wider community, and some parents may feel more comfortable, and indeed the funeral may be more meaningful, if the service is conducted in the home.

• They may need some help in making their decision about burial or cremation, and some information about infant graves so that their choice will be such that will avoid any later regrets.

D Guidelines for Community Support Persons

Effective Community Support may come from relatives, neighbours, friends, teachers, workmates, etc. as well as from professional responders.

• Acknowledge your own feelings of helplessness if that is how you feel.

• Let the parent decide what gives ease at any time rather than deciding for them.

• Avoiding the use of euphemisms and cliches can enable both parents and supporters to acknowledge the reality of the parent's experience.

• Allowing the parents to accept the reality as well as the fact of their baby's death is often helped by allowing expressions of: grief, guilt, anger/blame/pain.

• Recognise the parents' reactions to the death of their baby are 'normal for now'.

• If you can become aware that a friend's mood changes and swings may indicate what will give ease *today*, many misunderstandings between you and your friend can be avoided.

- Assume nothing.
- *Do* nothing most of the time: your physical presence may be all that is required.
- *Listen* with your heart.
- Allow parents to grieve in their own way and at their own pace.
- Provide *options* when parents ask for your help.
- Avoid telling parents why you think their baby died. There are many many theories about the causes of cot death, *none* of which have yet been proved.
- Become an informed and educated friend, neighbour or relative about:
  - (a) what *doesn't* cause cot death.
  - (b) the impact and effects of cot death.

E Guidelines for Doctors

For General Practitioners or other Doctors when they are called to a family in which a suspected cot death has occurred.

Formulated in consultation with The Victorian Academy for General Practice and the Sudden Infant Death Research Foundation

When you are called to a suspected cot death at the home of the baby it will probably be for one of the following reasons:

(a) You have been contacted immediately the parents have discovered their baby not breathing.

(b) You may have been called to the home where the baby is known to be dead, i.e. the police and/or ambulance officers are present, and the parents have asked for their private doctor's support and help.

In both circumstances the baby must be examined and attended to first, but in the latter circumstances it is the parents who need care and to whom the greatest time and skill has to be given. Even though these two different circumstances obtain, it is clear that common principles apply when you are called to the child's house – whether by parents, a baby sitter, grandmother or other responsible person.

1   As a doctor only you have the legal right to certify death, no matter how obvious the situation may be to other care givers.

2   If death is very recent, then you have to decide whether or not to commence resuscitation or continue this if it has already been started by those care-givers already at the scene. This decision to try may be taken because of the very real possibility of successful resuscitation of the baby, or because the parents need to have the attempt made. Either way, eventually in a S.I.D.S. case you will have to confirm the death.

3   Try to offer the parents an explanation of what did not cause the death — even if it is still not fully explicable — they will need, usually, to have a logic on which to hang their future trust in themselves and in living.

4   Let them hold the baby's body for as long as they wish and feel with them for their, and your incapacity, to reverse the inevitable. Eventually you will need to have the child taken either to the local hospital or the Coroner's Court for examination. This is best done now by using the Ambulance Service, but Ambulance Officers are nowadays trained to handle the situation of families involved with a S.I.D.S. baby and can be of great service to you in these circumstances. Removal of the baby's body by the Government Undertaker is an option that has proved to be least desired by families.

5   Stay with the parents for as long as they would appear to wish it, and offer as much comfort as you can. Advice, except for the practical matters of transport of the child's body etc., is rarely useful at this stage and unsolicited remarks such as 'Well, you are young enough to have another child' are likely to cause the parents more grief and anger than they can tolerate.

6   In general, sedation should be avoided because its use tends to interfere with the normal progress of grief and adjustment. Parents usually need a lot of 'working through' of the problems raised by this sudden death, and can benefit greatly from the early support of counsellors from the S.I.D.S. organisation, or other trained crisis care responders.

7   Parents are shocked by the unannounced arrival of the police. You can explain that police must investigate any sudden death, and will visit if they haven't already; that although the police will have to ask questions, it is the pathologist who will determine the cause of death.

8   If the mother is still lactating, then a decision of how this may be dealt with is useful either then or next day. The Nursing Mother's Association can often provide useful support at this time.

9   Your own role will be on-going and supportive for many months in most circumstances. This support includes reassurance that no fault of care is involved in S.I.D.S.

10 Recognise that guilt feelings, though unfounded, are inevitable and must be worked through. It is usual for the parents to express anger and hurt, and in such circumstances to concentrate their feelings on whoever is available — even you — at times. Parents at this time often move in and out of reality, especially during the first few hours after the discovery, hours which to them often assume overwhelming importance.

11 The fathers of S.I.D.S. children are as vulnerable as the mothers, but in our culture they frequently try to mask their emotions by adopting acceptable male roles of coping, of managing, or supporting those around them. Although they are 'coping' they may need permission to express their feelings at some later time.

12 Where older children are concerned they may feel considerable guilt about the circumstances of the sudden unexplained death for all sorts of real or imagined reasons. Younger children also may experience some guilt reactions as well as confusion and hurt by their parents' apparent withdrawal at their time of need.

13 Your role may well be to assist baby-sitters, grandparents, aunts or good friends meet their own particular needs in individual ways, particularly if they had the care of the baby at the time of death. The relationship between the parents and such bereaved others is very important, fragile and vulnerable to hurt at these times. You, as the attending doctor, have an especially demanding role in such situations.

F Guidelines for Emergency Staff of Hospitals

Prepared by emergency staff at the Royal Children's Hospital, Melbourne, Victoria and in consultation with S.I.D.R.F.

The first two points vary slightly dependent upon the baby arriving dead or needing resuscitation.

1   If parents arrive with their dead baby with the ambulance or with the police:

(a) Meet the parents at the door, show them into a private room and let them hold the baby as long as they want to. They will eventually give the baby up of their own accord.

(b) A doctor will talk to the parents and confirm their baby is dead. Even though the parents have been holding the baby, they need a doctor's acknowledgement of the reality.

2   If the baby is rushed in by parents or by ambulance for resuscitation:

(a) Continue, or initiate resuscitation.

(b) Give the parents a private room and make sure a member of nursing or medical staff give frequent reports on what is happening.

(c) As soon as resuscitation attempt has finished a doctor will talk to the parents and explain that their baby has died in spite of all attempts.

(d) Take parents into resuscitation room; let them hold their baby and take him/her back to the private room if they wish.

3   Allow parents to ask questions about the death, and explain what Sudden Infant Death Syndrome is, and is not.
There are two questions frequently asked by parents:

(a) Parents might ask whether a post-mortem is necessary. Explain it is necessary to try and establish a cause of death.
     You could explain that during this examination their baby will be treated with great care and respect by the pathologist. Parents might then ask what seems a very obvious question. 'Does that mean she/he will be cut?' There is only one answer you can give. 'Yes'. You can try to minimise the anguish this answer must give by explaining truthfully and gently that it is only by performing an examination of this kind that the pathologist can determine the cause of death. Difficult as your task might be, you can be assured the parents feel an immediate relief when the autopsy either confirms Sudden Infant Death Syndrome, or reveals some other condition that explains why their baby died.

(b) 'Where will my baby go now?' Parents need an answer to this question. Explain precisely where the baby will be. For example, 'to the mortuary in this hospital until the cause of death is determined. When you have selected the Funeral Company of your choice, your baby will be taken there. You will be able to see him again there if you wish'.

4 Let parents have the use of a private phone to contact friends or relatives if they so wish.

5 If the baby is discoloured or fixed in an unusual position, explain to the parents that this is normal and occurs after death. If parents are disturbed by this, tell them they can see the baby at the funeral parlour and she/he will be much more like the baby they remember.

The baby should be wrapped in a coloured blanket or towel rather than a clinical white sheet. Give them time to say goodbye alone.

6 It has been our experience that parents don't mind, and are not afraid of you showing them that the death of their baby has affected you.

7 Finally, remember the Foundation is available to you as well as the S.I.D.S. family.

8 If other children or friends or relatives are involved, include them in discussion and let them see or hold the baby too. Remember if the baby was with a babysitter or grandparent at the time of death they will need reassurances the death was not their fault, and will want most of the information that is naturally given to the parents.

9 Parents may appreciate your looking after other very young children, or they may not. *Ask* them if you can be of assistance. Older children may want to stay with their parents, and the parents may need them for comfort. You may need to assure a child they did not cause the death of their brother or sister. Remember many cultures expect children to be fully involved in the grieving process, and that any family may wish their children to be included in all that is taking place.

How to Look After Yourself:

1 Be aware, or become aware, that you will have feelings, reactions

and responses to the death of this baby. You may regard some feelings as negative, anger is a good example. The whole department may have been thrown out of kilter, and the 'flatness' that has been talked about previously may make it difficult for the department to operate at its normal efficient level. You, and other staff members may be irritable or depressed as a result of the death. If the department is 'too busy' for you to deal with your feelings – do it later.

2   A spontaneous release of your feelings may help you to recover fairly rapidly. If you are not comfortable showing your feelings in front of other staff, your rights in this regard should be respected. Whichever way you deal with your feelings needs to be respected by others.

3   It has been shown that setting aside a time for all staff involved in a S.I.D.S. to talk about the experience they have shared is beneficial to all concerned. Try to ensure you are given this opportunity.

4   A good friend or understanding partner or spouse can be an invaluable source of comfort at this time.

5   The Foundation and other S.I.D.S. organisations are as available to you as to the family. They understand you may need to express your feelings and explore your needs.

G Guidelines for Funeral Directors

For the Funeral Director (formulated in association with the Australian Funeral Directors' Association):

- Acknowledge the difficulty of the child's funeral, particularly if you have a child yourself, or if you are a grandparent. Identification with the baby, child or teenager could be strong.

- If you have feelings of pain, helplessness and anger at this 'unjust' death, try to acknowledge them.

- Seek out self-support systems in your Company or Industry, and/or try to promote their introduction.

- Remind yourself that, despite feelings of sorrow or inadequacy, the family being served needs and expects professional service.

For the bereaved family:

- It has been suggested that a phone call to the family on the day of the death allows you to begin planning the funeral and to commence the legal side of the arrangement. Slowing down the process may give everyone involved time to make considered decisions, and help the funeral to be less traumatic.

- Most parents come to this experience unprepared. It could be helpful to everyone to remember this, and to acknowledge to the family that *you* understand this.

- To facilitate a 'team' approach you could ask the family if anyone else is involved in the arrangement, or if anyone else has already given advice about how to proceed. This will require of the funeral director an understanding and acceptance that all professionals involved can help each other to do their work better.

- Ask the family if you can come and discuss the different ways the funeral can be arranged.

- Brothers and sisters of the baby may have a need to be part of the funeral service; certainly they can be included indirectly even if they do not attend for example, preparing a letter or drawing, or flower gift. Care in explaining this to families is an obvious requirement.

- Encourage family participation in the arrangement and planning of the funeral of their choice.

- When you are with the family, you can suggest alternatives: e.g. a funeral service at home, hospital, church, chapel or graveside. Families may need *time* to decide which option they want.

- Parents are deeply shocked, and verbal communication may be difficult. They may have desires that need time to surface, and slowing down the process allows for this need.

- You may wish to ask the family if past bad experiences with funerals will colour or shape their needs in arranging this funeral now.

- Avoid the use of cliches and euphemisms: 'The sudden death of your baby/child must be a tremendous shock—I am so sorry' is more meaningful than 'God works in mysterious ways' or 'I'm sorry you lost your baby'.

- You may need to be aware you are the last person the parents expected, or wanted to see today, their anger may be directed at you, and it is difficult not to take it personally.

Viewing and dressing the baby:

- The decision to view their baby/child or not must always be left with the parents.

- If parents choose to see their child again, they will need information about the condition of their child, and preparation for what they will see.

- If parents wish to dress their baby for burial, they will need to be prepared for the task. They will need gentle truths about the lifelessness of their baby, instruction, and almost always assistance with the dressing of their child.

- If in your opinion, it is likely to be a horrifying experience for the parents to see their child again, you should describe the child's condition as gently and as truthfully as you can. If this is not done, the parents may be left with a fantasy that is worse than the reality. If the parent decides to view under these circumstances, make sure someone is with them. Sometimes you may need to have another person present, who is closer to the parents, to help with this explanation.

- When viewing is being considered, it is important to allow for a change of mind by the parents, or other members of the family. When parents decide to view they rarely change their minds, but when a parent or relative says no at first, they often reconsider. When talking with a family, a simple 'if you change your mind, we can make the arrangements' lets the parent know the option is still open.

H Guidelines for Infant Welfare Sisters

These guidelines for Infant Welfare Sisters when responding to a cot death were formulated in consultation with Barbara Potter, Coordinator of In-service Education Programs, Maternal and Child Health Section of the Community Services, Victoria, and the Sudden Infant Death Research Foundation.

- As for any person, professional or otherwise, when called upon

to visit a family who has experienced cot death, it is important
to *be there*,
to *listen*,
and to *acknowledge the parent's reality*.

- As one of the people outside the family who may know the baby best, and with whom a close bond may have been established, *be aware you may have intense feelings of personal loss and sadness*.

- As a health professional who may have had recent contact with the baby, you may experience feelings of guilt, helplessness, frustration and anger. ('What did I miss?') You could be aware that the expectations society has of professional people — and those you have of yourself — can leave you open to such feelings.

- Feelings of fear and anxiety about what you can say to the parents are normal.

- Be aware that anger expressed by parents is usually generalised, and is not being directed at you personally.

- You may be concerned that the parents will blame you for the child's death. If you have recently pronounced the baby as 'doing well', it is important to remember that there is no way *anyone* could have predicted or prevented the death.

- As the Infant Welfare Sister will be seen as a reliable source of information, it is important to avoid speculation about causes and airing personal theories, and to stress that to date no one has the answers.

- Parents need to talk about their baby. Not only can you talk about the baby, thus allowing your expression of sadness at the infant's death, but together you can speak of him/her in a way that may facilitate the parent's mourning.

- Sharing the parent's experience is more meaningful than exchanging platitudes or cliches. Tears shed are a rarely misunderstood expression of sadness, and parents have reported they remember with affection the person, and this includes the professional, who has been so moved by the death of their baby.

- Continuing support can be offered over a lengthy period, and contact from you at anniversaries, birthdays, etc. will always be appreciated, as will some acknowledgement at approximately eight to fourteen weeks after the death, that whatever the parent is feeling at that time is 'normal for now'.

• If the link between the family and the Infant Welfare Sister is maintained, other issues may arise as time goes on. For example:

— reactions from, and effects on siblings.
— effects on relationships within the family.
— concerns about whether and when to have another baby.
— concern following the birth of a subsequent child.

The S.I.D.R.F., and other S.I.D.S. organisations can provide you with information about these and other subjects.

• Infant Welfare Sisters have expressed their need to acknowledge and have recognised the impact an infant's death has had on them — they have suggested:

—talking to a colleague
—talking to a partner or friend
—ringing a S.I.D.R.F. counsellor
—writing about their responses
—forming (self-help) support groups for themselves

The Infant Welfare Sister has an important role to play in the lives of families. By being non-judgemental and caring she can represent for the family a knowledgeable person in whom they feel safe to confide.

I Guidelines for Police Officers at the Scene of a Cot Death.

Formulated in consultation with the Community Policing Squad of the Victoria Police Force and the Sudden Infant Death Research Foundation.

If you get a call to a suspected cot death:

1 Explain to the parents that the police must investigate any sudden death.

2 You can explain that this obligation requires police to ask certain questions about the last few hours, and that you will endeavour to ask the questions with a view to their distress. Your task is to take notes and complete the relevant documents.

3 You need to be aware that your presence may be disturbing to other children and concerned adults who are in the home.

4 If the baby is not in the room where you are talking to the parents, ask them if they will take you to the baby. You can take your lead from the parents as to how you refer to the dead baby; for example, by name or third person.

5 Having established that the death is a *probable* cot death, if you are the first emergency responder to arrive, remember:

   (a) you can still call the ambulance even if the baby is obviously dead. We have been assured of the co-operation of the Ambulance Service in this regard.

   (b) reassure the parents that if it is a cot death there is nothing known that they or anyone else could have done to prevent it.

   (c) Because parents need to express their shock and disbelief, you may need to be aware that some parents become very distressed while others are immobilised by the shock. Also, different cultures express their mourning in different ways. Be aware that some families may need to undertake certain rituals that can seem strange to you.

6 You could consider the possibility of calling in the Community Policing Squad. If you decide to do this, inform the family of their special welfare role, otherwise you could add to their distress when two more uniformed police officers arrive. You can also tell them of the existence of the Sudden Infant Death Research Foundation, and that support and information is available through this organisation.

7 When compiling a statement of evidence, while it is necessary to be thorough, the circumstances should be considered and the information obtained as sensitively as possible.

8 Be aware that subsequent identification at the Coroner's Court is not required and that in lieu of formal identification, it is sufficient for you to take a statement from one or both of the parents.

9 Given the demands on your time during your rostered period of duty, allow as much time as the real situation permits.

10 Parents want to know what is going to happen to their baby next

and where they can see their baby again. Tell the parents the *name* of the hospital to which their baby is being taken, and if the death occurs in the Melbourne Metropolitan area, that their baby will then be transported via the Coroner's Court to the Royal Children's Hospital where the pathologist will determine the cause of death.

Before you leave:

- Ask the parents if they have any questions.
- Ask them if you can contact/ring anyone for them (friend, neighbour or relative) especially if they are alone in the house.
- Leave your name, Station and telephone number with parents for any subsequent queries.

After you leave:

- The death of this baby will affect the lives of many people. A child's death is always disturbing, and you too may feel the effects for a time.
- How you acknowledge these effects (to a colleague or at home) is your personal choice.
- The Sudden Infant Death Research Foundation is also available to you if you would like to talk about any issues that concern you.

REFERENCES AND BIBLIOGRAPHY

Aries, P., *The Hour of Our Death*, Translated Weaver, H., Alfred A. Knopf Incorporated, U.S.A., 1983.

Barr, P., and de Wilde D., 'Supportive Counselling of Parents after a Stillbirth', in Practical Pediatrics in *Australian Family Physician*, Vol. 1, No. 8., August, 1984, Victoria, Australia.

Beal, S., Sudden Infant Death Syndrome, *Australian Family Physician*, Vol. 8, December, 1979, Victoria, Australia.

Berezin, N., *After a Loss in Pregnancy*, Simon and Schuster, New York, 1982.

Bergman, A.B., 'Psychological Aspects of Sudden Unexpected Death in Infants and Children', in *Pediatric Clinics, U.S.A.*, 21, 1974.

Binik, Y.M. 'Psychological Predictors of Sudden Death: A Review and Critique', in *Social Science and Medicine*, Vol. 20, No. 7, 1985, Oxford, Great Britain.

Blake, A., 'The Loss of a Baby,' in *Nursing 85*, Part 43, Oxford, Great Britain.

Bluglass, K., 'Psychiatric Morbidity after Cot Death', in *Practice of Medicine*, Year Book, Vol. 224, May, 1980, Chicago.

Bluglass, K., Annotation, 'Psychosocial Aspects of the Sudden Infant Death Syndrome, ("Cot Death")', in *Journal of Child Psychology and Psychiatry and Allied Disciplines*, Vol. 22, No. 4, 1981, Oxford, Great Britain.

Borg, S., and Lasker, J., *When Pregnancy Fails*, Beacon Press, Boston, 1981.

Cornwell, J., Nurcombe, B., and Stevens, L., 'Family Response to Loss of a Child by Sudden Infant Death Syndrome', in *Medical Journal of Australia* 1, 1977, Glebe, N.S.W.

Emery, J.L., 'Cot Deaths in Australia', in *Medical Journal of Australia*, No. 144, April, 1986, Glebe, N.S.W.

De Forest, J., 'Home Apnea Monitoring In Infancy', in *Canadian Nurse*, 1984, May, 80 (5).

Frain, de, J., Taylor, J., and Ernst, L., *Coping with Sudden Infant Death*, D.C. Heath and Company, Canada, 1982.

Friedman, G.R., Franciosi, R.A. and Drake, R.M., 'The Effects of Observed Sudden Infant Death Syndrome (SIDS) on Hospital Staff', in *Pediatrics*, Vol. 64, No. 4, October, 1979, U.S.A.

Friedman, S., *The Child and Death*, Mosby Company, St. Louis, U.S.A., 1978.

Golding, J., Limerick S., and Macfarlane A., *Sudden Infant Death, Patterns, Puzzles and Problems*, Open Books Publishing Ltd., England, 1985.

Gordon, A.L., 'Wormwood and Nightshade' in *Adam Lindsay Gordon*, C.F. MacRae, Twayne, New York, U.S.A., 1968.

Griffin, G.M., *Talking about Death*, The Joint Board of Christian Education of Australia and New Zealand, Victoria, 1976.

Higgins, G.L., 'The Lost Infant: Impact on the Family', in *Canadian Family Physician*, Vol. 26, November, 1980.

Jones, H.J., 'Death of an Infant: Counselling Parents, Psychiatric Clinics', in *Patient Management Journal*, June, 1982, Australia.

Knapp, R.J., and Peppers L.G., 'Funeral Arrangements for the Newborn', in *American Funeral Director*, Vol. 101, No. 11, November 1978.

Kubler-Ross E., *Death the Final Stage of Growth*, Prentice Hall U.S.A., 1975.

Lewis, E., 'Mourning by the Family after a Stillbirth or Neonatal Death', in *Archives of Disease in Childhood*, 1979, U.K.

Lewis E., 'Inhibition of Mourning by Pregnancy: Psychopathology and Management', in *British Medical Journal*, July, 1979, 2.

Lewak, N., Zebal, B.H., and Friedman S.B., 'Management of Infants with Apnea and Potential Apnea', in *Clinical Pediatrics*, July, 1984, Philadelphia, U.S.A.

Lewis, C.S., *A Grief Observed*, Faber and Faber, London, 1961.

Lewis, S.N., 'Maternal Anxiety Following Bereavement by Cot Death and Emotional Security of Subsequent Infants', in *Child Psychiatry and Human Development*, Vol. 14, (1), Fall, 1983, U.S.A.

Limerick, S., 'Sudden Infant Death: Prevention', in *Nursing Times* March, 1984, England.

Limerick, S., 'Support and Counselling Needs of Families Following a Cot Death Bereavement', in *Proceedings Royal Society of Medicine*, Vol. 69, November, 1976, U.K.

Matthews, T.G., and O'Brien, S.J., 'Perinatal Epidemiological Characteristics of the Sudden Infant Death Syndrome in an Irish Population', in *Irish Medical Journal*, September, 1985, Vol. 78, No. 9.

Mayer, M., 'On Death' in *The Great Ideas Today*, Encyclopaedia Britannica, Chicago, U.S.A., 1965.

Miller, W.A., *When Going to Pieces Holds You Together*, Augsburg Publishing House, Minneapolis, U.S.A., 1976.

McClain, M., 'Sudden Infant Death Syndrome: An Update', in *Journal of Emergency Nursing*, Vol. 11, No. 5, September/October, 1985, Chicago, U.S.A.

MacNab, F., 'The Remains and What Remains', in *Australian Funeral Director*, May, 1983.

O'Connor, P., *Understanding the Mid-Life Crisis*, Sun Books, Melbourne, 1981.

Peppers, L.G. and Knapp, R.J., *Motherhood and Mourning*, Praeger Publishers, New York, 1980.

Peterson, D.R., Sabotta, E.E., and Dalling, J.R., 'Infant Mortality among Subsequent Siblings of Infants who Died of Sudden Infant Death Syndrome', in *Journal of Pediatrics*, Vol. 108, June, 1986, U.S.A.

Powell, J., Machin, D., and Kershaw, C.R., 'Unexpected Sudden Infant Deaths in Gosport — Some Comparisons Between Service and Civilian Families', in *Journal of the Royal Naval Medical Service*, 1983; 69, U.K.

Raphael, B., *The Anatomy of Bereavement*, Basic Books Incorporated, New York, 1983.

Rudolph, M., *Should the Children Know?*, Schocken Books Incorporated, New York, 1978.

Russell-Jones, D.L., 'Sudden Infant Death in History and Literature', in *Archives of Disease in Childhood*, 60, 1985, U.K.

Schatz, W.H., *Healing a Father's Grief*, Medic Publishing Company, Redmond, U.S.A., 1984.

Schiff, H.S., *The Bereaved Parent*, Crown Publishers, U.S.A. 1977.

Segal, S., 'Counselling Parents — Sudden Infant Death Syndrome' in *Report of the 20th Annual Scientific Session Section of General Practice British Columbia Medical Association*, British Columbia Chapter College of Family Physicians of Canada, April, Canada 1974.

Sheehy, G., *Pathfinders*, Bantam, New York, 1981.

Sheridan, M.S., 'Things that Go Beep in the Night: Home Monitoring for Apnea', in *Health and Social Work*, 0360-7283/85, 1985, New York, U.S.A.

Szybist, C., *The Subsequent Child*, National Sudden Infant Death Syndrome Foundation, Illinios, U.S.A., 1973.

Szybist, C., 'Thoughts of a Mother' in *The Child and Death*, S. Friedman, Mosby Company, St. Louis, U.S.A., 1978.

Szybist, L.A., 'Thoughts of a Sister', in *The Child and Death* S. Friedman, Mosby Company, St. Louis, U.S.A., 1978.

Spitzer, A.R., and Fox W.W., 'Infant Apnea—An Approach to Management', in *Clinical Pediatrics*, Vol. 23, No. 7, 1984, Philadelphia, U.S.A.

Thompson, K. *What Men Really Want*, New Age, U.S.A., 1982.

Thoreau, H.D., *Walden*, Twayne, New York, U.S.A. 1962.

Valdes-Dapena, M.A., 'Sudden Infant Death Syndrome: A Review of the Medical Literature 1974-1979', in *Pediatrics*, October, 1980, U.S.A.

Wasserman, A.L., 'A Prospective Study of the Impact of Home Monitoring on the Family', in *Pediatrics*, Vol. 74, No. 3, September, 1984, U.S.A.

Williams, M.L., 'Sibling Reaction to Cot Death', in *Medical Journal of Australia*, 2, 1981, Glebe, N.S.W.

Williams, R.A. and Nikolaisen, S.M., 'Sudden Infant Death Syndrome: Parents' Perceptions and their Responses to the Loss of their Infant', in *Research in Nursing and Health*, 1982, 5, New York, U.S.A.

Wilson, J., 'Cot Death—A Shattering Separation', in *Ambulance World*, June/August, 1982, Vol. 6, No. 2, Melbourne, Australia.

Wise Brown, M., *The Dead Bird*, Addison-Wesley Publishing Company Incorporated, Massachusetts, U.S.A. 1965.

Zebal, H., and Woolsey, M.S., 'SIDS and the Family: The Pediatricians Role', in *Pediatric Annals*, New York, 13:3, March, 1984.

Unpublished Papers and Articles

Davey, B., and Henning, I., Parental Perceptions and Utilization of Social Support Networks following a Sudden Infant Death, Sociology Research Project, Swinburn Institute, Melbourne, Australia, 1984.

Edgcumbe, G., Fr., Death, Grief, Life, Faith, Discussion paper presented to the National S.I.D.S. Workshop, Melbourne, Australia, April, 1985.

Henning, I., and Davey, B., Sudden Infant Death Syndrome: Parents' Perceptions and Responses to the Loss of Their Infant, Psychology Practical Report, Swinburn Institute, Melbourne, Australia, 1984.

Hirschfeld, B., Sr., Grief — Endpoint or Journey? Paper presented at the Fourth Annual General Meeting of the Queensland Sudden Infant Death Foundation, Brisbane, Australia, July, 1982.

Lord, J., Birth/Death — A Paradox, Journal of the National Obstetrics and Gynaecology Group of the Australian Physiotherapy Association, 1985.

Lurie, S., and Rowntree, J., Grandparents Grieve Too, S.I.D.R.F. Newsletter No. 27, Autumn, 1986, Victoria, Australia.

Lurie, S., A Visit You May Dread, Maternal and Infant Health Newsletter No. 37, May, 1986, Australia.

Maloney, J., (Prof.) How to Evaluate Media Reports on Cot Death. Presented at Centre for Continuing Education, Monash University Seminar Unravelling The Mystery of Sudden Infant Death, Melbourne, June, 1983.

Maloney, L., Cot Death — Some Effects on Families, S.I.D.R.F. Newsletter No. 13, March, 1982.

Porter, M., When a Baby Dies, Church Scene, July, 1984.

S.I.D.R.F., The Facts About Sudden Infant Death Syndrome, (S.I.D.S.), 2nd Edition, Melbourne.

Sundin, J., Grief During the Childbearing Year, Journal of the National Obstetrics and Gynaecology Group of the Australian Physiotherapy Association, Vol. 3, No. 1, April, 1984.

Trivan, R., Children and Their Understanding of Death, S.I.D.R.F., Newsletter, No. 12, August, 1981, Victoria, Australia.

Index

A

ambulance officers
  account by, 6-10
  as emergency responders, 14-20, 267
  guidelines for, 252-3
  immediate impact, 7-8
  removal of baby, 35, 258
  temporary diagnosis by, 16-17, 252
  training of, viii
anger, 39, 71-3, 84, 86, 207-8, 252,
    255
anniversaries, 43, 58, 210, 226, 265-6
  reminders of baby, 90-1, 127
ante-natal classes
  after S.I.D.S., 228-30
anxiety, 85, 228-45
  about health of other children,
    242-5
apnoea (cessation of breathing), 64,
    234-5
attentive listening, 42-3
autopsy ('examination'), 11, 35-6, 97,
    106, 107, 252, 260

B

babies, other people's
  parents' reaction to, 89-90
babies, subsequent, 61, 88, 199,
    215-27
  ambivalence about, 215-6, 245
  birth of, 230-4
  change in pattern of pregnancy, 219
  cot death during pregnancy, 224-5
  difficulties concerning, 228-45
  impossibility of, 246-9
  inhibited by grief, 225-7, 226-7
  misunderstandings about, 215-6
  possibility of further S.I.D.S.,
    219-20

recognition of previous S.I.D.S.,
    238-42, 245
  the 'replacement baby', 220-1
baby (victim of S.I.D.S.)
  affirmation of existence, 120-1
  baptism of, 121-2
  disfigurement, 17-18, 36, 105, 252,
    261
  dressing for burial, 107-10, 140, 264
  health prior to death, 11
  name used, 18, 252, 256, 267
  reincarnation, 224
  viewing before burial, 36, 41,
    103-13, 140, 264
babysit, S.I.D.S. mother refuses to,
    144
babysitters
  effect of cot death on, 143-4
birth weight, 238-9
blame, 13, 59-60, 84, 91, 138-9, 207-8
bonding, 12, 254
breakdown, 176-9
breast-feeding, 254, 259
  drying-up of milk, 6
  and S.I.D.S., 239
breathing, 64, 234-5
bruising, 28
burial
  grave site, 128-31, 256
  health regulations, 97
  multiple burials, 128, 130-1

C

casualty staff
  training of, viii
cause of death
  lack of explanation, 11
childbirth educators
  guidelines for, 253-5
  see also, ante-natal classes

children
  ability to cope with reality, 7, 10,
    185-6, 253
  anxiety about health of siblings,
    242-5
  behaviour difficulties, 88
  blame selves for death, 50, 88-9,
    261
  cemetery visits, 185, 186-8
  concept of death, 182-8, 203-4
  conflicting messages given to, 11,
    253
  effects of death on, 9-10, 58, 259
  euphemisms of death avoided, 182,
    203-4
  explaining death to, 43, 77-9, 142-3,
    181-97, 194-7
  explaining reason for death, 188-91
  'forgotten mourners', 10-11
  grieving of, 10, 88, 191-7
  involved in planning funeral, 126-7,
    263
  involvement at hospital, 50, 261
  'mis-matched' behaviour identified,
    184, 186
  reactions to death, 78-9
  viewing baby before burial, 104-5,
    127, 140
  wish-fulfillment, 189-9
choking, 34
citizens advice bureaux, 42
civil celebrant
  see, funeral celebrant (civil)
clergy, 116-21
  guidelines for, 255-6
  impact on, of S.I.D.S., 117-19
  involvement with bereaved, 117
  see also, funeral celebrant (civil)
collusion, 82
comforting, 199-201, 256
  permission to grieve in own way,
    210-11
communication between parents,
  162-80
community education, 28-9, 34-6,
  55-6, 211-12
Community Policing Squad, 267
  see also, police
community support, 198-212, 256-7
Coroner, 268
  legal requirements after cot death,
    21-2, 26, 252

cot death
  see, Sudden Infant Death Syndrome
cremation
  health regulations, 97

D

death
  certificate, 97, 257
  children's concept of, 182-8
  denial of, 96, 121
  explained to children, 43, 77-9,
    142-3, 181-97, 194-7
  reason for, 188-91
depression, 44
disbelief, 4, 31-2, 33, 201-2, 252
divorce, 174, 248
doctors, 252
  anger, 39
  educational role, 36
  expectations of, 38
  guidelines for, 257-9
  guilt, 39
  helplessness, 38
  'hidden agenda' of bereaved parents
    considered, 44
  reactions to S.I.D.S., 30-4
  responses of, 33-7
  role of, 32, 33, 37-8, 257-9
  self-awareness, 37
  supportive therapy, 39-44
dreams, 84-5, 217
drug therapy, 44, 258

E

Early Childhood Development
  Program, 247-8
Edgcumbe, Fr Grant, 116-21 *passim*
education
  see, community education
embalming, 106-7
emergency responders, 14-29, 40, 188
  emotional impact of S.I.D.S. on,
    50-1
emotional preparation lacking, 11-12
Ernst, L., de Frain, J. & Taylor, J.
    *Coping with Sudden Infant
    Death*, 174, 175
eulogy, 255
euphemisms about death, 182, 203-4,
  256, 263
'examination'
  see, autopsy

F

fathers, 259
  behavioural patterns, 166-70
  body language, 150-1
  communication of grief, 153-61
  grief ignored and denied by others,
    157-8
  grieving of, 146-61
  impact on, 259
  role loss of, 218
  roles of, 148-50
  see, parents
  silence and escapism, 156-7
  see also, parents
feeding methods, 35, 54, 139, 239
friends and relatives
  assist grieving, 70-1
  collusion, 82
  at the death, 3-7, 14-16, 31, 47-9
  as effective supporters, 198-212,
    256-7
  as exhausted supporters, 82
  funeral, 96, 98-100, 113-14, 121-3,
    255
  guilt, blame and anger, 84, 91
  men's needs from, 146-7, 153-5,
    158-61
  misconceptions, 81, 89-90, 94-5
  and the next child,
    loyalty conflicts of parents
      between, 226-7
    messages given to parents by, 221
    misunderstandings, 215-16, 223
  parents' accounts with, 185-6, 190-1
  parents' loyalty conflict with, 86, 91
  parents' reactions to, 87-8, 94-5
  the ripple effect on, 69, 142-4
  viewing, 104
funeral, 60, 73, 80
  arrangement of, 50, 96-113
  ceremony, 112-16, 122-4
  children involved in planning,
    126-7, 263
  civil ceremony, 124-8
  eulogy, 120-1
  parents choice of, 97, 115, 122-4,
    125-7, 256, 263
  parents' role before, 103-113
  slow down arrangements of, 98-100,
    263
funeral celebrant (civil)
  account of, 124-8
first meeting with parents, 124-5

  guidelines for, 255-6
  planning of funeral, 125-8
  reactions of, 80
  role, 73-4, 114-16
funeral director
  ancillary services, 102-3
  counselling and education services,
    102-3
  guidelines for, 262-4
  pressures on, 97
  public image of, 101-2
  reactions of, 98, 262
  role, 97, 99-102, 110-11

G

grandparents' grief, 80, 142, 143
grief
  chain of reactions, 135
  of children, 10, 88, 191-7
  community support for, 198-212
  cultural differences in expressing,
    46, 50, 141-2
  discussing, 253-5
  expressed differently by mother and
    father, 88, 135-7, 146-61, 162-80
  expression of emotions necessary,
    204-8, 258
  individual responses to, 69-70, 175,
    210-11
  inhibited by pregnancy, 221-3
  inhibits pregnancy, 225-7
  'journey through grief', 73, 76-95,
    210-11, 216-17
    diagram, 75
  men's communication of, 146-61
  men's 'rejection' and 'isolation' in,
    151-2
  of 'other mother', 191-2
  'ripple effect', 142-4
  sexual relationships affected by,
    147, 177
  stages of, 69-70, 71, 75
  times of intense emotion, 43, 58,
    90-1, 127, 210, 226, 265-6
  'wasteland', 85-6
guilt, 12-13, 17, 32, 39, 49, 83, 91,
    111, 137, 138, 139, 190, 205-7,
    255, 259

H

hallucinations, 42-3, 80, 208-9, 217,
    224-5

health prior to death, 11
health regulations, 97
  burial, 97
  cremation, 97
helplessness, 33, 38, 45, 46, 199, 256
hospital staff
  communication with, 244-5
  emotional support provided by,
    244-5
  feeling of helplessness, 46
  guidelines for, 259-62
  impact on, 261-2
  patients' history, procedures for
    recording, 230-1
  role defined, 49-50
  role on arrival of S.I.D.S. baby,
    44-51, 260
  S.I.D.S. discussed in maternity
    ward, 231-2
hospitals, 42, 252

I

immunisation
  and S.I.D.S., 54
infant welfare sisters
  account by, 53-6, 59-60, 64-5
  community education role, 55-6
  emotional impact on, 62-3, 265
  feelings of inadequacy, 55
  funeral attendance by, 60
  guidelines for, 264-6
  involvement with family, 52, 265-6
  reaction after S.I.D.S., 53-5, 265
  reassure parents, 64-5
  subsequent babies, advice on, 61
  support group for, 61, 266
  training of, viii
  visit to parents, 55, 56-60, 265
isolation, 82-3, 199

K

Kubler-Ross, Dr Elizabeth, 69

L

'life-line' counselling, 42
loyalty to baby, 86, 216, 223-4

M

marriage
  failure linked to S.I.D.S., 175
  strained, 179

memories, 93, 116-17, 125-6, 127,
    192-7, 226
men
  see, fathers, parents
Michael (poem by David Morawetz),
    159-61
misconceptions about grief, 90
Mobile Intensive Care Ambulance
    Unit (M.I.C.A.), 5, 7, 8
monitors, 62, 64, 234-8
  deciding to use, 236-7, 240-2
  literature about, 237
  problems with, 241
mortality after conception, 228-9
mothers
  account of reactions, 22, 23, 27,
    64-5, 94, 163-5, 173
  behavioural patterns, 166-8
  grief of, 135-45
  implicated in babies' deaths, 137-9
  instinctive responses of, 139-41
  nurturing role of, 177-8
  role loss of, 218-19
  see also parents
mourning, 252, 267
  inhibited by pregnancy, 221-3
  inhibits pregnancy, 225-7
  memories confused with, 93, 226
  misconceptions about, 83

N

'natural order' reversed, 12, 80
nightmares, 84-5, 208-9
'normal for now' reactions, 208-10,
    256
numbness, 81-2, 85
Nursing Mothers' Association of
    Australia (N.M.A.A.), 239, 259
nurturing role of women, 177-8

O

'other mother', 191-2
'overlaying', 138-9

P

parenting role, 87
  expectations of, 217-18
  loss of, 217-20
  restoration of, 221

parents
  account of reactions, 18-19, 22,
    47-8, 94-5, 119-20, 129-30, 185-6,
    187
  acknowledgment of feelings of,
    173-4
  avoid reference to baby, 57, 94-5
  behaviour 'normal for now', 208-10,
    256
  choice of funeral, 97
  communication between, 162-80
  community support for, 198-212
  conflicting pressures on, 226-7
  decision-making, 41, 76-7, 168-9,
    252, 256, 263
  effect on relationships of S.I.D.S.,
    162-80
  expressions of emotions, 204-8
  failure, feelings of, 218
  future after S.I.D.S., 246-9
  at the hospital, 48-51
  immediate impact, 8, 267
  loyalty to baby, 86, 216, 223-4,
    226-7
  'mis-matched' behaviour identified
    by children, 184
  need to talk about baby, 57, 93,
    94-5
  needs of, during bereavement, 201
  participation with emergency
    responders, 19-20
  period of grief, vii-viii, 76-95
  reaction to other people's babies,
    89-90
  role before funeral, 103-113
  sanity doubted, 208-10
  self-esteem, 87-8
  self-image after S.I.D.S., 136-7, 168
  separation from baby, 18-20, 48,
    50, 252, 258, 260
  sources of comfort for, 199-201
  support groups for, 237-8, 252
  support of, 73-4
  volunteer visitors, ix
  wish-fulfillment, 189-9, 217
  see also fathers; mothers
pathologists, 36, 49, 97, 188, 258,
  260, 268
pertussis
  see whooping cough
philosophical issues, 86-7
police
  after involvement with S.I.D.S.,
    25-7, 268
  as emergency responders, 21-9
  Form 83 (statement of evidence), 21,
    267
  guidelines for, 266-8
  involvement, 6, 35, 49, 97, 111,
    252, 258, 266-8
  questioning of parents, 21-7
  training of, viii
post-mortem examination
  see autopsy
pregnancy
  see subsequent babies
primary maternal preoccupation,
  221-2

R

Raphael, Beverley, *Anatomy of
  Bereavement*, 78, 93
reality, 255, 256
  avoidance of, 25, 203-4
  decision-making encouraged, 40-1
recognition of emotions, 208-10
reincarnation, 224
relationships, 88, 94-5, 146-7, 259
  effect of S.I.D.S. on, 162-80
  evaluation of, 180
  roles within, 165-72
relatives
  see, friends and relatives
religious beliefs, 86-7, 116-24, 182,
  183, 184, 186, 204, 255-6
reminders of the baby, 76
  see also, memories
renewal, 176-9
'replacement' baby, 220-1
  community pressure about, 221
  impact of early 'replacement', 222-3
resuscitation, 5, 7, 16, 31, 64, 252,
  258, 260
'ripple effect', 69, 142-4
Rudolph, Marguerita, *Should the
  Children Know?*, 182

S

'saying goodbye', importance of, 10,
  69, 103-113, 140
sedation
  see, drug therapy
self-forgiveness, 91
sexual relationships affected by grief,
  147, 177
shock, 19, 77, 79, 81, 252, 254
sibling rivalry, 189, 192

sleep patterns, 235
subsequent babies
  see, babies, subsequent
Sudden Infant Death Research
  Foundation(s), viii, 48, 49, 65,
  251, 252, 267
  *A Common Sense Approach to Cot
  Death*, 64
  Counselling and Support Service,
  28, 237, 258
  counselling for professional staff,
  51, 253, 254-5, 262, 268
  *Facts about Sudden Infant Death
  Syndrome*, 253
  initial contact, 20, 41
  lectures by staff, 15
  parents' mutual support, 58
  volunteers, 15
Sudden Infant Death Syndrome
  (S.I.D.S.), 34-5, 49
  age at death, 12, 35
  ante-natal discussions, 228-30
  anxiety about, 228-45
  defined, vii, 11
  during pregnancy, 224-5
  effect on relationships of, 162-80
  historical references to, 137-9
  immediate impact, 3
  marriage failure resulting from, 175
  'monitors prevent' (claim), 234-8
  'non-causes', 17, 54, 188-91, 206-7,
  252, 257, 258, 260, 265, 267
  organisations' role, 42
  recognised at next pregnancy,
  229-30

statistics, 64, 229, 235-6, 254
suffocation, 23, 24, 34, 35, 138
suicide after cot death, 13
support groups, 237-8
supportive therapy, 39-44, 244-5

T

talking and sharing to adjust
  emotionally, 10, 37, 51, 262, 265
telephone counselling, 42
training of professionals involved, viii
'turning point' in grief, 92-3

V

vasectomy, 246-7
viewing baby before burial, 36, 41,
  103-13, 140, 264

W

'wasteland' of grief, 85-6
When I Was a Child (poem by Shirley
  Rutherford), 194-7
whooping cough
  vaccine not linked to S.I.D.S.,
  206-7
Why so Young? (poem by Emily
  Patterson), 193-4
wish-fulfillment, 189-90
women
  see, mothers, parents

Index prepared by Kerry Herbstreit
and sponsored by Tobin Brothers Foundation